G
CIDER
GUIDE

DAVID KITTON

ALMA
BOOKS

Getting around the cider country

Contents

Pub facilities

Snacks: sandwiches, rolls, pies and pasties

Meals: at least one hot and/or cold dish, with vegetables; often a full three courses

Garden: this can vary from a small patch by the car park to several acres; it can be assumed that children accompanied by an adult may be admitted. Outdoor drinking area is the urban equivalent of the above, often more cramped and less likely to provide comfortable eating conditions, with notable exceptions

Restaurant: a separate room or space set aside specifically for meals

Children's room: a room or space within the pub which children may occupy if accompanied by an adult: many pubs do not permit children within the bar area though in some cases this may be varied if a full meal is being taken

Outlets

(P) Pubs, hotels, restaurants and clubs having a licence for the consumption of cider on the premises

(OL) Premises at which cider may be purchased to take away only

Cider makers from which cider may be purchased to take away only

Dispense

(B) Bottle (BB) Bag in box (CK) Carry keg (E) Cask and electric pump (F) Flagon (H) Cask and hand pump (J) Glass jar (PC) Polycask (PL) Plastic container (PP) Polypin (W) Wooden cask

Maps

● Principal town with traditional cider outlet

• Other town or village with traditional cider outlet

○ Principal town with no traditional cider outlet, included for location purposes

▲ Location of cider maker selling direct to public from premises

Cover design: Robert Howells

First published October 1987
© Alma Books Ltd, 34 Alma Road, St Albans, Herts AL1 3BW
Alma Books is a wholly-owned subsidiary of the Campaign for Real Ale Ltd
ISBN 1-85249-010-1. Printed by McCorquodale Confidential Print Ltd, Wolverton, Milton Keynes MK12 5LX

Welcome to the Good Cider Guide

This is a book to broaden your drinking horizons. If you think that "cider" is just a fizzy drink with a vaguely apple taste, then you are missing out on a lot. Cider *can* be that if you stick to the mass produced commercial ciders advertised on television and on the supermarket shelf. But there is much, much more – *still* made by the original methods, and *still* tasting of the real thing.

This book is the appleholic equivalent of CAMRA's *Good Beer Guide:* to lead you through the maze of mass production to some of the cider makers who still turn out the genuine article, good, old fashioned, and natural.

It is not as easy to define an honest pint of cider as it is real ale. In theory it should be made strictly from the juice of cider apples, fer-

mented in their own yeasts with sweetness controlled by racking off, without any filtration, artificial colour, or pasteurisation, for serving without the use of extraneous carbon dioxide and it should be matured only in oak casks.

If we were to stick rigidly to this definition the Guide would be a thin pamphlet, for few cider makers adhere to every point. There are some that do, and you will discover them within; but many more, often for good reasons, such as basic hygiene, or producing a consistent product, bend the rules a bit. Every cider in the Guide should, however, satisfy all but the most exacting palates, and even they should find enough to keep them happy too. You will discover an infinite variety of ciders, from robust rough to sophisticated smooth, ciders to quaff and ciders to sip.

It is difficult also to know what to call it. Many people refer to it as "scrumpy", but this tends to get some cider makers in a ferment. They would rather talk about "traditional cider", believing that scrumpy conjures up visions of an unpredictable drink, leading to unpredictable behaviour – though often it is the drinker's lack of understanding about the drink that is to blame. But while some use "scrumpy" to describe the rough stuff made from the windfalls (or "scrumps") for others, such as Derek Inch, from Devon, it means the finest cider, from selected, better apples, slowly fermented and matured for much longer.

Perhaps "traditional cider" says it best, for it is cider made by the age-old methods, with nothing to get between you and the authentic taste of properly fermented and matured apple juice. That is what you will get here, from the biggest firms in the land (for even the Big Three make their traditional ciders) right down to the farmer's gate. Some may not be to your taste – it would be surprising if all were – but we are sure you will find many more that will become your friends for life.

Just a word of warning. Scrumpy/farmhouse/traditional cider, call it what you will, is strong stuff. Left to ferment out it will be up to 8 per cent alcohol content, though many are less. But even the national brands of traditional cider will be around $4\frac{1}{2}$ per cent. To put that in perspective, a good draught beer is about $3\frac{1}{2}$ per cent. If you bear that in mind, and pace yourself, you won't go far wrong. Good hunting, and good health!

Apples, the only ingredient

Apples come in four main types: Sweet, Bittersweet, Bittersharp and Sharp. They are categorised according to the degree of acidity and tannin which they contain, which naturally has a bearing on their uses.

Sweets are the blandest of the four, being low in both acid and tannin: among these are dessert fruit. Bittersweets are low in acid but high in tannin; it is this class that is most used in cider making. Rich in sugar, which ferments to alcohol, and not too acid, they give the cider maker plenty of flexibility, with their wide number of varieties and flavour characteristics, in blending to perfection. Bittersharps, high in acid and tannin, were once more used in cider making than now. They do not possess the wide spectrum of flavour of the Bittersweet, though like them they have a high sugar content. Sharps, the last of the four, are as the name implies high in acidity, but low in tannin; they include cooking apples such as Bramleys.

In the west cider apples are the tradition, and few would dream of making cider from any other. The cider apple is more related to the crab apple than to dessert or culinary fruit, but does appear in all four classes. The Sweets are used for blending with other more assertive fruit; an example still in use is Sweet Coppin. Most cider apples fall into the Bittersweet and Bittersharp categories: there are literally hundreds of varieties, some with names that commemorate their place of first cultivation,

4

such as Kingston Black, others named after their growers, like Tom Putt. You will come across numerous examples in the Guide, and it is good to note that although the varieties have been drastically reduced in recent years and new strains have been introduced in their place, these modern apples continue to be given similar traditional sounding names.

In the east the tradition has been quite different. From Sussex to Norfolk a mixture of cooking apples and dessert fruit is used for cider making: bearing in mind the characteristics of each category shown above, it would seem that a balanced cider would be hard to achieve; true the culinary apples provide plenty of acidity, but neither they nor the desserts yield much tannin. However, the results have been, and are being, eagerly consumed in such parts: a more acid, and crisp drink, but without the same subtlety of flavour as west country cider. It is however interesting to obse... makers in the east a... ning to use cider fruit and in some cases are their own Bittersweets.

There is in fact quite a lot of two way traffic. In a bad year in the west it is not unknown for an urgent cry to go out for lorry loads of Bramleys to augment the supplies of local fruit, and again you will notice that some western firms, from Bulmer downwards, while professing the authenticity of their traditional cider, do admit to always adding a small proportion of culinary fruit. Apples such as Bramleys, which possess a similar flavour and balance to the Sharp cider apples, can be substituted with a clear conscience. Though east and west would never admit it, cider making is more a question of good British compromise, within the limitations and strengths of each apple, rather than counsels of perfection.

Cider then and now

It all began in prehistory, when forests covered much of the land. Among the trees our ancient ancestors discovered the crab apple, and probably by chance found that the fermented juice had an interesting kick. Soon they were enjoying another one for the woad.

Certainly cider making was established in Britain well before the coming of the Romans. The old custom of wassailing for instance dates from pre-Christian times, and was intended to persuade the pagan gods to produce a good apple crop for the coming year.

The word cider itself is of ancient origin, coming from the Anglo Saxon "seider", which in turn derived from the Latin "sicra": but the early Britons called all strong drink "shekar", a word used by the wandering peoples of Spain and Northern France, so perhaps it was they who encouraged our ancestors to cultivate apple trees and begin making cider.

As with most things, the Norman Conquest had a profound effect. The Normans brought with them their already well developed cider expertise; they introduced new varieties of apple, and organised orchards and cider making as part of the pattern of monastic farming. The climatic conditions in southern England were very similar to those of northern France, and during the next 200 years apples were grown, and cider made, from Cornwall to East Anglia, and as far north as the Humber.

By the 13th century we find mention being made of the cider apple, which is really only a development of the original crab apple; quite different from dessert and culinary fruit, with a fibrous texture, which makes it easier to extract the juice: high in tannin and sugar, but low in acid.

In Tudor times the apple orchard became an established feature of the English countryside, with a general increase in interest in gardening and horticulture. Cider was by now the drink of the ordinary people, but it was also used by the highest in the land, who drank it as an alternative to table wine, in elegant engraved cider glasses. Lesser mortals took it in pottery mugs, often two-handled affairs, sometimes highly decorated. There was much literature on fruit culture and cider making, the most notable publication being in 1678 by John Worlidge, who wrote a detailed study of the care and growing of apple trees, and invented an improved form of cider mill, which he was convinced would put paid to French wine once and for all.

The various periods of war with our continental neighbours had done much to reduce trade, and encourage the production of our national drink. But by the 1700s relations were becoming more settled, trade was increasing and imported wine came into fashion. Agriculture was also gradually changing, too, turning to arable crops, and the resultant products facilitated the production of cheap beers and spirits. As if this was not enough, the government, desperate to raise funds for the Seven Years War, slapped a tax on cider makers of four shillings per hogshead. This caused a national uproar, for it was the first time that the customs man had been given authority to enter private property in search of goods subject to duty. William Pitt the Elder became quite irate and uttered the now famous phrase "an Englishman's home is his castle". A few years later the tax was repealed, amid great rejoicing.

At this time farm workers received up to a fifth of their wages in cider, amounting to about four pints a day, and much more during harvest. Every farm, large or small, made its own cider, and this had the added benefit of providing work at the end of the year, when there was little to do outside. The surplus was sold locally, to the village inns and cider houses.

The industrial revolution led to a drift to the new manufacturing towns, which were well catered for by a profusion of breweries that had sprung up. Unlike apples, which only grew regionally, barley was universally obtainable, and the 18th and 19th centuries saw a further decline in cider drinking, which remained a small-scale operation, mostly on the farm, with a limited market.

Revival came in the late 19th century, thanks largely to the initiative of several enthusiasts, who saw the potential for selling cider to the towns. Chief among these individuals was Mr. Radcliffe Cooke, member of Parliament for Herefordshire, who plugged the product for all he was worth, to the extent that he became known as the "member for cider". He affirmed that "regular drinkers of cider are practically exempt from many distressing maladies. They are not subject to gravel or stone; they enjoy immunity from disorders of a choleric nature" – and here he warmed to his subject – "no case of Asiatic chloera has *ever* been known in Herefordshire". With such rhetoric how could cider fail to make a comeback! That it did so was as much due to the development of the railways, which enabled a maker to send his cider all over the country, as to Radcliffe Cooke's campaigning. With the right commercial climate new cider makers emerged, such as H. P. Bulmer, and by the start of the century it was available to a new urban market.

Since then cider drinking has increased, most rapidly of all in recent years. For instance in the early 1970s about 30 million gallons were drunk in Britain per year, and today that figure has doubled.

At one time cider was a reasonably cheap drink, a fact which did much to give it a bad reputation, as the "lads" soon discovered it was a good way to get drunk without getting skint. It was certainly cheaper than beer and it was also stronger.

Popularity, as in the 1760s, eventually led to the attentions of the Chancellor, and in 1976 tax was again imposed. Almost every Budget since has brought an increase, and it is hardly surprising that cider is now comparable with beer in price per pint. However, remember is is *still* stronger, so it still represents better value.

More than 90 per cent of the market is accounted for by just three firms, Bulmer, Taunton, and Coates-Gaymer. When most people think of cider it is their keg and bottled brands that come to mind. But, as this Guide shows, there are a multitude of smaller firms, from the man making a few gallons as a side line, to firms such as Symonds, Merrydown and Westons, each turning out over a million gallons a year; others, such as Inch's from Devon, are not far behind.

Of the Big Three only one, H. P. Bulmer, is independent. Coates-Gaymer is part of the Allied Lyons Group, while Taunton is backed by a host of breweries, including Guinness, Courage, and Scottish & Newcastle—even Young's of Wandsworth is part of the consortium. Where cider goes hand in glove with beer the obvious advantage is that it automatically guarantees its outlets: Taunton Keg Blackthorn, for example, now graces every Young's pub, while you will find such ciders as Olde English in Ind Coope houses. Every cider maker needs a market place, and many have reached an agreement with a brewer by which he stocks their product. Some of the more ambitious makers now sell their cider under contract, for brewers to offer as their own brands: this has enabled a wider public to become exposed to the delights of some of the smaller firms. Weston's, though still independent, produce a keg brand "Stowford Press", for Camerons Brewery of Hartlepool.

It is, however, a dangerous business making friends with a tiger. With beer sales dormant, and cider sales increasing, brewers had been taking more interest in the cider trade, and it was only a matter of time before a big brewer, Greenall Whitley, bought up one of the small makers, Symonds, and created from it their own in-house cider for their expanding pub empire. Overnight, out went all the previous brands, and in came Greenalls/Symonds. Such instant change can severely affect the whole balance of the cider industry, and I suspect that those brands which were ousted are still licking their wounds, and perhaps even planning drastic action of their own to recover their position.

It is unlikely that we have yet seen the end of such brewers' acquisitions. It would be surprising if in due course others do not follow Greenall's example: any cider maker in the million gallon league must be seriously concerned. So too should its customers, for to judge by the Symonds take over, it is not the firm's traditional brands which will flood into the brewery pubs, but a keg alternative. In takeovers there are no winners.

The Cider Maker's Year

January

What makes an otherwise rational man go out into his orchards in the depth of winter with a shot gun and fire off a salvo at his apple trees? Well, 'tis the wassailing moi dear! "Wassail" comes from the Anglo Saxon "Be of Good Health", and was originally used as a greeting. Over the years it developed into a mid-winter festival, in which people wished health and prosperity to each other and their crops for the year ahead – a sort of pre-harvest festival. The animals in the barns would be toasted, much to their amazement, and then the happy farmer's family and villagers would troop out to the orchards to bless the trees.

The ceremony took place at different times around the country, but mostly either on Old Christmas Eve (January 5) or Old Twelfth Night (January 17). The gathering in the orchard would pour cider over the roots of the best tree, and address it in song:

Here's to Thee, old apple tree,
Be sure Thee bud, be sure Thee blow,
And bring forth apples good enow.
Hats full, caps full,
Buckets full and bags full.
Hurrah! Hurrah!

The unfortunate tree then had to suffer the indignity of being beaten with sticks, shot at and shouted at, to the accompaniment of the bashing of kettles and tin trays. All the company then took a piece of toast soaked in cider and ate it, placing one piece in the branches for the robins.

The Goddess of the apple trees, Pomona, must have had little sleep that night, and surely got the message. Actually shooting at the trees did have some practical purpose, for it was supposed to dislodge the insects from the bark, and these would then be devoured by the birds.

Nowadays the average cider maker is rather more remote from his trees, buying in most of his supplies from local growers, who would probably resent him turning up late at night and cavorting fully armed round his orchard. But

8

the custom has not quite died out: for instance it is still enacted every January 17 behind the Butchers Arms at Carhampton in Somerset, and in the same county no less a body than the Taunton Cider Company has reintroduced it, apparently with effective results. I suspect that there are more than a few cider makers, and apple growers, who still say a little prayer in darkest January.

April

Apple blossom time, a season loved by writers of romantic songs: but for the cider maker it is nail biting time, as he watches anxiously for a late frost, which could literally nip his plans in the bud. A wet spring can also spell disaster for the year's crop. It is at this stage that he wishes he had had a longer session with Pomona back in the winter.

Apple trees tend to be biennial, a habit accentuated by the two hot dry summers in the mid 1970s. If the previous crop was heavy the trees will be reluctant, and the developing buds will need all the help they can get. Careful husbandry and judicious pruning in a "good" year can however do much to correct this imbalance.

August

Though this may sound early, it is possible to start harvesting and cider making. There are a few varieties of apple, such as Morgan Sweet, which can be gathered at this time. They make a quick fermenting cider, and if you have access to an orchard of these you can be one jump ahead of the competition. They are, however, something of a maverick in the cider world, and are regarded by some only as a stop gap.

September

The cider maker will grow restless, excuse himself from conversation, and plead "pressing business elsewhere". From now on the pressure is indeed on, not only him but his apples, which will be arriving by the truck load from his suppliers. If he has orchards of his own he will not need even this reminder, for a walk through the trees will tell him all he should know.

Harvesting has changed greatly over the years. In the old days the apples were left to drop when they were ready, or were sometimes knocked off the tree with a pole, both procedures which could badly bruise the crop. This did not seem to concern some makers, but could affect the final strength and quality of the cider. In the old orchards, with tall standard trees, the stock which normally grazed there would have to be banned for the duration. Modern orchards consist of much shorter bush trees, closer together, designed for mechanical harvesting. The process is much quicker, but if anything the damage to the fruit is greater, and once gathered the apples must be taken without delay to the mill.

At the mill the fruit is sorted, and if in good condition can be left to soften for a week or two. The cider maker tests the apples, pushing his thumb into the fruit – if it punctures the first time, the apple is ripe. The principle of extracting the juice has varied little, breaking down the apples into pulp, and then extracting the juice from the pulp.

Firstly the apples are crushed in a mill. Most people are familiar with pictures of the old horse drawn, stone wheel running in a stone trough, filled with apples, which were gradually reduced to an evil looking brown mush. As early as the 1760s John Worlidge invented an improved method, which dispensed with the horse and much of the labour, comprising a large metal roller with spikes which tore the apples to pieces, and could be turned by hand. In essence most modern mills are only variants of this, though now with high-speed blades reducing the fruit to pulp.

The second stage involves the cider press. Here the pulp is built up on a flat bed to form a sort of many layered giant apple sandwich, some four feet square and much the same height. Originally the layers were separated by straw, or horse hair, both easily acquired, though these have been superseded by modern materials such as nylon. A board is placed on top of the sandwich, or "cheese" as it is known, and pressure applied from above, the juice trickling out down the sides into a trough. Originally presses were made entirely of wood, even to the great screw shaft that formed the mainstay of the machine. Eventually the screws were replaced by metal, but for many years the press remained hand operated. Later powerful hydraulic presses came into use, and today in large firms even more sophisticated machines are employed, working like giant pistons.

The juice now enters the vats, where yeast ferments the natural sugars into alcohol – the cider maker may apply sulphur dioxide to kill off the wild natural yeast, and introduce a wine or champagne yeast of known performance in its place. Once the desired degree of fermentation has been achieved the cider, as it now is, gets transferred to storage vats to mature until required. The cider maker will at this stage blend the cider with that of other vats, to give the desired flavour and character, and may also bring in cider from the previous year to contribute to the final product.

January

The cider maker's work is now done, save for the all important task of selling what he has produced. As described, it is "traditional cider", ready for you to drink and enjoy, without carbonation, pasteurisation or other cosmetic surgery. With the help of this Guide you should be able to find it waiting for you in its natural state, and in enough quantity to last through the year, whenever you call.

By January you might expect the cider maker would relax. But no, he is already thinking ahead to the next season. Wassail to him, and his apple trees.

Pre-war Bulmer advertisement

10

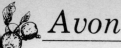

Avon

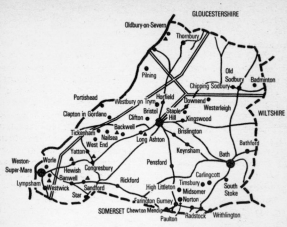

GLOUCESTERSHIRE

Oldbury-on-Severn
Thornbury
Pilning
Old Sodbury
Chipping Sodbury
Badminton
Portishead
Westbury on Trym
Horfield
Downend
Westerleigh
WILTSHIRE
Clapton in Gordano
Bristol
Clifton
Staple Hill
Westerleigh
Kingswood
Backwell
Brislington
Tickenham
Nailsea
Long Ashton
Bathford
West End
Yatton
Keynsham
Bath
Weston-Super-Mare
Worle
Hewish
Congresbury
Pensford
Carlingcott
Lympsham
Banwell
Rickford
Timsbury
South Stoke
Westwick
Sandford
High Littleton
Midsomer
Star
Faringon Gurney
Norton
SOMERSET
Chewton Mendip
Radstock
Writhlington
Paulton

BACKWELL

WILLIAMS BROS.▲
Backwell Common
Tel: Flax Bourton
(027 583) 2740

BADMINTON

Village Club (P)
High Street
Tel: Badminton (045 421) 234
Weston (PC)

BANWELL

Ship (P)
West Street
Tel: Banwell (0934) 822522
Taunton (PC)
Meals including Sunday;
skittle Alley; table skittles.

Whistling Duck (P)
Weston Road
Tel: Banwell (0934) 822763
Thatcher (H)
Modern pub on edge of town.
Meals, lunchtime and
evening; garden; live music.

BATH

Beehive (P)
3 Belvedere, Lansdowne Road
Tel: Bath (0225) 20274
Taunton (H)
A sturdy stone built pub on
the hillside, but well worth
the climb. An enthusiastic
cider outlet and friendly local.
Snacks 10.30-2.30; full meals
12-2 and 6-10.

County Wine Vaults (P)
21 Westgate Street
Tel: Bath (0225) 310463
Taunton (H)
Near the theatre. Snacks.

Golden Fleece (P)
1-3 Avon Buildings, Lower
Bristol Road
Taunton (PC)
Interesting mural in darts
area. Meals and snacks
lunchtime; live music.

Hadley Arms (P)
Combe Down
Tel: Bath (0225) 837117
Thatcher (H)
Snacks all sessions; meals
lunchtime; outdoor drinking
area; skittles; table skittles;
pool; accommodation.

New Westhall (P)
Upper Bristol Road (A4)
Tel: Bath (0225) 25432
Weston (H)
Meals and snacks lunchtime;
live music.

Oddbins (OL)
3-5 Beau Street
Tel: Bath (0225) 60148
Weston (full range)

Pulteney Arms (P)
37 Daniel Street
Tel: Bath (0225) 63923
Taunton (H)
Side street local with gas
lighting. Meals and snacks
lunchtime and evening.

Ram (P)
20 Claverton Buildings,
Widcombe
Tel: Bath (0225) 21938
Bulmer (H)
Near first lock on Kennet &
Avon Canal. Meals and
snacks lunchtime and
evening.

Rose & Crown (P)
6 Brougham Place, St.
Saviours Road, Larkhall
Tel: Bath (0225) 25700
Thatcher (H)
Friendly out of town local.
Pool.

Royal Oak (P)
Summerlays Place, Pulteney
Road, Widcombe
Tel: Bath (0225) 335587
Bulmer (H)
Accent on food. Meals and
snacks lunchtime and
evening; skittles.

White Horse (P)
4 Northampton Street
Tel: Bath (0225) 25944
Taunton (H)
Snacks; large pool room.

Ye Olde Farmhouse (P)
1 Lansdown Road
Tel: Bath (0225) 316162
Taunton (H)
Snacks; live music.

BATHFORD

The Inn (P)
54 Bathford Hill
Tel: Bath (0225) 858528
Bulmer (H)
Split level local. Garden.

BRISTOL

Apple Tree (P)
Philip Street, Bedminster
Taunton (H)
Probably smallest pub in
Bristol; glorious cider house
of character. Meals and
snacks lunchtime and
evening.

Beaufort (P)
High Street, Clifton
Tel: Bristol (0272) 735906
Bulmer (H)
Smart back street local with
accent on food. Meals and
snacks lunchtime and
evening.

B.J's Off Licence (OL)
Bedminster
Broad Oak (B) (E)

Bellvue Stores (OL)
Bellvue Park, Brislington
Tel: Bristol (0272) 777898
Richards (PC)

Black Horse (P)
5 Nelson Parade, Bedminster
Taunton (H)
Busy two bar local. Outdoor
drinking area.

Brays Food Store (OL)
Bedminster Road
Broad Oak (PC)
Richards (PC)

Brewery Stores (OL)
99 Ashley Down Road,
Horfield
Tel: Bristol (0272) 46127
Thatcher (PC)

Brewery Stores (OL)
125 Two Mile Hill Road,
Kingswood
Tel: Bristol (0272) 672154
Thatcher (PC)

Britannia Off Licence (OL)
93 Nags Head Hill, St. George
Tel: Bristol (0272) 614985
Richards (PC)

Carpenters (OL)
387 Gloucester Road,
Horfield
Tel: Bristol (0272) 429283
Thatcher (E) (PL)

Coach & Horses (P)
25 Gloucester Lane, St. Judes
Tel: Bristol (0272) 553836
Taunton (H)

Coronation Tap (P)
8 Sion Place, Clifton
Tel: Bristol (0272) 739617
Bulmer (W) (PL)
Taunton (W) (PL)

Clifton village drinking pub
near Suspension Bridge, with
no pub games or juke box.
Meals and snacks 12-2pm.

Cotham Porter Stores (P)
15 Cotham Road South,
Cotham
Tel: Bristol (0272) 491198
Taunton (PC)
One bar cider house.

Crown & Anchor (P)
12 New Kingsley Road, St.
Philips
Tel: Bristol (0272) 277908
Taunton (PC)
Small back street cider
drinkers' local. Meals and
snacks lunchtime; outdoor
drinking area; live music.

Cumberland (P)
St. Lukes Road, Totterdown
Tel: Bristol (0272) 777382
Coates
Snacks; bar billiards.

Elston Stores (OL)
509 Wells Road, Hengrove
Tel: Bristol (0272) 775957
Broad Oak (PC) (B)

Empire Wines (OL)
Southmead Road
Broad Oak (PC) (B)

Essex Arms (P)
237 Two Mile Hill Road,
Kingswood
Tel: Bristol (0272) 674161
Taunton (H)
A noted cider house. Snacks;
garden.

Friendship (OL)
High Street, Kingswood
Broad Oak (PC) (B)
Richards (PC)

Gillmore (OL)
2 Birchwood Road, St. Annes
Tel: Bristol (0272) 716906
Richards (PC)

Grahams General Store (OL)
176 Ashton Drive
Tel: Bristol (0272) 663484
Richards (PC)

Greenbank Off Licence (OL)
Broad Oak (PC) (B)

Greville House (OL)
50 North Street, Bedminster
Tel: Bristol (0272) 664466
Broad Oak (PC) (B)

Hengaston Off Licence (OL)
77 Garnet Street, Bedminster
Tel: Bristol (0272) 635145
Broad Oak (PC) (B)

Hit or Miss (P)
199 Easton Road, Easton
Tel: Bristol (0272) 557698

Bulmer (H)
Regulars' local. Snacks;
meals lunchtime; bar
billiards; pool.

Humpers Off Licence (OL)
26 Sandwell Road, Staple Hill
Tel: Bristol (0272) 565525
Richards (PC)

James Off Licence (OL)
Pembury Road, Bedminster
Broad Oak (PC) (B)

Jordans (OL)
Sydenham Road, Knowle
Richards (PC)

Kings Arms (P)
51 Stokes Croft
Tel: Bristol (0272) 49589
Taunton (H)

Kings Off Licence (OL)
Kingsdown
Broad Oak (PC) (B)

Lady Di's (OL)
419 Gloucester Road,
Horfield
Tel: Bristol (0272) 514232
Richards (PC)

Lion (P)
19 Church Lane, Clifton
Wood
Tel: Bristol (0272) 28492
Taunton (H)

Mardyke (P)
128 Hotwells Road, Hotwells
Tel: Bristol (0272) 20475
Coates (H)
A robust local. Snacks; meals
lunchtime; live music.

Mead Wines (OL)
St. George
Broad Oak (PC) (B)

Newsbuoy (P)
Mardyke Ferry Road
Broad Oak (B)

Oddbins (OL)
7 Princess Victoria Street,
Clifton
Tel: Bristol (0272) 738185
Weston (full range)

Oddbins (OL)
20 Union Street, Broadmead
Tel: Bristol (0272) 290147
Weston (full range)

Oddbins (OL)
116 Coldharbour Road,
Redland
Tel: Bristol (0272) 48423
Weston (full range)

Oddessey Wines (OL)
Westbury on Trym
Inch

12

Orchard (P)

Hanover Place

Taunton (H)

Back street cider house near
SS Great Britain. Snacks.

Plume of Feathers (P)

135 Hotwells Road, Hotwells
Tel: Bristol (0272) 276788

Weston (PC)

Popular pub about 1 mile
from city centre. Meals and
snacks lunchtime (not
weekends); live music.

Red Lion (P)

Worrall Road

Coates (PC)

Robertson Road Off Licence (OL)

Robertson Road

Broad Oak (PC) (B)

School Road Stores (OL)

114 School Road, Brislington
Tel: Bristol (0272) 717177

Broad Oak (PC) (B)
Richard (PC)

Spring Gardens (P)

188 Hotwells Road, Hotwells

Taunton (PC)

Meals and snacks lunchtime;
bar billiards.

Tasty Wines (OL)

68 Hollway Road, Stockwood
Tel: Whitchurch
(0272) 832943

Richards (PC)

Terracotta Off Licence (OL)

Hanham Road

Richards (PC)

Trinity Towers (OL)

29-37 Old Market
Tel: Bristol (0272) 550734

Broad Oak (PC)

Trooper (P)

Bryants Hill
Tel: Bristol (0272) 673326

Bulmer (H)

Refurbished main road pub.
Meals and snacks lunchtime;
garden.

Volunteer (P)

9 New Street, St. Judes
Tel: Bristol (0272) 557982

Taunton (H)

Cider drinkers' local; built at
time of Queen Anne. Live
music.

Wine Cask (OL)

17 High Street, Staple Hill
Tel: Bristol (0272) 568360

Richards (PC)

Open: 10-1.30 and 4.30-10pm.
Sunday 12-2 and 7-10pm.

Wine Store (OL)

16 Duncombe Road,
Speedwell
Tel: Bristol (0272) 671092

Richards (PC)

White Swan (P)

North Street, Downend
Tel: Bristol (0272) 560261

Taunton (PC)

Meals and snacks lunchtime
and evening.

CARLINGCOTT

Beehive (P)

Tel: Radstock (0761) 34442

Bulmer (H)

Panoramic views from
garden. Snacks; garden;
skittles.

CHEWTON MENDIP

Chewton Cheese Dairy (OL)

on B3114
Tel: Chewton Mendip
(076 121) 666

Burrow Hill (PL)
Perry (PL)
Sheppy (B)

A working cheese maker with
a produce shop and
restaurant. You can watch
the cheese being made while
you eat. Restaurant open
April to December. Shop
hours Monday to Friday
8.30-5pm; weekends 9-5pm.

CHIPPING SODBURY

Portcullis (P)

Horse Street (A432)
Tel: Chipping Sodbury
(0454) 312004

Taunton (H)

Meals lunchtime and evening
except Sunday;
accommodation.

Elegant façade of Beehive Inn, Bath

CLAPTON-IN-GORDANO

Black Horse (P)
Clevedon Lane (off A369)
Tel: Portishead (0272) 842105
Taunton (H)
Unspoilt country pub with
original stone floor. Garden;
children's room.

CONGRESBURY

RICHARDS CIDER▲
The Corner Cottage,
Smallway
Tel: Yatton (0934) 832054

FARRINGTON GURNEY

Miners Arms (P)
on A362
Tel: Temple Cloud
(0761) 52158
Taunton (H)
Snacks; garden; skittles.

HEWISH

CROSSMAN'S PRIME FARMHOUSE CIDER▲
Mayfield Farm
Tel: Yatton (0934) 833174

LANGDON'S WEST COUNTRY CIDERS▲
The Cider Mill
Tel: Yatton (0934) 833433

Palmers Elm (P)
on A370
Tel: Yatton (0934) 832245
Crossman (PC)
Meals and snacks lunchtime
and evening; garden;
childrens' room.

HIGH LITTLETON

BROAD OAK CIDER
Greyfield Road
Tel: Bristol (0272) 333154

Dandos Off Licence (OL)
Tel: Timsbury (0761) 70495
Broad Oak (PC) (B)

Star Inn (P)
High Street (A39)
Tel: Timsbury (0761) 70433
Taunton (E)
Meals and snacks lunchtime;
garden; pool.

KEYNSHAM

Gators Off Licence (OL)
Queens Road
Broad Oak (PC)

Hicks Gate Farm Shop (OL)
Broad Oak (PC) (B)
Broad Oak Perry (B)

Trout Tavern (P)
46 Temple Street
Tel: Keynsham (027 56) 2754
Taunton (H) (PC)
18th century former coaching
inn, the cider centre of the
town. Snacks; live music.

LONG ASHTON

Little Tipple (OL)
50 Weston Road
Tel: Long Ashton
(0272) 392508
Crossman (BB)

LONG ASHTON SUPERIOR QUALITY CIDER▲
The Cider House, Long
Ashton Research Station
Tel: Long Ashton
(027 580) 2181

Miners Rest (P)
Providence Lane
Tel: Long Ashton
(0272) 393449
Taunton (PC)
On hill above village, with
fine views through valley.
Snacks; garden.

Robin Hood's Retreat (P)
Providence Lane
Tel: Long Ashton
(0272) 393217
Taunton (PC)
Wood panelled bar with
atmosphere. Snacks; garden.

LYMPSHAM

Sanders Super Fruit (OL)
West Home Nurseries
Tel: Bleadon (0934) 812652
Sheppy

MIDSOMER NORTON

Crown (P)
Station Road, Welton
Tel: Midsomer Norton
(0761) 412811
Taunton (H)
Snacks; garden; pool.

Kings Arms (P)
Chilcompton Road
Tel: Midsomer Norton
(0761) 412313

Taunton (H)
Snacks; pool; separate games
room.

Royal Oak (P)
Taunton (H)

White Hart (P)
The Island, Market Place
Tel: Midsomer Norton
(0761) 412957
Taunton (PC)
Snacks; skittles; live music.

NAILSEA

White Lion (P)
Silver Street
Tel: Nailsea (0272) 852776
Taunton (F)
Cooked snacks all sessions.

NAILSEA WEST END

Blue Flame (P)
Tel: Nailsea (0272) 856910
Bulmer (PC)
Remote country pub 2 miles
west of Nailsea. Snacks.

OLDBURY-ON-SEVERN

COWHILL CIDER▲
Cowhill Farm

Ship (P)
Tel: Thornbury (0454) 413257
Bulmer (PC)
Ask for "the scrumpy", it's not
on show. Good value bar
meals; Sunday lunches;
garden.

PAULTON

Exton Stores (OL)
Winterfield Road
Tel: Midsomer Norton
(0761) 412269
Broad Oak (PC)

Lamb Inn (P)
Park Road
Taunton (H)
Cider house with no
distracting frills. Snacks;
pool.

Red Lion (P)
High Street
Tel: Midsomer Norton
(0761) 412157
Taunton (H)
Town centre pub. Meals and
snacks lunchtime and
evening; skittles;
accommodation.

Somerset Inn (P)
Bath Road
Tel: Midsomer Norton
(0761) 412828
Taunton (H)
Old fashioned pub with no
juke box or fruit machines.
Snacks; outdoor drinking
area.

Winterfield Inn (P)
Salisbury Road
Tel: Midsomer Norton
(0761) 412022
Taunton (H)
Meals and snacks lunchtime;
garden.

PENSFORD

Rising Sun (P)
Church Street
Tel: Compton Dando
(076 18) 516
Bulmer (H)
Snacks; lunches Monday to
Saturday; evening meals
Tuesday to Saturday;
riverside garden; children's
room.

PILNING

Plough (P)
Tel: Pilning (045 45) 2556
Bulmer (PC)
Just outside the village,
convenient for the industrial
companies, but still a country
pub. Meals lunchtime
Monday to Friday; skittle
alley.

PORTISHEAD

Plough (P)
High Street
Tel: Portishead (0272) 842433
Taunton (PC)
Small local in shopping area.
Snacks; garden; skittles;
children's room.

Welcome (OL)
6 The Triangle, West Hill
Tel: Portishead (0272) 842316
Broad Oak (PC)

RADSTOCK

Railway Hotel (P)
Wells Road
Tel: Radstock (0761) 35100
Taunton (H)
Snacks; garden.

RICKFORD

Plume of Feathers (P)
off A368
Tel: Blagdon (0761) 6249
Taunton (PC)
In small village at foot of
Mendips, popular with
ramblers and potholers.
Garden; accommodation.

SANDFORD

THATCHER'S CIDER▲
Myrtle Farm, Station Road
Tel: Banwell (0934) 822862

SOUTH STOKE

Packhorse (P)
off B3110
Tel: Coombe Down
(0225) 832060
Taunton (PC)
Unspoilt 15th century village
pub. Snacks; garden.

STAR

Star Inn (P)
on A38 near Shipham
Tel: Winscombe
(0934 84) 2569
Bulmer (E)
Meals and snacks lunchtime
to 1.45pm; evening meals
Friday only, 7.30-8.45pm;
garden.

THORNBURY

Wheatsheaf (P)
Chapel Street
Tel: Thornbury (0454) 412366
Bulmer (PC)
Meals and snacks lunchtime
and evening; garden; skittle
alley/children's room.

TICKENHAM

Post Office Stores (OL)
Clevedon Road, Nailsea
Tel: Nailsea (0272) 852102
Wilkins (PC)

TIMSBURY

Guss & Crook (P)
South Road
Tel: Timsbury (0761) 70373
Taunton (PC)
Large village pub. Meals and
snacks lunchtime and
evening; garden; pool.

WESTERLEIGH

Olde Inne (P)
Westerleigh Road
Tel: Chipping Sodbury
(0454) 312344
Taunton (PC)
Village pub, reputed to be
haunted. Meals lunchtime

and evening; garden;
children's room.

WESTON-SUPER-MARE

Bunters Bar (P)
Birnbeck Road
Rich (PC)

Paddle Steam Tavern (P)
The Old Pier
Rich (PC)

Salamis (OL)
44 Orchard Street
Tel: Weston-Super-Mare
(0934) 22213
Inch

WESTWICK

PLUM TREE CIDER▲
Plum Tree Farm, Summer
Lane
Tel: Weston-Super-Mare
(0934) 510707

WORLE

Lamb (P)
High Street
Tel: Weston-Super-Mare
(0934) 513075
Taunton (PC)

Olde Kings Head (P)
The Scaurs
Tel: Weston-Super-Mare
(0934) 510377
Taunton (PC)

WRITHLINGTON

Fir Tree (P)
Frome Road (A362)
Tel: Radstock (0761) 33139
Taunton (PC)
Large pub outside village.
Snacks; garden; skittles.

YATTON

Butchers Arms (P)
31 High Street
Tel: Yatton (0934) 833377
Bulmer (PP)
17th century building.
Snacks at lunchtime; garden.

SS Great Britain, landmark of the Orchard Cider House, Bristol

Bedfordshire

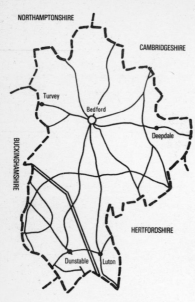

NORTHAMPTONSHIRE

CAMBRIDGESHIRE

Turvey

Bedford

Deepdale

BUCKINGHAMSHIRE

HERTFORDSHIRE

Dunstable   Luton

DEEPDALE

Locomotive (P)
on B 1042
Tel: Potton (0767) 260365
Bulmer (H)
Near bird sanctuary and
Sandy TV transmitter. Meals
and snacks lunchtime and
evening; garden.

DUNSTABLE

The Wheatsheaf (P)
82 High Street,
North Dunstable
Tel: Dunstable (0582) 62571
Bulmer (H)
Meals lunchtime; snacks
10.30-2.30; outdoor eating
and drinking area; live bands
Monday and Wednesday;
music lunchtimes and
evenings.

LUTON

Barn Owl (P)
Leyhill Drive
Tel: Luton (0582) 29532
Bulmer (H)
Meals and snacks 12-2 and
7-10 Monday to Saturday;
large play area for children;
garden; children's room.

TURVEY

Three Fyshes (P)
on main Bedford to
Northampton road (A428)
Tel: Turvey (023 064) 264
Guest Ciders (PC)
Riverside pub on border of
Bedfordshire and Bucks.
Meals and snacks; garden;
children's room.

The Three Fyshes at Turvey

*Your recommendations
are welcomed for future
editions of the Guide
Please use the inspection
form at the back*

Berkshire

BUCKINGHAMSHIRE

OXFORDSHIRE

Batts Green
Hare Hatch
Ruscombe
Fifield
Windsor
Reading
Shefford Woodland
Frilsham
Marsh Benham
Newbury
Ascot
Kintbury

HAMPSHIRE

ASCOT

Oddbins (OL)
5 Hermitage Parade,
High Street
Tel: Ascot (0990) 22370

BATTS GREEN

Dewdrop Inn (P)
South of Hurley (turn up road
by Grassland Research
Centre, and right at end)
Tel: Littlewick Green
(062 882) 4327
Coates (PC)
Snacks all sessions; barbeque
in summer, garden.

FIFIELD

Royal Foresters (P)
Drift Road (off Bracknell to
Maidenhead road – A330)
Tel: Maidenhead
(0628) 27987
Bulmer (H) & (E)
Until recently a Bulmer cider
house, now "privatised", but
still maintaining the
tradition. Snacks; garden.

FRILSHAM

Pot Kiln (P)
on Yattenden to Bucklesbury
road
Tel: Hermitage (0635) 201366
**West Country Scrumpy
(PC)**
Isolated country cottage,
within sound but fortunately
not reach of M4. Make for
Frilsham *Common* rather
than the village. Meals and
snacks Monday to Saturday
12-2 and 6.30-10; rolls on
Sunday; garden; children's
room.

HARE HATCH

Whippit Inn (P)
Blakes Lane
Tel: Wargrave (073 522) 2227
**Whippit Inn Farmhouse
Cider (PC)**
Just east of village – turn
north off A4 at sign for Upper
Wargrave. Meals Lunchtime
and Friday and Saturday
evening; garden;
accommodation.

KINTBURY

Crossways Inn (P)
Inkpen Road
Tel: Kintbury (0488) 58398
Bulmer (E)
About 1 mile from village,
used to be the village school.
Meals and snacks all sessions;
restaurant, terrace.

MARSH BENHAM

Red House (P)
off A4
Tel: Newbury (0635) 41637
Perry (PC) summer
Thatched pub in old estate
hamlet, just north of Kennet
& Avon Canal. Check first for
availability of the cider.
Snacks 12-2 and 6.30-10.30
all sessions; meals evening
from 7.30 except Sunday;
restaurant; garden with
children's cabin; miniature
passenger carrying railway.

NEWBURY

Newbury Beer Shop
(OL)
3 Saddlers Court,
The Broadway
Tel: Newbury (0635) 35171

Rich (PC)
Symonds (PC)

Sun Store (OL)
Marsh Lane
Tel: Newbury (0635) 30825
Weston (PC) (PL)

READING

Grog Shop (OL)
11 London Road
Tel: Reading (0635) 587847
Weston (H)

RUSCOMBE

Royal Oak (P)
Ruscombe Lane
Tel: Twyford (0734) 345190
Bulmer (PC)
Meals and snacks Monday to
Friday lunchtime; garden.

SHEFFORD
WOODLANDS

Pheasant (P)
Baydon Road
near A338/M4
Tel: Great Shefford
(048 839) 284
Bulmer (PC) summer
Tile hung country inn. Meals
lunchtime and evening;
garden; children's room.

WINDSOR

Jon Hallam (OL)
34 Devereux Road
Tel: Windsor (0753) 852609
**Farm ciders and perries
(BB) (PC)**
Traditional small farm
produced cider/perry in "live"
unfiltered state supplied in
your own container (from 1
gal.)

Oddbins (OL)
44 Peascod Street
Tel: Windsor (075 35) 59882
Weston (J)

Two Brewers (P)
Park Street
Tel: Windsor (0753) 855426
Town centre pub strategically
placed between Castle and

Windsor Great Park. A good
base for a day out, don't miss
Madame Tussaud's
Exhibition at the GWR
station. Meals lunchtime all
days.

Buckinghamshire

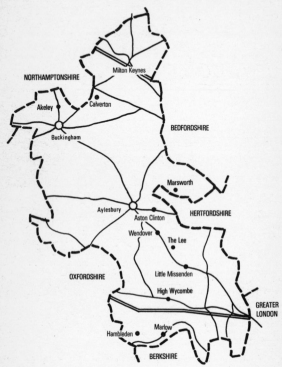

AKELEY

Bull and Butcher (P)
The Square (A413)
Tel: Lillingstone Dayrell
(028 06) 287
Bulmer (H)
In the centre of the village.
Meals lunchtime except
Sunday, evenings except
Sunday and Monday;
restaurant; garden.

ASTON CLINTON

Gerrard Harris Ltd.
(OL)
2 Green End Street
Yearlstone (B)
Yearlstone Apple Wine (B)

CALVERTON

Shoulder of Mutton
(P)
Lower Weald (nr. B4033)
Tel: Milton Keynes
(0908) 562183
Bulmer (H) summer

HAMBLEDEN

Stag & Huntsman
Inn (P)
Tel: Henley (0491) 571227
Bulmer (H)
In picturesque brick and flint
Trust village. Meals and
snacks all sessions except
Sunday evening; garden;
accommodation.

HIGH WYCOMBE

The Brewer (OL)
19 Desborough Avenue
Tel: High Wycombe
(0494) 25538
Weston (PC)

LITTLE
MISSENDEN

The Crown (P)
off A413
Bulmer (PC)
Lunchtime hot food.

MARSWORTH

Red Lion (P)
90 Vicarage Road

18

Tel: Cheddington
0242) 668366
Weston (PC)
Near Grand Union Canal and
Tring nature reserve.
Improved but unspoilt. Meals
and snacks except Sunday;
garden.

MARLOW

Two Brewers (P)
Bulmer (H)

MILTON KEYNES

Oddbins (OL)
15 Acorn Walk
Tel: Milton Keynes
(0908) 604599
Weston (J)

THE LEE

Gate Inn (P)
Swan Bottom
Tel: The Lee (024 020) 368

Bulmer (H)   .
Remote and rural. Meals and
snacks lunchtime only;
garden; children's room.

WENDOVER

Red Lion Hotel (P)
High Street (A413)
Tel: Wendover (0296) 622266
Bromell (PC)
Snacks 12-2.30 and 6-10.30;
meals 12-2.30 and 7-9.30;
restaurant; garden;
accommodation.

Cleveland

(map see page 93)

BILLINGHAM

Off Licence (OL)
25 Ruseberry Road
Cornish Scrumpy

HARTLEPOOL

Sun Inn (P)
Durham Street
Tel: Hartlepool (0429) 67759
Bulmer (H)
Bar meals at lunchtime.

REDCAR

**Newbigging Hotel
(P)**
Queen Street/Turner Street
Tel: Redcar (0642) 482059
Scrumpy (PC)
Choice of two ciders at all
times, type changed every
fortnight. Meals and snacks
12-2 and 7-9; restaurant;
outdoor drinking area;
accommodation; children
welcome.

*Your recommendations
are welcomed for future
editions of the Guide
Please use the inspection
form at the back*

Getting to the core of the problem . . .

C AMRA, the Campaign for
Real Ale, defends the
interests of beer and cider
lovers.

In more than 15 years of lobbying
and campaigning, CAMRA has
shaken the drinks industry from
top to bottom.

It has shown how giant combines
manipulate the market and dep-
rive drinkers of choice.

It has exposed the fraud of brews
that masquerade as "traditional"
but are little better than keg beer
and cider. It has produced a
series of carefully researched
reports arguing for the break up
of the drinks oligopolies and has
called for government action to
prevent further take-overs.

The pint of traditional cider
you are enjoying possibly owes
its existence to CAMRA. Why
not strengthen our arm and
ensure your enjoyment by joining today? A year's membership
costs £9 and brings you a
monthly newspaper, What's
Brewing, and generous discounts
on the Good Beer Guide and
other books. Send a cheque to
CAMRA, 34 Alma Road, St
Albans, Herts AL1 3BW.

Cambridgeshire

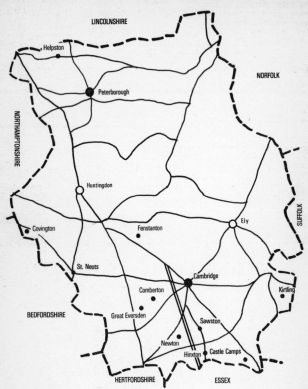

CAMBRIDGE

Alma Brewery (P)
26 Russell Court
Tel: Cambridge (0223) 64965
Weston (H)
Snacks lunchtime.

Salisbury Arms (P)
Tenison Road
Tel: Cambridge (0223) 60363
Weston (H)
Lunchtime bar food.

Jug & Firkin (OL)
90 Mill Road
Tel: Cambridge
(0223) 315034
James White (B)

Oddbins (OL)
14 Regent Street
Tel: Cambridge (0223) 67000
Weston (J)

CASTLE CAMPS

New Inn (P)
Saffron Ciders (PC)

COMBERTON

Grape Vine (P)
5 Green End
Tel: Comberton
(022 026) 3059
Saffron Ciders (PC)

COVINGTON

Red Cow (P)
Tel: Huntingdon
(0480) 861336
Saffron Ciders (H)

FENSTANTON

King William IV (P)
High Street
Tel: St. Ives (0480) 62467
Merrydown (BB)
Taunton (BB)
16th century inn, heavily
beamed with inglenook
fireplaces. Meals and snacks
all sessions; restaurant;
garden.

GREAT EVERSDEN

Post Office Stores (OL)
Tel: Comberton
(022 026) 2205
Saffron Ciders (B)

GUESTING-THORPE

Pheasant (P)
Saffron Ciders

20

HELPSTON

Bluebell (P)
10 Woodgate
Tel: Peterborough
(0733) 252314
Bulmer (H)
Next to poet John Clare's
cottage. Snacks any time,
garden; accommodation.

HINXTON

Red Lion (P)
High Street
Tel: Saffron Walden
(0799) 30601
Saffron Ciders (PC)

KIRTLING

Queens Head Inn (P)
Tel: Newmarket
(0638) 730253

Bulmer (PC)
A beautiful Elizabethan inn
in attractive countryside, on
border with Suffolk. Home
made food, good range of bar
snacks, 10.30-2 and 7-11;
garden; accommodation.

NEWTON

Queens Head (P)
off B1368
Tel: Cambridge
(0223) 870436
Bulmer (PC)
Cellar dates from 1450, rest
from 1680. Snacks all
sessions; garden; children's
room.

PETERBOROUGH

Gladstone Arms (P)
Gladstone Street
Tel: Peterborough
(0733) 44388

Bulmer (H)
Saffron Perry (PC)

Harrier (P)
Gunthorpe Road
Gunthorpe (near A47)
Tel: Peterborough
(0733) 75362
Taunton (H)
Prize winning design new
pub. Meals lunchtime;
garden.

ST. NEOTS

Globe (P)
Huntingdon Street
(off B1043)
Tel: Huntingdon
(0480) 72590
Bulmer (H)

SAWSTON

University Arms (P)
84 London Road
Tel: Cambridge (0223) 32165
Saffron Ciders (PC)

21

Cornwall

Padstow

St. Columb

Newquay

Trerice

Perranporth

Penhallow

St. Agnes

Chacewater

Truro

Portreath

Blackwater

Tregony

Redruth

Veryan

St. Ives

Philleigh

Zennor

Hayle

Pendeen

Crowntown

St. Mawes

Penzance

Marazion

Falmouth

Long Rock

Helford Passage

St Michaels Mount

Praa Sands

St. Kerverne

ALBASTON

Queens Head (P)
off A390
Tel: Tavistock (0822) 832482
Taunton (PC)
Lively local in old mining
area. Snacks.

BLACKWATER

**Blackwater Stores
(OL)**
Tel: Truro (0872) 560320
Apple Blossom (B)

BOSCASTLE

Cobweb Inn (P)
Bude Road
Tel: Boscastle (084 05) 278
Countryman (PC)
300 year old wine and spirit
cellar where cobwebs
insulated the roof and spiders
kept other bugs at bay. Meals
and snacks 11.30-2.30 and
6-10; restaurant; garden;
children's room.

Napoleon (P)
on B3266
Tel: Boscastle (084 05) 204
Countryman (PC)
16th century inn set high
above the village. Meals
lunchtime and evening;
garden.

Wellington Hotel (P)
The Harbour
Tel: Boscastle (084 05) 203
Inch (BB) (PP)
Former coaching inn, listed
400 year old building. Close to
Elizabethan harbour,
surrounded by National
Trust walks. Snacks 12-2 and
6.30-9.30; full meals
7.30-9.30; restaurant;
garden; children's room;
accommodation.

BOTUS FLEMING

Rising Sun (P)
Tel: Saltash (075 55) 2792
Local cider (PP) (W)

BUDE

**Beville House Wines
(OL)**
22 Lansdown Road
Tel: Bude (0288) 2320
Cornish Scrumpy

Brendon Arms (P)
Tel: Bude (0288) 2713
Wonnacott (PC)
Quayside pub overlooking
Inner Harbour. Meals and
snacks lunchtime and
evening; children's room;
accommodation; facilities for
disabled.

**Mister Wonnacotts
(OL)**
Wonnacott (PC)

**WONNACOTT'S
CIDER ▲**
Lansdown Yard
Tel: Bude (0288) 3105

CALLINGTON

Bulls Head (P)
Tel: Liskeard (0579) 83387
Inch (PC)
Town centre pub. Snacks;
accommodation.

CARGREEN

Spaniards (P)
off A388
Tel: Saltash (075 55) 2830
Local cider (PC)
Riverside inn set in beautiful
Tamar Valley. Meals
lunchtime and evening;
garden; children's room;
accommodation; facilities for
disabled.

CHACEWATER

Kings Head (P)
Fore Street
Tel: Truro (0872) 560652
Bulmer (PC)
Unspoilt pub in former
mining village. Meals and
snacks lunchtime and
evening; garden;
accommodation.

CHAPEL AMBLE

Maltsters Arms (P)
Tel: Wadebridge
(021 881) 2473
Cornish Scrumpy (PC)
16th century inn with 3ft
thick walls and ancient ship's
timbers; slate floors. Snacks
and lunchtime meals; garden;
camping nearby; facilities for
disabled.

CHARLESTOWN

The Rashleigh (P)
Tel: St. Austell (0726) 73635
Apple Blossom (P)
Close to harbour and beaches.
Snacks lunchtime; large
garden/outdoor drinking
area; pool; accommodation.

CHILSWORTHY

White Hart Inn (P)
Tel: Tavistock (0822) 832307
Countryman (W)

Ancient village inn with superb views over Tamar Valley, renowned for widest range of real ales and ciders in Cornwall. Snacks all sessions; gardens; children's room.

CRACKINGTON HAVEN

Coombe Barton Hotel (P)
Tel: St. Gennys (084 03) 345
Cornish Scrumpy (PC)
Sheppy (PC)
By the beach in a beautiful Cornish bay. Snacks lunchtime and evening till 10pm; full meals evening 7-9.30pm; restaurant; garden; accommodation.

CROWNTOWN

Crown Inn (P)
near Helston
Tel: Helston (032 65) 2660
Bulmer (PC)
Pleasant village inn. Meals and snacks lunchtime and evening; garden; children's room; accommodation.

DELABOLE

Spar Stores (OL)
75 High Street
Tel: Camelford (0840) 212303
Inch

FALMOUTH

Chesters (OL)
28 Church Street
Tel: Falmouth (0326) 312022
Cornish Scrumpy

Victoria Wines (OL)
7a Killigrew Street
Tel: Falmouth (0326) 311839
Local cider

GUNNISLAKE

Rising Sun (P)
Calstock Road, Hatches Green (off A390)
Tel: Tavistock (0822) 832201
Hill (PC)
17th century local overlooking Tamar Valley. Snacks; garden.

HAYLE

Old Quay House (P)
Griggs Quay
Tel: Hayle (0736) 753988
Cornish Scrumpy (PC)
Meals and snacks lunchtime and evening; garden; children's room; accommodation.

HELFORD PASSAGE

Ferry Boat Inn (P)
near Mawnam Smith
Tel: Falmouth (0326) 250625
Bulmer (H)
In riverside setting, with private beach. Snacks 12-2 and 7-10; full meals 12-2 and 7.30-10; restaurant; garden; children's room; accommodation; boat hire; private swimming pool, sauna, sun bed.

KILKHAMPTON

Spar Shop (OL)
Inch

LANHYDROCK

National Trust Restaurant (P)
2½ miles south east of Bodmin
Tel: Bodmin (0208) 3320
Apple Blossom (PC)
Victorian reconstruction of 17th century house, fine gardens. Open April to end of October, 11am to 6pm; November to end of March garden only open.

LISKEARD

Jenrich (OL)
2 Lower Lux Street
Tel: Liskeard (0579) 45151
Inch

LONG ROCK

Mexico Inn/Rock Inn (P)
Tel: Penzance (0736) 710625
Cornish Scrumpy (H)
Old Favourite (W)
Snacks 12-2.15; full meals 7-10.30; restaurant; outdoor drinking area; children's room; accommodation; log fires; lots of jazz; quiet bars; 60s bar.

LOOE

Allsorts (OL)
Higher Market Street, East Looe
Tel: Looe (050 36) 2615
Cornish Scrumpy

Peter Dominic (OL)
Fore Street
Tel: Looe (050 36) 2992
Local cider

Portbyhan Hotel (P)
West Looe
Tel: Looe (050 36) 2071
Cornish Scrumpy

Trevanian Hotel (P)
Hannafore
Tel: Looe (050 36) 2003
Cornish Scrumpy

LOSTWITHIEL

Earl of Chatham (P)
Grenville Road
Tel: Bodmin (0208) 872269
Local Cider (PC)
On the road to Lerryn. Meals
and snacks lunchtime and
evening; garden;
accommodation.

MARAZION

**Marazion
Pharmacy (OL)**
Apple Blossom (B)
To be taken three times daily
during and after meals.

MARHAMCHURCH

Bullers Arms (P)
Tel: Widemouth Bay
(028 885) 277
Sheppy (PC)
Farmers Scrumpy (PC)
In completely unspoilt village
2 miles from sea. Meals all
sessions; Sunday lunches;
garden; accommodation.

METHERILL

**Carpenters Arms
(P)**
Lower Metherill
Tel: Liskeard (0579) 50242
Countryman (PP)
15th century inn close to
National Trust House and
holiday village. Snacks
11-1.30; full meals 7-9.30;
garden.

MEVAGISSEY

Cellar Bar (P)
2a St. Georges Square
Tel: Mevagissey
(0726) 842951
Local Cider (PC)
Meals and snacks 12-2 and
6-10.30; outdoor drinking
area; children allowed inside
within main eating/drinking
area; charcoal barbeque in
summer season.

Fountain (P)
Cliff Street
Tel: Mevagissey
(0726) 842320
Bulmer (PC)
Cosy pub near harbour.
Snacks; children's room;
accommodation.

Rising Sun (P)
Portmellon
Tel: Mevagissey
(0726) 843235
Cornish Scrumpy

**Somerby Wines
(OL)**
18 Fore Street
Tel: Mevagissey
(0726) 843865
Cornish Scrumpy

NEWQUAY

**Cornish Goodies
(OL)**
Apple Blossom (B)

**Harbour Lights
(OL)**
Inch

**Booker Cash &
Carry (OL)**
Treloggan Road
Merrydown (BB)

**Hendra Tourist
Park (OL)**
Tel: office-Newquay
(0637) 875778
shop-Newquay (0637) 875996
Cornish Scrumpy

**Two Clomes Motel
Country Club (P)**
Quintrell Downs
Tel: Newquay (0637) 873485
Cornish Scrumpy

**White Acres
Holiday Park (OL)**
Caravan Site
Tel: St Austell (0726) 860220
Cornish Scrumpy

PADSTOW

Henwoods (OL)
Strand
Tel: Padstow (0841) 532325
Apple Blossom (B)

**Seafood Restaurant
(P)**
Station Road
Tel: Padstow (0841) 532485
Apple Blossom (F)

PAR

Par Inn (P)
2 Harbour Road
Tel: Par (072 681) 3961
Bulmer (PC)
Close to the docks. Snacks;
accommodation.

PENDEEN

**Trewellard Hotel
(P)**
on B3318
Tel: Penzance (0736) 788634
Cornish Scrumpy

Meals and snacks lunchtime
and evening; garden;
children's room;
accommodation; camping
nearby; facilities for disabled.

PENDOGGET

Cornish Arms (P)
on B3314
Tel: Port Isaac (020 888) 263
Weston (PC)
17th century house, popular
with holiday makers from
nearby beaches and coves.
Meals lunchtime and
evening; restaurant; garden;
children's room (lunchtime);
accommodation.

PENHALLOW

**CORNISH
SCRUMPY ▲**
Callestock Cider Farm
Tel: Truro (0872) 573356

PENZANCE

Old Bath Inn (P)
Cornwall Terrace
Tel: Penzance (0736) 64244
Cornish Scrumpy

**Old Coastguard
Hotel (P)**
Mousehole
Tel: Penzance (0736) 731222
Cornish Scrumpy

PERRANPORTH

Bamboo Club (P)
1 St. Michaels Road
Tel: Truro (0872) 573355
Cornish Scrumpy

Bics Wine Bar (P)
Boscawen Road
Tel: Truro (0872) 573865
Cornish Scrumpy

Corkscrew (OL)
Cornish Scrumpy

Ponsmere Hotel (P)
Tel: Perranporth
(087 257) 2225
Cornish Scrumpy (PC)
Close to 3 mile long beach.
Snacks; outdoor drinking
area; children's room,
accommodation; camping
nearby. Not open lunchtime
during winter.

PHILLEIGH

Roseland Inn (P)
off A3078 on King Harry
Ferry Road
Tel: Portscatho (087 258) 254
Taunton (PC)
17th century pub close to
King Harry Ferry, with cob
walls, low ceilings, and
wooden seats. Meals
lunchtime; evening in
summer; garden.

POLPERRO

Claremont Hotel Off Licence (OL)
Tel: Polperro (0503) 72536
Cornish Scrumpy

Crumplehorn Mill (P)
Tel: Polperro (0503) 72348
Churchward (PC)
—summer only
Near entrance to village.
Meals lunchtime and
evening; garden,
accommodation.

Noughts & Crosses (P)
Tel: Polperro (0503) 72239
Churchward (PC)
—summer only

PORTREATH

Basset Arms (P)
Tregea Terrace
Tel: Portreath (0209) 842077
Merrydown (BB)
Meals and snacks all sessions;
outdoor drinking area.

PRAA SANDS

Welloe Rock Inn (P)
Tel: Germoe (073 676) 3516
Cornish Scrumpy
Situated on the beach. Meals
and snacks lunchtime and
evening; outdoor drinking
area; children's room;
camping nearby.

REDRUTH

Oxford Inn (P)
28 Fore Street
Tel: Redruth (0209) 215651

Bulmer (H)
Snacks all sessions; full meals
10.30-2; outdoor drinking
area; accommodation.

Wine Shaft (OL)
12 Penryn Street
Tel: Redruth (0209) 211025
Apple Blossom (B)

ST. AGNES

Churchtown Stores (OL)
5 Churchtown
Tel: St. Agnes (087 255) 2459
Apple Blossom (B)

ST. AUSTELL

Sun Valley Holiday Park (P)
Pentewan Road
Tel: St. Austell (0726) 843266
Cornish Scrumpy (BB)
Meals and snacks 12-2 and
7.30-11; restaurant; garden;
children's room; holiday
homes for hire; camping and
touring; heated swimming
pool.

Victoria Wines (OL)
10 Fore Street
Tel: St. Austell (0726) 65693
Local cider

ST. BLAZEY

Cornish Arms (P)
Tel: Par (072 681) 3001
Bulmer (PC)

ST. COLUMB

Julius Street (OL)
Inch

ST. DOMINIC

Cotehele House (P)
Barn Restaurant
Countryman (PC)

Who'd Have Thought It Inn (P)
Tel: (0579) 50214
Inch (BB)
Near Cotehole House. Meals
and snacks 12-1.45 and
7.30-9.45.

ST. IVES

Johns Off Licence (OL)
Cornish Scrumpy

ST. KEW HIGHWAY

Red Lion (P)
Tel: St. Mabyn (020 884) 271
Inch (PC)
17th century village inn.
Snacks; garden; children's
room.

ST. MABYN

St Mabyn Inn (P)
off B3266
Tel: St. Mabyn (020 884) 266
Bulmer (H)
15th century inn next to the
village church. Meals and
snacks 12-2 and 6.30-9;
separate dining room;
garden; children's room.
(Reduced winter menu;
kitchen closed Monday and
Tuesday during winter).

ST. MAWES

Victory Inn (P)

Pub on the beach. Port William at Trebarwith Strand

Victory Steps
Tel: St. Mawes (0326) 270324
Merrydown (H)
Old village pub in the
Roseland. Snacks all sessions;
gardens; children's room;
accommodation.

ST. MICHAELS MOUNT

Sail Loft Restaurant (P)
Apple Blossom (PC)
A National Trust property.

ST. TUDY

Cornish Arms (P)
near B3266
Tel: Bodmin (0208) 850
Inch (PC)
Meals and snacks lunchtime
and evening; garden;
children's room.

STRATTON

Tree Inn (P)
Fore Street
Tel: Bude (0288) 2038/2931
Inch (PL)
Historic scheduled building,
home of the last of the
Cornish giants, Anthony
Payne, 7ft 4 inches tall, and
weighing 38 stone! Snacks
11-2 and 7-10; meals 12-1.45
and 7-10; restaurant; garden;
children's room;
accommodation; games room.

TINTAGEL

Cornishman (P)
Fore Street
Tel: Camelford (0840) 770238
Countryman (PC)
Meals and snacks lunchtime
and evening; garden;
children's room; camping
nearby.

Flowers Supermarket (OL)
Tel: Camelford (0840) 770323
Inch
Wonnacott (PC)

King Arthurs Arms (P)
Fore Street
Tel: Camelford (0840) 770304
Countryman (PC)
14th century building with 2
ft thick walls. Meals and
snacks lunchtime and
evening; garden; children's
room; camping nearby.

TREBARWITH STRAND

Port William (P)
Tel: Camelford (0840) 770230

Countryman (H)
Beachside pub, once the
harbour master's house and
stables. Meals and snacks all
sessions; terrace; children's
room; self catering
accommodation.

Trebarwith Strand Hotel (P)
Tel: Camelford (0840) 770326
Cornish Scrumpy (PC)
Countryman (PC)
Good bathing beach.
Accommodation.

TRELISSICK GARDEN

National Trust Restaurant (P)
Feock (4 miles south of Truro)
Tel: Truro (0872) 862090
Apple Blossom (PC)
Extensive park and gardens
beside River Fal with rare
plants and shrubs. Open from
April to end of October,
11-6pm.

TRERICE

National Trust Restaurant (P)
St. Newlyn East, near
Newquay
Tel: Newquay (063 73) 5404
Apple Blossom (PC)
Restaurant set in
Elizabethan barn adjoining
16th century manor house
and small museum tracing
the history of the lawn
mower. Open from April to
end of October, 11-6pm.

TRURO

APPLE BLOSSOM CIDER
Trevean Farm, Coombe Kea
Tel: Truro (0872) 77177

Cheese Board Creation Centre
Lemon Quay
Tel: Truro (0872) 70813
Apple Blossom (B)

Pottles (P)
Pannier Market, Lemon
Quay
Tel: Truro (0872) 71384
Cornish Scrumpy (PC)

Walter Hicks (OL)
4 River Street
Tel: Truro (0872) 72100
Cornish Scrumpy

Wine Ale & Cheese Shop (OL)
Bridge House, St. Clement
Street
Tel: Truro (0872) 72091
Apple Blossom (PC)
Inch (PP)

Tarka Apple Brandy
Weston (PP)

TYWARDREATH

New Inn (P)
off A3082
Tel: Par (072 681) 390
Bulmer (E)
In quiet area near coast.
Meals lunchtime except
Sunday; garden;
accommodation; camping
nearby.

UPTON CROSS

Caradon Inn (P)
on B3254
Tel: Liskeard (0579) 62391
Haymaker (E)
18th century country inn.
Snacks 12-2 and 6-10; garden.

VERYAN

New Inn (P)
Tel: Truro (0872) 501362
Bulmer (PC)
18th century pub in beautiful
countryside near beaches.
Snacks 12–2 and 6.30-9;
outdoor drinking area;
accommodation.

WADEBRIDGE

Wadebridge Wines (OL)
Polmorla Road
Tel: Wadebridge
(020 881) 2692
Apple Blossom (B)

WEEK ST. MARY

Green Inn (P)
Tel: Week St. Mary
(028 884) 450
Wonnacott (PC)
Snacks; garden;
accommodation, camping
nearby.

WIDEMOUTH BAY

Widemouth Manor (P)
Tel: Widemouth Bay
(028 885) 263
Countryman (PC)
Inch (PC) (BB)
Seaside bar and hotel. Meals
and snacks all sessions;
restaurant; outdoor drinking
area; children's room;
accommodation.

ZENNOR

Tinners Arms (P)
on B3306
Tel: Penzance (0736) 796927
Inch (PL)
Thornton (PL)
An old church house,
Meals and snacks
lunchtime and evening;
garden; children's room,
camping nearby.

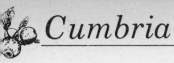

Cumbria

AMBLESIDE

Skelwith Bridge Hotel (P)
on A593 2½ miles west of town
Tel: Ambleside (0966) 2155
Bulmer (H)
Accommodation.

CARLISLE

Denton Wine Lodge (P)
50 Denton Street
Tel: Carlisle (0228) 33639
Cornish Scrumpy

Friars Tavern (P)
Devonshire Street
Tel: Carlisle (0228) 23757
Bulmer (H)
Lively town centre pub.
Meals lunchtime.

CARTMEL FELL

Masons Arms (P)
Strawberry Bank (off A5074)
Tel: Crossthwaite 044 88 486
Scrumpy (PC)
Vintage (PC)
Perry (PC)
A good selection of guest
ciders and perrys are
available on rotation basis,
also a bottled range, Long
Ashton, and Weston in 3 pint
jars. The pub is set in a
beautiful remote valley.
Meals and snacks 12-1.45 and
6-8.45 (Sunday 7-8.45);
garden; children's room;
accommodation. Stay a few
weeks and try the whole cider
cycle!

ELTERWATER

Britannia Inn (P)
off B5343
Tel: Langdale
(096 67) 382 or 210
Bulmer (H)
Good centre for fell walkers.
Pub dates back 400 years.
Snacks 12-1.45 and 6.30-9.00;
meals 7.30pm; restaurant;
garden; accommodation.

GREAT LANGDALE

Old Dungeon Ghyll (P)
on B5343
Tel: Langdale (096 67) 272

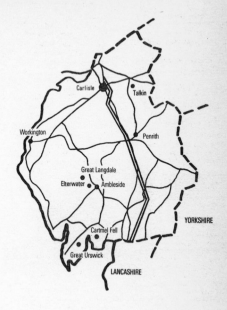

Bulmer (PC)
Climbers and walkers pub at
head of beautiful valley.
Home cooked meals,
lunchtime and evening;
garden; accommodation;
camping nearby.

GREAT URSWICK

General Burgoyne (P)
off A590, 2 miles west of
Ulverston
Tel: Bardsea (022 988) 394
Bulmer (PC)
Popular village inn. Meals
evening; garden.

PENRITH

The Cumbrian Cellar (OL)
1 St. Andrews Street
Tel: Penrith (0768) 63664
Merrydown (BB)

TALKIN

Hare & Hounds Inn (P)
Tel: Brampton (069 77) 3456
or 3457
Bulmer (H)
In the heart of the fells; once
used by monks as a stop over
on the way from
Armathwaite to Lanercost
Priory; excellent walking and
fishing country. Meals and
snacks every evening 7-9;
Saturday and Sunday lunch
12-1.30; garden; children's
room; accommodation.

WORKINGTON

Wine Cellars (OL)
2 Nook Street
Tel: Workington (0900) 4639
Cornish Scrumpy

Derbyshire

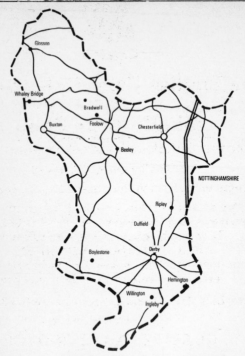

BRADWELL

Travellers Rest (P)
Brough Lane Head
Tel: Hope Valley
(0433) 20363
Bulmer (H)
Meals and snacks lunchtime,
and 6-8 during summer; large
garden with children's
facilities.

BOYLESTONE

Rose & Crown (P)
off A515
Tel: Great Cubley
(037 184) 518
Bulmer (PC)
Small white washed pub in
pleasant setting. Garden;
children's room.

DUFFIELD

Wheel (P)
Chapel Street, Holbrook
Tel: Derby (0332) 880006
Weston (F)

FOOLOW

Bulls Head Inn (P)
off A623
Tel: Hope Valley
(0433) 30873
Bulmer (H)
Oak beams and brasses.
Meals and snacks lunchtime
and evening; restaurant;
garden; camping; facilities for
disabled.

GLOSSOP

Coopers & Son (OL)
Symonds (PC)

HEMINGTON

Three Horseshoes (P)
Tel: Derby (0332) 810 408
Weston (F)

INGLEBY

LLOYDS COUNTRY BEERS
John Thompson Inn
Tel: Melbourne (033 16) 3426
or 2469

RIPLEY

Hollybush (P)
Brook Lane (off A61)
Tel: Ripley (0773) 42558
Bulmer (H)
Good view of cricket ground.
Meals evening; garden;
facilities for disabled.

WHALEY BRIDGE

Fermentation (OL)
1a Canal Street
Tel: Whaley Bridge
(066 33) 4214
Westrays (F)
Stock up for your canal cruise!

WILLINGTON

Rising Sun (P)
1 The Green
Tel: Burton on Trent
(0283) 702116
Bulmer (PC)
In village on Trent & Mersey
Canal, good for overnight
stop. Meals and snacks
lunchtime; garden.

ENGLISH FARM CIDER CENTRE

The English Farm Cider Centre
AND
Middle Farm Shop

Taste free samples of many of England's finest Farm 'Scrumpy' Ciders

Brought to you from the length and breadth of England

We have Cider from Sussex – Cider from Kent – Cider from Hereford & Worcester – Norfolk & Suffolk Cider – Devon and Somerset Cider – and of course, REAL FARM SCRUMPY CIDER
Containers supplied – but our Ciders & Perry will be even better value if you bring your own!

Suppliers of Real Farm Ciders to the Licensed Trade

See also a selection of

QUALITY FARM PRODUCE

from Middle Farm Shop

THE ENGLISH FARM CIDER CENTRE AND MIDDLE FARM SHOP
Firle, Lewes, East Sussex.
Telephone: Ripe (032 183) 303 or 411

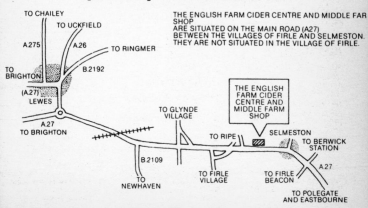

THE ENGLISH FARM CIDER CENTRE AND MIDDLE FARM SHOP
ARE SITUATED ON THE MAIN ROAD (A27)
BETWEEN THE VILLAGES OF FIRLE AND SELMESTON.
THEY ARE NOT SITUATED IN THE VILLAGE OF FIRLE.

Devon

ALPHINGTON

New Inn (P)
76 Church Road
Tel: Exeter (0392) 72584
Inch (PC)

Sydney Road Dairy (OL)
Gray (PL)

APPLEDORE

Bell Inn (P)
New Quay Street
Tel: Appledore (023 72) 74769
Inch (H)
Slipway to the Torridge Estuary, and seating on the sea wall. Snacks 11-2.30; outdoor drinking area; children's room.

Mace Stores (OL)
Inch (BB) (J)

ASHBURTON

Bay Horse (P)
North Street
Tel: Ashburton (0364) 52838
Inch (PL)
Snacks 11-2 and 5-8; children's room.

Exeter Inn (P)
26 West Street
Tel: Ashburton (0364) 52559
Local cider (PC)
12th century pub where Sir Walter Raleigh was arrested. Meals; accommodation.

Ford Stores (OL)
12 North Street
Tel: Ashburton (0364) 52546
Local cider

Golden Lion Hotel (P)
East Street
Tel: Ashburton (0364) 52205
Local cider (PC)
Meals; outdoor drinking area; accommodation.

Holne Chase Hotel (P)
Tel: Poundsgate (036 43) 471
Local cider (BB)
Snacks 12-1.45; meals 7-8.30; accommodation.

London Hotel (P)
West Street
Tel: Ashburton (0364) 52478

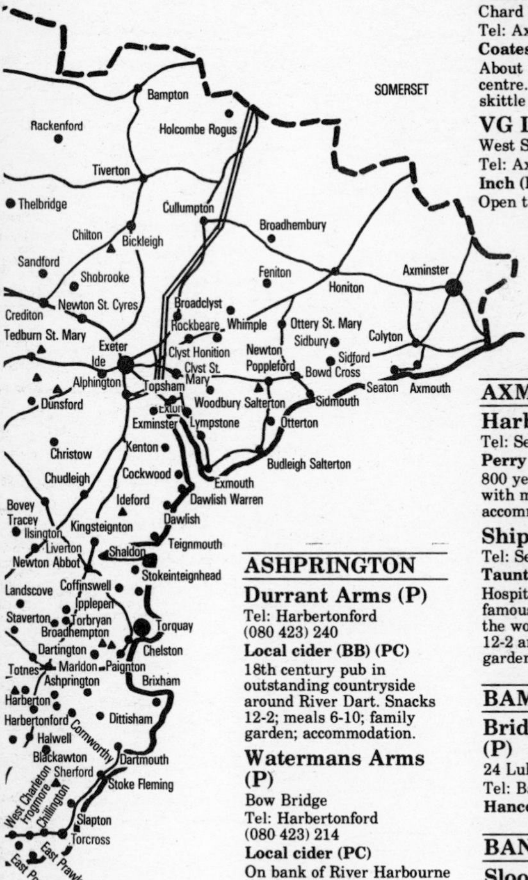

Map labels (Devon/Somerset area):
SOMERSET, Bampton, Rackenford, Holcombe Rogus, Tiverton, Thelbridge, Cullompton, Broadhembury, Chilton, Bickleigh, Sandford, Shobrooke, Feniton, Axminster, Crediton, Newton St. Cyres, Broadclyst, Honiton, Tedburn St. Mary, Rockbeare, Whimple, Ottery St. Mary, Colyton, Exeter, Clyst Honiton, Sidbury, Ide, Clyst St. Mary, Newton Poppleford, Sidford, Alphington, Topsham, Bowd Cross, Dunsford, Eaton, Woodbury Salterton, Seaton, Axmouth, Exminster, Sidmouth, Christow, Kenton, Lympstone, Otterton, Chudleigh, Cockwood, Budleigh Salterton, Bovey Tracey, Ideford, Exmouth, Ilsington, Kingsteignton, Dawlish Warren, Newton Abbot, Dawlish, Shaldon, Teignmouth, Landscove, Stokeinteignhead, Coffinswell, Ipplepen, Staverton, Torbryan, Torquay, Broadhempton, Dartington, Chelston, Totnes, Marldon, Paignton, Ashprington, Brixham, Harberton, Harbertonford, Dittisham, Halwell, Blackawton, Dartmouth, Sherford, West Charleton, Frogmore, Chillington, Stoke Fleming, Slapton, Torcross, East Prawle, East Portlemouth

ASHPRINGTON

Durrant Arms (P)
Tel: Harbertonford (080 423) 240
Local cider (BB) (PC)
18th century pub in outstanding countryside around River Dart. Snacks 12-2; meals 6-10; family garden; accommodation.

Watermans Arms (P)
Bow Bridge
Tel: Harbertonford (080 423) 214
Local cider (PC)
On bank of River Harbourne beside picturesque Bow Bridge. Meals; garden.

ASHWATER

Manor Inn (P)
Inch (PC)
Sheppy (PC)
Meals 11-2 and 6-10.15; garden; ¾ size grass tennis court; full size snooker table; pool; bar billiards.

Local cider (PC)
Meals.

Royal Oak (P)
East Street
Tel: Ashburton (0364) 52444
Local cider (PC)
Meals.

AXMINSTER

New Commercial Inn (P)
Trinity Square
Tel: Axminster (0297) 33225
Coates (H)
Comfortable town centre local. Snacks 10.30-2.30 and 6-10; meals 7.30am-5pm in separate restaurant; coffee shop.

Millwey (P)
Chard Road (A358)
Tel: Axminster (0297) 32774
Coates (PC)
About 1 mile from town centre. Meals and snacks; skittle alley.

VG Late Shop (OL)
West Street
Tel: Axminster (0297) 34415
Inch (BB) (J)
Open till 9pm.

AXMOUTH

Harbour Inn (P)
Tel: Seaton (0297) 20371
Perry (PC)
800 year old thatched inn with many rooms. Meals; accommodation.

Ship Inn (P)
Tel: Seaton (0297) 21838
Taunton (PC)
Hospital for birds & animals; famous collection of dolls of the world. Meals and snacks 12-2 and 7.30-10; restaurant; garden.

BAMPTON

Bridge House Hotel (P)
24 Luke Street
Tel: Bampton (0398) 31298
Hancock (F)

BANTHAM

Sloop Inn (P)
near A379
Tel: Kingsbridge (0348) 560489
Local cider (PC)
16th century inn 300 yards from the beach; excellent surfing. Meals and snacks 12-2 (1.30 on Sunday) and 7-10; restaurant; accommodation; holiday cottages; garden; children's room.

BARNSTAPLE

Albert Inn (P)
Diamond Street
Tel: Barnstaple (0271) 72640
Taunton (H)
Town centre cider pub.
Childrens' room.

Corner Shop (OL)
54 Newport Road
Tel: Barnstaple (0271) 78129
Hancock (B)

Imperial Hotel (P)
Taw Vale Parade
Tel: Barnstaple (0271) 45861
Inch (PC)

Lynwood House Restaurant (P)
Fortescue Road
Tel: Barnstaple (0271) 43695
Inch (PC)

Oakland Stores (OL)
Oakland Park
Inch (BB) (J)

Sherrys Restaurant (P)
54 Boutport Street
Tel: Barnstaple (0271) 45499
Inch (PC)

Union Inn (P)
Princess Street
(off Vicarage Street)
Tel: Barnstaple (0271) 42863
Taunton (E)
Snacks all sessions; children's
room; skittle alley; pool.

BEAFORD

Globe (P)
on B3220
Tel: Beaford (080 53) 261
Inch (PC)

BELSTONE

Tors Hotel (P)
Tel: Okehampton
(0837) 840689
Gray (PC)
Solid Victorian hotel on edge
of Dartmoor. Meals and
snacks 12-2 and 7-9.30;
restaurant; garden;
children's room;
accommodation; riding and
pony trekking immediately
available – just phone to
book.

BERRYNARBOR

Manor Stores (OL)
near Ilfracombe
Hancock (B)

BICKLEIGH

Bickleigh Mill Farm Shop (OL)

Tel: Bickleigh (088 45) 419
Yearlstone (B)
Yearlstone Wine (B)

BIDEFORD

Bideford Wines (OL)
Old Town
Tel. Bideford (023 72) 70507
Inch (BB) (J)

J & K Wines (OL)
Inch (BB) (J)

Joiners Arms (P)
Inch (PC)

Old Custom House (P)
1 Bridgeland Street
Tel: Bideford (023 72) 70044
Inch (BB)
Meals and snacks 12-2 and
6.45-10; restaurant.

Portobello (P)
Silver Street (A39)
Tel: Bideford (023 72) 2991
Taunton (H)
Corner house local, popular
with young. Meals lunchtime
and evening; outdoor
drinking area; children's
room; facilities for disabled.

BIGBURY

Post Office (OL)
Hill

Royal Oak (P)
on B3392
Tel: Bigbury-on-Sea (054 881)
313
Hill (PC)
Meals; garden.

BLACKAWTON

Normandy Arms (P)
Tel: Blackawton
(080 421) 316
Stancombe Farm Cider (PC)
16th century pub, but named
after the Normandy landings:
the British troops did their
pre-invasion training here!
It's quieter now. Snacks 12-2
and 6.30-9.30; meals 12-1.30
and 7-9.30; restaurant;
garden; children's room;
accommodation.

BOVEY TRACEY

Cromwell Arms (P)
on B3344
Tel: Bovey Tracey
(0626) 833473
Local cider (PC)

BOW

White Hart (P)
on A3072

Inch (PC)
18th century pub. Meals;
garden; children's room;
accommodation.

BOWD CROSS

The Famous Bowd Inn (P)
on A3052
Tel: Sidmouth (039 55) 3328
Bulmer (PC)
Large, old and popular pub on
main road. Meals and snacks
12-2 and 7-10; separate
dining room; garden;
children's room;
accommodation.

BRANSCOMBE

Masons Arms (P)
near A3052
Inch (PC)
Old, thatched, and attractive.
Meals; garden;
accommodation.

Three Horseshoes (P)
on A3052 (outside village)
Tel: Branscombe
(029 780) 251
Local cider (H)
Meals lunchtime and
evening; garden; children's
room; accommodation;
camping nearby.

BRAUNTON

Braunton Wines (OL)
26 Caen Street
Tel: Braunton (0271) 812054
Inch (BB) (J)

BRIDESTOWE

Royal Oak (P)
Tel: Bridestowe (083 786) 214
Inch (PC)
Meals; garden;
accommodation.

White Hart (P)
Fore Street
Tel: Bridestowe (083 786) 318
Inch (PC)
Old coaching inn. Meals;
restaurant; garden;
accommodation.

BRIXHAM

Breakwater Restaurant (P)
Breakwater Beach,
Berry Head Road
Tel: Brixham (080 45) 6738
Churchward (PC)

Brixham Co-op (OL)
75 Fore Street
Tel: Brixham (080 45) 2888
Local cider

Cullinaria (OL)
60 Middle Street
Tel: Brixham (080 45) 4364
Local cider

Grape Vine (OL)
1 Churchill Court,
Bolton Street
Tel: Brixham (080 45) 4909
Local cider (BB) (PL)
Greengrocer and video
library.

BRIXTON

Brixton Off Licence (OL)
Local cider

BROADHEMBURY

Drewe Arms (P)
off A373
Tel: Broadhembury
(040 484) 267
Bulmer (PC)
Ancient thatched pub. Snacks
all sessions; meals 11.45-1.45
and 7-9.45; garden; children's
room; accommodation.

BROADHEMPSTON

Coppa Dolla Inn (P)
Tel: Ipplepen (0803) 812455
Local cider (BB)
Meals and snacks lunchtime
and 7-10; restaurant; garden.

Monks Retreat (P)
Tel: Ipplepen (0803) 812203
Local cider (PP)
Resident ghost! Meals and
snacks lunchtime and
evening; accommodation; self
contained holiday flat.

BUCKFAST

Buckfast Retail Shop (OL)
Tel: Buckfastleigh
(0364) 42882
Local cider
The modern Benedictine
Abbey should be visited.

BUCKFASTLEIGH

Buckfastleigh Wines (OL)
3-4 Fore Street
Tel: Buckfastleigh
(0364) 43790
Inch (BB)
Luscombe (PL)

Dart Bridge Inn (P)
Totnes Road (A384)
Local cider (PC)
Meals; garden.

LUSCOMBE CIDER▲

Luscombe Farm
Tel: Buckfastleigh (0364)
42373

Watermans Arms (P)
Market Street
Tel: Buckfastleigh (0364)
43200
Local cider (PC)
13th century coaching inn.
Meals and snacks 12-2 and
7-10; accommodation.

White Hart (P)
2 Plymouth Road
Tel: Buckfastleigh
(0364) 2336
Local cider (PC)
Garden; children's room;
accommodation.

BUDLEIGH SALTERTON

Creamery (OL)
Fore Street
Local cider
Inch (BB) (J)

Peter Dominic (OL)
13 High Street
Local cider

White Hart Hotel (P)
Local cider (PC)

BURGH ISLAND

Pilchard Inn (P)
Tel: Bigbury-on-Sea
(054 881) 344
Bulmer (H)
Coates (H)
Built in 1336, possesses
smuggler's ghost. The island
can only be reached on foot at
low tide; at other times you
travel on the world's only
giant sea tractor! Meals and
snacks all sessions;
restaurant; garden; wild
flowers and seabirds on
island.

CHAGFORD

Blacks Wine Stores (OL)
28 The Square
Tel: Chagford (064 73) 3545
Inch (BB) (J)

Globe (P)
High Street
Tel: Chagford (064 73) 3483
Inch (PC)
In good centre for northern
Dartmoor.

CHAWLEIGH

Portsmouth Inn (P)
Tel: Chulmleigh (0769) 80204
Inch (PP)
Meals and snacks 12-2 and
7-10; restaurant; garden;
children's room.

Royal Oak (P)
Tel: Chulmleigh (0769) 80427
Inch (PC)

CHELSTON

Chelston Manor Hotel (P)
Tel: Torquay (0803) 605142
Local cider (PC)
Accommodation.

CHERITON BISHOP

Old Thatch Inn (P)
on old A30
Tel: Cheriton Bishop
(064 724) 204
Bromell (PC) April to
September
Meals 12-1.45 and 6.30-7.30;
accommodation.

CHILLINGTON

New Inn (P)
on A379
Tel: Kingsbridge
(0548) 580245
Local cider (PC)
Garden; accommodation.

Post Office (OL)
Tel: Kingsbridge
(0548) 580371
Local cider

Union Inn (P)
on A379
Tel: Kingsbridge
(0548) 580241
Local cider (PC)
Meals; garden.

CHILTON

YEARLSTONE CYDERS▲
Yearlstone Vineyard,
(near Bickleigh)
Tel: Bickleigh (088 45) 450

CHITTLEHAM HOLT

Exeter Inn (P)
Tel: Chittleham Holt
(076 94) 281
Hancock (W)

CHRISTOW

Artichoke (P)
Tel: Christow (0647) 52387
Local cider (PC)
12th century pub in centre of
village. Meals lunchtime and
evening; garden.

Teign House Inn (P)
on B3193
Tel: Christow (0647) 52286
Bromell (PC) (PL)
Meals; garden; children's
room; accommodation.

CHUDLEIGH

Taylors Off Licence (OL)
Local cider

CHULMLEIGH

Barnstaple Inn (P)
South Molton Street
Tel: Chulmleigh (0769) 80388
Inch (PC)
Historic coaching inn. Meals;
children's room;
accommodation.

Corner Shop (OL)
Hancock (B)

Dairy (OL)
Fore Street
Tel: Chulmleigh (0769) 80598
Inch (BB) (J)

Globe (P)
Church Street
Tel: Chulmleigh (0769) 80252
Inch (PC)
Meals; childrens' room.

Red Lion (P)
Tel: Chulmleigh (0769) 80384
Inch (PC)

CLOVELLY

New Inn (P)
near A39
Inch (PC)
Meals; garden; childrens'
room; accommodation.

CLYST HONITON

Young Hayes Farm Shop (OL)
on A30 Exeter to Honiton
road
Tel: Whimple (0404) 822201
Gray (PL)
Yearlstone (B)
Full range of local produce.
No cider sold on Sunday.

CLYST ST. MARY

Half Moon Inn (P)
Tel: Topsham (039 287) 3515
Inch (PC)

COCKWOOD

Anchor Inn (P)
Tel: Starcross (0626) 890203
Taunton (H)
16th century inn overlooking
small harbour between
Dawlish Warren and
Starcross. Log fires and
beams. Fresh seafoods daily.
Snacks all sessions; meals
12-2 and 7-10; restaurant;
outdoor drinking area.

Ship (P)
Tel: Starcross (0626) 890373
Taunton (H)
Harbourside inn. Meals
lunchtime and evening;
children's room.

COFFINSWELL

The Linney (P)
off A380
Tel: Kingskerswell
(080 47) 890373
Churchwood (PC)
14th century thatched
farmhouse. Meals and snacks
lunchtime and evening.

COLEFORD

New Inn (P)
Tel: Copplestone (036 34) 242
Inch (PC)

COLYTON

Kingfisher (P)
Dolphin Street
Tel: Colyton (0297) 52476
Coates (H)
Take the miniature tram
from Seaton. Meals and
snacks 12-1.45 and 7-10;
garden; family room.

COMBE MARTIN

Beaumont Stores (OL)
Hancock (B)

Pack of Cards (P)
Tel: Combe Martin
(027 188) 3327
Inch (PC)

Wine Shop (OL)
Inch (BB) (J)

COPPLESTONE

Cross Hotel (P)
Tel: Copplestone (036 34) 273
Inch (PC)

CORNWORTHY

Hunters Lodge (P)
near A381
Tel: Harbertonford
(080 423) 204
Beenleigh (W)
Meals; garden.

CREDITON

Lees Wine Store (OL)
21 High Street
Tel: Crediton (036 32) 2561
Gray (PL)

CULLOMPTON

Cullompton Wine (OL)
35 Fore Street
Tel: Cullompton (0884) 32760
Bromell (PL)

Fosters Off Licence (OL)
Inch (BB) (J)

Pony & Trap (P)
Exeter Hill
Tel: Cullompton (0884) 33254
Bulmer (H)

DARTINGTON

Cider Press Centre (OL)
Shinners Bridge
Tel: Totnes (0803) 864171
Beenleigh (PL)
Local cider (PL)
Inch (BB) (J)
Yearlstone (B)
Once a cider press, now a
complex of craft shops and
restaurants: annual cider
festival in August, with free
tastings. Restaurant with full
meals 10-5; outdoor eating
area; traditional Devon farm
foods on sale.

Cott Inn (P)
Tel: Totnes (0803) 863777

Handsome thatched antiquity — the Copper Key Inn, North Tawton

Copper Key Inn

34

Local cider (E) (PC)
Thatched inn dating from
1320. Snacks 12-2.30; full
meals 7-10.30; Sunday
lunches; restaurant; garden;
accommodation.

The Stores (OL)
Tel: Totnes (0803) 863476
Local cider

DARTMOUTH

Cherub (OL)
11 Higher Street
Tel: Dartmouth (080 43) 2571
Yearlstone (B)
Yearlstone Wine (B)

Dartmouth Vintners (OL)
The Butterwalk, Duke Street
Tel: Dartmouth (080 43) 2602
Several west country ciders (PL)

Floating Bridge Inn (P)
Sand Quay
Tel: Dartmouth (080 43) 2354
Bulmer (H)
Old fashioned pub by the
river, near Higher Ferry.
Meals lunchtime and
evenings; garden; children's
room; facilities for disabled.

Tall Ships Restaurant (P)
South Embankment
Tel: Dartmouth (080 43) 2641
Beenleigh (PL)

DAWLISH

Exeter Inn (P)
Beach Street
Tel: Dawlish (0626) 865677
Local cider (PC)
In small alley off main street
near station. Meals and
snacks lunchtime.

Gays Creamery (OL)
20 Brunswick Place
Tel: Dawlish (0626) 863341
Gray (PL)
Local cider (PL)
West Country Fayre (B) (J) (PL)
Home made cooking to take
away; Devon clotted cream,
also by post; groceries.

Golden Sands Holiday Camp (P)
Week Lane
Tel: Dawlish (0626) 863099
Bromell (PC)

Lansdowne Stores (OL)
4 Park Road
Tel: Dawlish (0626) 863891
Inch (BB) (J)
Selection of about 30 cheeses;
ideal with the cider!

Peter Dominic (OL)
1 The Lawn
Tel: Dawlish (0626) 863127
Inch (BB) (J)

Railway Inn (P)
Beach Street
Tel: Dawlish (0626) 863226
Bulmer (PC)
Opposite the Exeter. Display
of railway relics. Snacks;
childrens' room.

Red Lion (P)
Old Town Street
Tel: Dawlish (0626) 863084
Local cider (PC)
Friendly local at back of town.

Swan Inn (P)
Old Town Street
Tel: Dawlish (0626) 863677
Bulmer (E)
Snacks till ½ hour before
closing; garden.

DAWLISH WARREN

Post Office (OL)
Tel: Dawlish (0626) 862090
Inch (BB) (J)

The Welcome Holiday Park (OL)
Tel: Dawlish (0626) 862070
Bromell (PL)

DEVONPORT

Antics Restaurant (OL)
184 Albert Road
Tel: Plymouth (0752) 564529
Beenleigh (PL)

Devonport Wines (OL)
58 George Street
Tel: Plymouth (0752) 569472
Inch (BB) (J)

Off Licence (OL)
23 Marlborough Street
Local cider

DITTISHAM

Red Lion Inn (P)
Tel: Dittisham (080 422) 235
Local cider (W)
Inch (PC)
Overlooking River Dart.
Meals and snacks all sessions;
restaurant; terrace and
garden; children's room;
accommodation.

DOLTON

Rams Head (P)
South Street
on B3217
Tel: Dolton (080 54) 255
Inch (PC)
Meals; garden; children's
room, accommodation.

Royal Oak (P)
The Square
Tel: Dolton (080 54) 288
Inch (PC)
16th century pub in
delightful village between
Dartmoor and Exmoor. Meals
and snacks 12-2.15 and
6-10.30; restaurant; garden;
accommodation; pool parties.

DREWSTEIGNTON

Drewe Arms (P)
Bulmer (PC)
Ancient thatched pub of great
character, a real experience.

DUNSFORD

BRIMBLECOMBE'S DEVON FARMHOUSE CIDER▲
Farrants Farm
Tel: Longdown (039 281) 456

Royal Oak Inn (P)
Tel: Christow (0647) 52256
Brimblecombe (PC)
In village of thatched cob
cottages, at edge of Dartmoor
National Park, near Steps
Bridge nature reserve. Home
cooking lunchtime and
evening; restaurant; garden;
children's room;
accommodation.

EAST PORTLEMOUTH

Post Office (OL)
Tel: Salcombe (054 884) 2382
Local cider

EAST PRAWLE

Pigs Nose Inn (P)
Tel: Chivelstone
(054 851) 209
Local cider (E) (PP)
16th century pub on the green
in a fishing village; the most
southerly inn in Devon.
Snacks 12-2; full meals
7.30-10; children's room;
accommodation.

EGGBUCKLAND

Off Licence (OL)
65 Delamere Road
Local cider

Speedwell Mini Market (OL)
131 Speedwell Crescent
Tel: Plymouth (0752) 788448
Local cider

EGGESFORD

Fox & Hounds Hotel (P)
on A377 100 yards from
Eggesford Station

Tel: Chulmleigh
(0769) 80345
Inch (PC)
25 ft. wooden bar top in one
piece, cut from centre of a
Monterrey Pine tree. Meals
and snacks 11-1.45 and 6-10;
restaurant; garden;
children's room;
accommodation.

EXBOURNE

Red Lion (P)
Tel: Exbourne (083 785) 683
Inch (BB)
Snacks all sessions; meals
evening; restaurant; garden;
accommodation.

EXETER

Bananas (P)
North Street
Tel: Exeter (0392) 50608
Local cider (PC)
City centre restaurant with
mainly young clientele.

British Railways
Staff Club (P)
Beacon Avenue, Polsloe
Bridge
Tel: Exeter (0392) 73319
Coates (PC)

City Cellars (OL)
3 Upper Paul Street
Tel: Exeter (0392) 214565
Inch (BB) (J)
Yearlstone (B)

Clifton Inn (P)
off Heavitree Road
Tel: Exeter (0392) 73527
Local cider (PC)
An old pub surviving in the
midst of modern Exeter.
Young clientele. Meals
lunchtime; pool.

Continental Food
Store (OL)
120 Old Tiverton Road
Tel: Exeter (0392) 58633
Bromell (H) (PL)

Crossways Stores
(OL)
92 Cowick Street
Tel: Exeter (0392) 72842
Gray (PL)

Dawsons Stores
(OL)
Heavitree
Gray (PC) (PL)

Devon Foods (OL)
15 Gandy Street
Gray (PL)
Yearlstone (B)

Double Locks (P)
Canal Bank
Tel: Exeter (0392) 56947
Gray (PC)
Inch (PP)

About 1 mile out of town on
towpath of Exeter Canal.
Snacks 11-2 and 5.30-10.30
(10 in winter); Sunday
12-1.30 and 7-10; meals to
order; 3 acres of garden;
children's room.

Exwick Stores (OL)
29 Exwick Villas
Tel: Exeter (0392) 55737
Bromell (PL)

H & M Central
Stores (OL)
1 Burnthouse Lane
Tel: Exeter (0392) 72077
Traditional ciders (PP)
(BB) (PL)
Snacks 8am to 6pm.

John Bull (P)
St. Davids Hill
Tel: Exeter (0392) 74754
Bulmer (H)
Popular local near St. David's
Station. Snacks 12-2 and 5-9;
accommodation.

H. A. Kasba (OL)
5 Well Street
Tel: Exeter (0392) 34323
Bromell (PL)

Locomotive (P)
New North Road
Tel: Exeter (0392) 75840
Local cider (PC)
Taunton (PC)
Cider Pub near city centre.

Lion Holt Off
Licence (OL)
Well Street
Tel: Exeter (0392) 55179
Bromell (PL)

Mr. Bradfords Off
Licence (OL)
Bonhay Road
Bromell (PL)

Red Cow (P)
Red Cow Village
Tel: Exeter (0392) 72318
Bulmer (PC)
Coates (PC)
Taunton (PC)
The cider centre of Exeter,
conveniently placed near St.
David's Station. snacks;
outdoor drinking area.

Ropemakers Arms
(P)
29-30 Blackboy Road
Tel: Exeter (0392) 75080
Taunton (H)

Wavy Line Stores
(OL)
Howell Road
Local cider

Whipton Inn (P)
54 Whipton Village Road
Tel: Exeter (0392) 67615
Inch (H)
Taunton (H)
Good cider pub in east of the
city. Meals and snacks
lunchtime and early

evenings; children's room;
pool table; family garden;
accommodation.

EXMINSTER

Geralds Enterprises
(OL)
Pitthayes
Tel: Exeter (0392) 832406
Bromell (PL)

Turf Hotel (P)
Tel: Exeter (0392) 833128
Gray (PC)
Out on the Exe estuary at
entrance to the Exeter Canal,
only approached by track
from Exminster, or towpath
from Exeter. The Turf runs its
own canal boat, the Water
Mongoose, from Countess
Weir to the pub; phone for
details. Snacks all sessions;
full meals on Sunday; garden;
children's room;
accommodation.

EXMOUTH

Builders Arms (P)
Princes Street
Tel: Exmouth (0395) 3858
Taunton (H)
Survives amid car parks and
new blocks. Snacks all
sessions; live groups; discos.

Country House Inn
(P)
176 Withycombe Village
Road, Withycombe
Tel: Exmouth (0395) 263444
Taunton (H)
Snacks all sessions; large
garden with aviary.

First & Last (P)
10 Church Street
Tel: Exmouth (0395) 272086
Bulmer (E)
Snacks lunchtime; garden.

Pilot Inn (P)
Chapel Hill
Tel: Exmouth (0392) 263382
Taunton (H)
Snacks 12–2 during week.

Pines Road Stores
(OL)
Pines Road
Tel: Exmouth (0392) 263905
Inch (BB) (J)

Queens Hotel (P)
2-4 Victoria Road
Tel: Exmouth (0392) 272091
Bulmer (H)
Between station and beach.
Meals and snacks 12-2 and
6-8; childrens' room;
accommodation.

Royal Oak (P)
31 Exeter Road
Tel: Exmouth (0392) 272932
Taunton (H)
Snacks all sessions.

Southwestern (P)
The Parade
Tel: Exmouth (0392) 263649
Taunton (H) (PC)
Adjoins railway station.
Snacks 12-2 and 6-10; full
meals 12-2; pool table.

EXTON

Puffing Billy (P)
near Exton Station
Tel: Topsham (039 287) 3152
Taunton (PC)
Just a good old fashioned pub.
Snacks 12-1.45 and 7-9.45;
garden.

FENITON

Nog Inn (P)
Ottery Road
Tel: Honiton (0404) 850210
Taunton (H)
Adjacent to Feniton Station.
Snacks all sessions; skittles;
pool; squash; children's room;
accommodation; ballroom
and cat.

FILLEIGH

Stags Head (P)
Tel: Filleigh (059 86) 250
Hancock (F)

FINGLE BRIDGE

Anglers Rest (P)
Tel: Drewsteignton
(064 721) 2287
Bromell (PC)
On edge of Dartmoor by well
known beauty spot, popular
with fishermen and ramblers.
Open daily at lunchtimes all
year, in winter Friday and
Saturday evenings only.
Meals and snacks 12-2 and
7-9; restaurant; riverside
terraces; children welcome.

FROGMORE

Globe Inn (P)
on A379
Tel: Frogmore (054 853) 351
Stancombe (PL)
Traditional inn catering for
all the family. Home cooked
food. Meals and snacks 12-2
and 6.30-10; restaurant;
garden; children's room;
accommodation.

GEORGEHAM

Rock Inn (P)
off B3231
Bulmer (H)
Meals lunchtime and
evening; garden; children's
room.

GULWORTHY

Harvest Home (P)
on A390
Tel: Tavistock (0822) 2755
Countryman (PC)
Inch (PC)

HALWELL

Old Inn (P)
Tel: Blackawton
(080 421) 329
Churchward (PC)
Snacks 11-2.30; full meals
6.30-10.30; restaurant;
garden; children's room;
accommodation.

HARBERTON

**Church House Inn
(P)**
Tel: Totnes (0803) 863707
Inch (PC)

HARBERTONFORD

**BEENLEIGH
MANOR CIDER ▲**

Beenleigh Manor
Tel: Harbertonford
(080 423) 738

HARTLAND

Quay Hotel (P)
Tel: Hartland (050 15) 218
Inch (PC)
Snacks 12-2.30 and 6–9; full
meals 7-8; restaurant;
accommodation.

HATHERLEIGH

George Hotel (P)
on A386
Tel: Okehampton
(0837) 810454
Inch (BB) (PL)
15th century thatched
coaching inn; open all day
Monday and Tuesday
(Market Days). Snacks all
sessions; meals evening
except Sunday; restaurant;
outdoor drinking area;
accommodation; outdoor
unheated swimming pool.

Tally Ho Inn (P)
on A386
Tel: Okehampton
(0837) 810306
Inch (PC)
Meals; garden.

HEMERDON

Miners Arms (P)
near Plympton
Tel: Plymouth (0752) 33252
Countryman (PC)
Former tinminers pub.
Garden.

HEXWORTHY

Forest Inn (P)
near A384
Tel: Poundsgate (036 43) 211
Local cider (PC)
A Dartmoor pub. Meals;
garden; childrens' room;
accommodation.

HEYBROOK BAY

Eddystone Inn (P)
Tel: Plymouth (0752) 862356
Local cider (PP)
Panoramic sea views. Snacks
11.30-2 and 6.30-10; meals
11.30-2 and 7-10; garden and
sun patio; accommodation.

HOLBERTON

Dartmoor Union Inn (P)
Fore Street
Tel: Holberton (075 530) 288
Local cider (PC)
18th century building once a
workhouse. Meals; children's
room.

Mildmay Colours Inn (P)
Tel: Holberton (075 530) 248
Local (H)
Near sea, only ten miles from
Plymouth. Snacks 12-2 and
6.30-10; meals evenings;
restaurant; garden;
accommodation.

HOLCOMBE ROGUS

Prince of Wales (P)
Tel: Greenham (0823) 672070
Bulmer (H)
Meals lunchtime.

HOLNE

Church House Inn (P)
Tel: Poundsgate (036 43) 208
Local cider (PL)
14th century inn said to have
housed Oliver Cromwell
during the fighting at Totnes.
Old oak screen and beams
dating from 1530. Meals and
snacks 12-2 and 6-9.30;
restaurant; garden;
children's room;
accommodation.

HOLSWORTHY

Cleggs Chemist (OL)
The Square
Tel: Holsworthy
(0409) 253461
Inch (BB)

Golden Fleece (P)
Bodmin Street
Tel: Holsworthy
(0409) 253263
Countryman (PC)
Snacks 12-2 and 7-10;
childrens' room.

Huntsman (P)
Market Square
Tel: Holsworthy
(0409) 253750
Inch (PC)
Accommodation.

HONITON

Red Cow (P)
High Street
Tel: Honiton (0404) 2579
Taunton (H)
Popular town centre pub.
Snacks lunchtime only.

Volunteer (P)
177 High Street
Tel: Honiton (0404) 2145
Local cider (PC)
Snacks 11-2 and 7-10.30;
children's room.

World Wines (OL)
High Street
Inch (BB) (J)
Yearlstone (B)
Yearlstone Wine (B)

HOPE COVE

Hope & Anchor (P)
Outer Hope (near
Kingsbridge)
Tel: Kingsbridge
(0548) 561294
Local cider (PC)
Sandy beaches nearby.
Meals; children's room;
accommodation.

Hope Cove Stores & Post Office (OL)
Tel: Kingsbridge
(0548) 561249
Local cider (BB) (PL)
Hot and cold snacks
available.

Lobster Pot Inn (P)
Outer Hope
Tel: Kingsbridge
(0548) 561214
Local cider (PC)
Meals; accommodation.

HORNDON

Elephants Nest (P)
near Mary Tavy
Tel: Mary Tavy (082 281) 273
Countryman (PC)
Views across the Moors. The
name derives from the
physical appearance of a
previous landlord! Snacks
11.30-2 and 7.30-10; meals
7.30-10 except Thursday;
garden.

HORSEBRIDGE

Royal Inn (P)
Sydenham Damerel, 3 miles
off A384
Tel: Milton Abbot
(082 287) 214
Countryman (PC)
In superb setting on River
Tamar, formerly a nunnery.
Bar meals; patio and garden;
bar billiards.

IDE

Huntsman (P)
High Street (off A30)
Taunton (PC)
Ancient thatched village pub,
with longest sign in Devon.
Meals lunchtime and
evening; garden.

IDEFORD

REDDAWAY'S FARM CIDER ▲
Lower Rixdale, Luton
Tel: Teignmouth
(062 67) 5218

IDDESLEIGH

Duke of York (P)
on B3217
Inch (PC)
Meals; accommodation.

ILFRACOMBE

Cap Stone Restaurant (P)
St. James Place
Tel: Ilfracombe (0271) 63540
Inch (PC)

Cider Apple (P)
Bremore Road
Inch (PC)

St. James Dairy (OL)
24 St. James Place
Tel: Ilfracombe (0271) 62727
Inch (BB) (J)
Open 8am till late all week.

Salty Dog (P)
Capstone Parade
Tel: Ilfracombe (0271) 62267
Inch (PC)

Woolacombe Wines (OL)
Unit 3B Mullacott Cross
Industrial Estate
Tel: Ilfracombe (0271) 62016
Inch (BB) (J)
Wholesalers, delivery service
throughout north Devon.

INSTOW

Commodore Hotel (P)
Marine Parade
Tel: Instow (0271) 860347
Inch (PC)

ILSINGTON

Haytor Country House Hotel (P)
Tel: Haytor (036 46) 200
Gray (PC)

IPPLEPEN

Plough (P)
Fore Street
Tel: Ipplepen (0803) 812118
Bulmer (H)
Coates (PC)

Pick & Park (OL)
Park Hill Farm
Tel: Ipplepen (0803) 812613
Sheppy

IVYBRIDGE

Westerley Off Licence (OL)
Clare Street
Tel: Plymouth (0752) 895 335
Local cider

KENNFORD

Fair Winds Hotel (P)
Tel: Exeter (0392) 832911
Inch (PC)

KENTON

Devon Arms (P)
on A379
Tel: Starcross (0626) 890213
Bulmer (H)
18th century inn. Snacks all sessions; meals Tuesday to Saturday evening; restaurant; garden; pets corner; children's room; accommodation.

KINGSBRIDGE

Avon Farmers Ltd (OL)
Avon Centre, Wallingford Road
Tel: Kingsbridge (0548) 7321
Local cider

Grays Delicatessen (OL)
Fore Street
Tel: Kingsbridge (0548) 3625
Beenleigh (PL)

Hermitage Bar (P)
8 Mill Street
Tel: Kingsbridge (0548) 3234
Bulmer (H)
Town pub with unique carved woodwork. Meals lunchtime and evening during summer; accommodation.

Kingsbridge Creamery (OL)
28a Fore Street
Tel: Kingsbridge (0548) 2456
Beenleigh (PL)

King of Prussia (P)
Bulmer (H)

Maid Marion Stores (OL)
37 Fore Street
Tel: Kingsbridge (0548) 3625
Inch (BB) (J)

KINGSTEIGNTON

Conway Wines (OL)
Exeter Road
Local cider

Dew Drop Inn (P)
Fore Street
Tel: Newton Abbot (0626) 2786
Inch (PC)

Kings Arms (P)
Oakford Terrace
Tel: Newton Abbot (0626) 64859
Inch (PC)

KINGSTON

Post Office (OL)
near Modbury
Tel: Bigbury-on-Sea (054 881) 810263
Local cider

KNOWLE

Ebrington Arms (P)
Tel: Braunton (0271) 812166
Inch (H)
Taunton (H)
Snacks 12-2; full meals 7.30-10; restaurant; garden; children's room; accommodation.

LANDSCOVE

Live & Let Live Inn (P)
near A38
Tel: Staverton (080 426) 663
Local cider (PC)
Overlooking Dart Valley, with sound of steam trains on nearby Dart Valley Railway. Meals and snacks 12-2 and 7-10; garden in orchard across road; children's room.

LAPFORD

Old Maltscoop (P)
Tel: Lapford (036 35) 330
Inch (PC)
In centre of village overlooking Yeo Valley. Meals; accommodation.

Yeo Vale (P)
on A377 (near Station)
Tel: Lapford (036 35) 452
Inch (PC)
Meals; garden; children's room; accommodation.

LEWDOWN

Blue Lion (P)
Tel: Lewdown (056 683) 238
Inch (PC)

LIFTON

Fox & Grapes (P)
Inch (PC)

LIVERTON

Star Inn (P)
Tel: Bickington (062 682) 376
Taunton (PC)
Old unspoilt inn with character. Snacks 11.30-2; garden; large children's play area.

LYDFORD

Castle (P)
Countryman (PC)
16th century stone pub with massive fireplace and bread oven. Meals; garden; children's room; accommodation.

Dartmoor Inn (P)
on B386
Tel: Lydford (082 282) 221 or 374
Bulmer (PC)
Inch (BB)
16th century inn. Meals and snacks 12-2 and 7-10; restaurant; garden; accommodation.

Fox & Hounds (P)
Tel: Lydford (082 282) 206
Inch (PC)

Manor (P)
Lydford Gorge
Tel: Lydford (082 282) 208
Inch (BB) (PC)
By entrance to waterfall. Snacks 11.30-2 and 7-10; full meals 11.30 and 7-9.30; restaurant; garden; accommodation; skittle alley, for private hire when available.

LYMPSTONE

Globe Inn (P)
The Strand
Tel: Exmouth (0395) 263166
Taunton (PC)
Old pub in centre of small fishing village, easily accessible from Exeter and Exmouth by train. Famous for seafood. Meals Monday to Saturday 12-2 (1.45 in Lounge); Sunday 12-1.15.

Redwing (P)
Church Road
Tel: Exmouth (0395) 271656
Bulmer (H)
Meals and snacks all sessions; restaurant; garden; children's room; children's zoo; live entertainment and barbeques.

Swan (P)
The Strand
Tel: Exmouth (0395) 272284
Bulmer (H)
Near railway station. Snacks 12-1.45 and 7-9.30.

LYNMOUTH

Blue Ball (P)
Countisbury (On A39)
Bulmer (H)
17th century coaching inn.
Meals; garden;
accommodation.

LYNTON

Castle Hill House Hotel (P)
Yearlstone (B)
Yearlstone Wine (B)

Lynton Stores (OL)
Inch (BB) (J)

MALBOROUGH

Royal Oak (P)
off A381
Tel: Kingsbridge
(0548) 561481
Local cider (W)
Meals and snacks all sessions;
patio; children's room; pool
table; camping nearby;
accommodation; traditional
folk evenings every
Wednesday.

MANATON

Becky Falls Cafe (P)
Tel: Manaton (064 722) 267
Local cider (PC)
Well known beauty spot on
Eastern Dartmoor.

MARLDON

Church House Inn (P)
Tel: Paignton (0803) 558279
Bulmer (H)
Meals; garden; children's
room.

MARY TAVY

Mary Tavy Inn (P)
on A386
Tel: Mary Tavy (082 281) 289
Inch (H)
17th century pub. Snacks all
sessions; meals 12-2 and 7-10;
garden pool.

MEAVY

Royal Oak (P)
Inch (PC)
15th century village inn.
Garden.

MEETH

New Inn (P)
on A386
Tel: Okehampton
(0837) 810325
Inch (BB) (PL)

Ancient coaching inn with
inglenook fireplaces and
beamed ceilings. Snacks
12-2.30 and 6-10; meals
12-2.30 and 6-9.30;
restaurant; garden front and
rear; pool room; children's
room; accommodation.

MERRIVALE

Dartmoor Inn (P)
on B3357
Tel: Princetown
(082 289) 340
Countryman (PC)
Set amid the Dartmoor tors.
Meals lunchtime and
evening; garden; camping
nearby.

MILTON ABBOT

COUNTRYMAN CIDER▲
Felldownhead
Tel: Milton Abbot
(082 287) 226

Edgcumbe Arms (P)
on A384
Tel: Milton Abbot
(082 287) 229
Countryman (PC)
Superb moorland views, in
good touring area. Snacks
and meals all sessions;
garden.

MILTON COMBE

Who'd Have Thought It (P)
near A386
Tel: Yelverton (0822) 853313
Bulmer (H)
16th century village pub with
low beams. Meals lunchtime
and evening; garden.

MODBURY

Mackgills (OL)
Church Street
Tel: Modbury (0548) 830860
Beenleigh (PL)

Modbury Wines (OL)
28 Church Street
Local cider

MONK-OKEHAMPTON

Old Swan (P)
on B3217
Inch (PC)
Meals; garden; children's
room; accommodation.

MORCHARD BISHOP

London Inn (P)
Tel: Morchard Bishop
(036 37) 222

Inch (F)
Snacks 11.30-2; full meals
6.30-9.30; restaurant;
garden; skittle alley; pool
room; accommodation.

Sturt Arms (P)
on A377
Tel: Morchard Bishop
(036 37) 237
Inch (PC)
Meals; garden; children's
room; accommodation.

MORETON-HAMPSTEAD

Plymouth Inn (P)
Court Street
Tel: Moretonhampstead
(0647) 40266
Inch (PC)
Meals; outdoor drinking area.

White Hart Hotel (P)
The Square
Tel: Moretonhampstead
(0647) 40406
Coates (PC)

NEWTON ABBOT

Dartmouth Inn (P)
61 East Street
Tel: Newton Abbot
(0626) 3451
Coates (PC)

Keyberry Hotel (P)
Kingskerswell Road, Decoy
Tel: Newton Abbot
(0626) 2121
Local cider (PC)
Near Decoy Lake, with
fishing and wind surfing.
Snacks all sessions; meals
11.30-2; restaurant; skittle
alley.

Mears (OL)
103 Queen Street (near War
Memorial)
Tel: Newton Abbot
(0626) 65373
Local cider (BB) (PL)
Inch (BB) (J)

Pannier Market (OL)
Churchward (PL)

Saracens Head (P)
Fairfield Terrace
Tel: Newton Abbot
(0626) 65430
Bulmer (H)

Ship Inn (P)
6 Wolborough Street
Tel: Newton Abbot
(0626) 3409
Bulmer (H)
By Clock Tower. Full meals
except Sun. and Mon.
evenings.

Swan (P)
4 Highweek Street
Tel: Newton Abbot
(0626) 65056

Coates (H)
Snacks all sessions; pool table; euchre.

Vine & Video (OL)
12 Bank Street
Tel: Newton Abbot
(0626) 69413
Inch (BB) (PC)
Open to 9pm; Sunday 12-2 and 7-9.

Ye Olde Cider Bar (P)
99 East Street
Tel: Newton Abbot
(0626) 54221
Hunt (W)
Inch (W)
A cider house, selling a comprehensive range of vintage, draught farmhouse, and bottled ciders; the draught is dispensed from 40 gallon wood barrels. 17 fruit and grape wines. Substantial bar snacks all sessions; garden; children's room. Not to be missed.

NEWTON FERRERS

Dolphin Inn (P)
Riverside Road East
Tel: Plymouth (0752) 872282
Local (PC)
On estuary of the lovely River Yealm. Meals lunchtime; sunny south facing garden overlooking river.

NEWTON POPPLEFORD

FARMER JOHN'S FARMHOUSE CIDER▲
Parson's Farm
Tel: Colaton Raleigh
(0395) 68152

Jack & Marys (OL)
Glebe House, High Street
Tel: Colaton Raleigh
(0395) 68379
Inch (BB) (J)

Post Office & Spar Shop (OL)
High Street
Tel: Colaton Raleigh
(0395) 68225
Local cider (PL)

NEWTON ST. CYRES

Crown & Sceptre (P)
on A377
Tel: Exeter (0392) 815278
Inch (PC)
Meals and snacks lunchtime and evening; large garden with play facilities for children; children allowed into part of Lounge.

NORTH BOVEY

Ring of Bells (P)
Tel: Moretonhampstead (0647) 40375
Gray (PC)
13th century pub with thatched roof and low ceilings on the Moors; by village green. Snacks 12-2.30 and 7.30-10; meals 7.30-9.30; restaurant; garden with moorland views; children's room; accommodation.

NORTH LEW

Green Dragon (P)
Tel: Beaworthy (040 922) 228
Inch (PC)
Village local in main square. Meals; garden.

NORTH TAWTON

Copper Key (P)
Fore Street
Tel: North Tawton
(083 782) 357
Local (PC)
Tastefully restored 16th century thatched inn at western edge of town, with emphasis on food. Snacks 12-2 and 6.30-10; meals 7-10; restaurant; garden; children's room.

Railway Hotel (P)
Whiddon Down Road
Tel: North Tawton
(083 782) 789
Inch (BB)
A pub with no station, but railway atmosphere! Meals and snacks 12-2 and 6-10.30; restaurant; garden; children's room; accommodation.

Ring of Bells (P)
North Street
Tel: North Tawton
(083 782) 585
Inch (PC)
Meals; accommodation.

White Hart (P)
Fore Street

Tel: North Tawton
(083 782) 473
Inch (PC)
A family run 17th century coaching inn. Meals and snacks all sessions; restaurant; garden; children's room; skittle alley, discos; accommodation, resident ghost (but room for you too); angling club with regular sea and trout fishing trips; outdoor activities arranged.

NOSS MAYO

Old Ship Inn (P)
Tel: Plymouth (0752) 872387
Local cider (PC)
Meals; garden; accommodation.

OKEHAMPTON

Allins Dairy (OL)
Fore Street
Tel: Okehampton (0837) 2264
Inch (BB) (J)

Kings Arms (P)
St. James Street
Tel: Okehampton (0837) 2809
Bulmer (H)
Bar snacks lunchtime.

London Hotel (P)
West Street
Tel: Okehampton (0837) 2863
Inch (PC)

Red Lion Delicatessen (OL)
Red Lion Yard
Tel: Okehampton (0837) 4234
Inch (BB) (J)

White Hart (P)
High Street
Tel: Okehampton (0837) 2730
Inch (PC)
Meals; accommodation.

OTTERTON

Paynes of Otterton (OL)
Bromell (PL)

Harbourside Anchor Inn, Cockwood

OTTERY ST. MARY

Lamb & Flag (P)
Batts Lane
Tel: Ottery St. Mary
(040 481) 2616
Bulmer (E)
Snacks 12-2 on weekdays;
skittle alley.

London Hotel (P)
Gold Street
Tel: Ottery St. Mary
(040 481) 4755
Inch (PC)
Meals and snacks all sessions;
restaurant; patio; childrens'
room; pool room; skittle alley.

Plume of Feathers (P)
Yonder Street
Tel: Ottery St. Mary
(040 481) 2395
Taunton (PC)
Snacks lunchtime.

Potters Country Market (OL)
West Hill
Tel: Ottery St. Mary
(040 481) 2825
Inch (BB) (J)

PAIGNTON

Aircraft Museum (OL)
Barton Pines, Higher
Blagdon
Tel: Paignton (0803) 553540
Churchward (PL)

CHURCHWARDS CIDER ▲
Yalberton Farm
Tel: Paignton (0803) 558157

Ex Service Men's Club (P)
Churchward (H)

HUNTS DEVON CIDER▲
Higher Yalberton Farm,
Collaton St. Mary
Tel: Paignton (0803) 557694

Palace Place Social Club (P)
2 Palace Place
Tel: Paignton (0803) 553165
Churchward (H)

Spinning Wheel (P)
Esplanade
Tel: Paignton (0803) 555000
Coates (PC)
Busy sea front bars. Meals.

Three Beaches Wines (OL)
101 Dartmouth Road
Tel: Paignton (0803) 554917
Inch (BB) (J)

PARRACOMBE

Hunters Inn (P)
Heddons Mouth (off A39)
Tel: Parracombe (059 83) 230
Hancock (W)
Beautiful gardens with ponds
where peacocks and ducks
wander; walks around coast
and down to beach. Snacks
12-2 and 6-10; meals 7-9.30;
restaurant; children's room;
accommodation.

PLYMOUTH

Clifton Wines (OL)
67 Clifton Place
Tel: Plymouth (0752) 660758
Local cider

Cork & Bottle Off Licence (OL)
Cornwall Street
Local cider

Embankment Road Wines (OL)
Princerock
Local cider

Farm Stile (OL)
57 Mutley Plain
Tel: Plymouth (0752) 66740
Local cider

Jubilee Stores (OL)
176 Exeter Street
Tel: Plymouth (0752) 669538
Local cider

Leos Off Licence (OL)
252 Old Laira Road
Tel: Plymouth (0752) 667542
Bromell (PL)

Lipson Wines (OL)
8 Ladysmith Road
Tel: Plymouth (0752) 228866
Local cider

Peter Dominic (OL)
86 Cornwall Street
Tel: Plymouth (0752) 664748
Inch (BB) (PL)

Petes Mini Market (OL)
26 Waterloo Street
Local cider

Punchbowl Off Licence (OL)
15 Wolseley Road, Milehouse
Tel: Plymouth (0752) 569300
Local cider

Selleck Wine (OL)
St. Georges Terrace
Local cider

South Side Wines (OL)
49 Southside Street, Barbican
Tel: Plymouth (0752) 664846
Inch (BB) (J)

Star of the West (P)
7 Brownlow Street
Tel: Plymouth (0752) 229037
Addlestones (H)
Coates (PC)
Taunton (H)
Bar snacks.

VG Off Licence (OL)
124 Beacon Park Road,
Beacon Park
Tel: Plymouth (0752) 564362
Local cider (PL) (PP)
Open to 9pm.

West Side Stores (OL)
North Road West
Local cider

Woodside Inn (P)
12 Gasking Street
Tel: Plymouth (0752) 669700
Coates (PC)

Wren Pottery (OL)
The House that Jack Built,
11 Southside Street, The
Barbican
Tel: Plymouth (0752) 20655
Gasping Goose Scrumpy (PL)

PLYMPTON

Ace Wines (OL)
Ridgeway
Inch (BB) (J)

PLYMSTOCK

Plymstock Wines (OL)
23 Holland Road
Tel: Plymouth (0752) 44580
Local cider

POUNDSGATE

Leusdon Lodge (P)
Leusdon Lower Town
Tel: Poundsgate (036 43) 304
Local cider (PC)
Snacks 12-3; meals 12-2 and
7-9; restaurant; garden;
accommodation.

Tavistock Inn (P)
on A384
Tel: Poundsgate (036 43) 251
Taunton (PC)
Old traditional granite
moorland pub. Meals
lunchtime and evening;
garden; children's room.

PRINCETOWN

Prince of Wales (P)
Tavistock Road (B3357)
Tel: Princetown
(082 289) 219
Inch (PC)
Unspoilt Dartmoor pub.
Meals lunchtime and
evening; garden; children's
room.

RACKENFORD

Stag Inn (P)
near B3221
Tel: Rackenford
(088 488) 369
Inch (PC)
Reputedly Devon's oldest
pub. Meals; garden.

RINGMORE

Journeys End Inn (P)
Tel: Bigbury-on-Sea
(0548) 810205
Local cider (PC)(W)
14th century building which
acted as overnight lodging for
pack horse teams, in seaside
village. R. C. Sherriff wrote
his play here, and the name
stuck. Snacks 12-2 and
7-9.30; meals summer 8.30;
restaurant; garden;
accommodation (even
without pack horse).

ROCKBEARE

Bidgood Arms (P)
on A30
Tel: Whimple (0404) 822262
Bulmer (H)
Lively roadside local. Meals
lunchtime and evening;
garden; children's room;
accommodation; camping
nearby.

ST. ANNES CHAPEL

The Pickwick Inn (P)
on B3392
Tel: Bigbury-on-Sea
(054 881) 810241
Local cider (PP) (W)
Taunton (H)
Snacks 11.30-2 and 7-10;
meals 12-2 and 7-10;
restaurant; garden;
children's room;
accommodation.

ST. BUDEAUX

Beacon Park Wines (OL)
124 Beacon Park Road
Tel: Plymouth (0752) 54362
Local cider

Corner House (OL)
Inch (BB) (J)

The Stores (OL)
17 Roman Way
Local cider

SALCOMBE

Bower Wines (OL)
1 Fore Street
Local cider

Lambs Stores (OL)
Raleigh Road
Local cider

Ferry Inn (P)
Fore Street
Tel: Salcombe (054 884) 3349
Coates (PC)

Victoria Inn (P)
Fore Street
Tel: Salcombe (054 884) 2604
Local cider (PC)
Old yachting pub. Meals
lunchtime and evening;
outdoor drinking area;
children's room;
accommodation.

SAMPFORD COURTENAY

New Inn (P)
on A3072
Tel: North Tawton
(083 782) 247
Inch (PC)
Rambling unspoilt 16th
century inn. Meals; garden;
children's room;
accommodation.

SANDFORD

Lamb Inn (P)
Tel: Crediton (036 32) 3676
Inch (PC)
Meals.

SANDWAY

Sportsman (P)
on North Molton to Exford
road
Local (PC)
Sturdy stone Exmoor pub.
Meals.

SEATON

Seaton Wines (OL)
50 Queen Street
Tel: Seaton (0297) 22134
Inch (BB) (J)

SHALDON

Shaldon Wines (OL)
2 Fore Street
Tel: Shaldon (0626 87) 2217
Local cider (BB) (PL)

SHERFORD

STANCOMBE CIDER▲
Stancombe Farm
Tel: Frogmore (054 853) 634

SHOBROOKE

Red Lion (P)
Tel: Crediton (036 32) 2340
Inch (PC)

SIDBURY

Red Lion (P)
Tel: Sidbury (039 57) 313
Inch (PC)

SIDFORD

Blue Ball (P)
on A3052
Tel: Sidmouth (039 55) 4062
Taunton (PC)
Flagstone floored public bar,
inglenook fireplace. Meals
lunchtime and evening;
garden; children's room;
accommodation.

SIDMOUTH

Anchor Inn (P)
Old Fore Street
Tel: Sidmouth (039 55) 4129
Bulmer (E)
Meals and snacks lunchtime
and evening; large garden;
family room; children's
adventure playground;
unique collection of old farm
implements.

Peter Dominic (OL)
4 Fore Street
Tel: Sidmouth (039 55) 283
Local cider

Radway Inn (P)
1 Radway Place
Tel: Sidmouth (039 55) 3444
Taunton (PC)
Snacks 12-1.45; meals 7-9;
pool table.

Old Ship (P)
Old Fore Street
Tel: Sidmouth (039 55) 2127
Taunton (PC)
Restaurant with drink
licence; meals and snacks
11-3 and 6-10.30 (closed on
Sunday).

SLAPTON

Queens Arms (P)
Tel: Kingsbridge
(0548) 580800
Local cider (PC)
Snacks 12-2.30 and 6-11;
meals 12-2.30 and 7-11;
garden restaurant.

SOURTON

Highwayman (P)
Gray (PC)

SOUTH BRENT

Royal Oak (P)
Station Road
Tel: South Brent
(036 47) 2133
Local cider (H)

Old fashioned village local.
Meals lunchtime and
evening; skittle alley by
appointment;
accommodation.

SOUTH MOLTON

Beehive Wine Store (OL)
Tel: South Molton
(076 95) 2644
Inch (BB) (J)

HANCOCKS DEVON CIDER▲
Clapworthy Mill
Tel: South Molton
(076 95) 2678

Mill Inn (P)
Bish Mill
Tel: Bishops Nympton
(076 97) 437
Inch (BB)
Taunton (H)
Meals and snacks all sessions;
restaurant; garden;
children's room; barbecue in
part of restaurant; skittle
alley; accommodation.

SOUTH POOL

Millbrook Inn (P)
near Kingsbridge
Tel: Frogmore (054 853) 581
Local cider (PC)
Bar food: family room;
terrace.

SOUTH TAWTON

Seven Stars (P)
Tel: Okehampton
(0837) 840292
Local Farm Scrumpy (BB)
Snacks all sessions to 10pm;
meals 7.30-9pm; restaurant;
garden; monthly discos and
folk evenings;
accommodation.

SOUTH ZEAL

Kings Arms (P)
Tel: Okehampton
(0837) 840300
Inch (PC)

Oxenham Arms (P)
Tel: Okehampton
(0837) 840244
Gray (PP)
Unique ancient pub in centre
of village, once the dower
house of the Oxenham family;
on edge of Dartmoor. Meals
and snacks 12-2 and 7-9.30;
restaurant; garden;
children's room;
accommodation.

Poltimore Guest House (P)
Bromell (PC)

SPREYTON

Tom Cobbley Inn (P)
4 miles north of A30
Inch (PC)
Garden; children's room;
accommodation.

STAVERTON

Riverford Farm Shop (OL)
Tel: Staverton (080 426) 636
Beenleigh (PL)
Luscombe (PL)
Yearlstone (B)
Yearlstone Wine (B)

STICKLEPATH

Devonshire Inn (P)
on A30
Tel: Sticklepath
(083 784) 626
Gray (PC)
Inch (PC)
Meals; children's room.

STOKE FLEMING

London Inn (P)
Tel: Stoke Fleming
(0803) 770397
Local cider (PC)
Very close to Blackpool Sand
Beach. Snacks 12-2; meals
6-9.30; garden; childrens'
room.

Mace Stores (OL)
Local cider

STOKEIN-TEIGNHEAD

Church House Inn (P)
Tel: Shaldon (0626) 872475
Churchward (PC)
In centre of village. Meals and
snacks 12-2 and 7-10;
restaurant; garden;
children's room; large
collection of antique brass.

TEIGNHEAD FARM CIDER▲
Higher Farm
Tel: Shaldon (0626) 873394

STRETE

Kings Arms (P)
on A379
Tel: Stoke Fleming
(0803) 377
Churchward (PC)

TAVISTOCK

Duke of York (P)
Ford Street (A390)
Tel: Tavistock (0822) 3789
Taunton (PC)

Meals; outdoor drinking area;
accommodation.

Virtuous Lady (P)
Plymouth Road
Tel: Tavistock (0822) 5811
Inch (PC)

TEDBURN ST. MARY

BROMELL'S DEVON FARM CIDER▲
Lower Uppacott
Tel: Tedburn St. Mary
(064 76) 294

GRAY'S FARM CIDER▲
Halstow
Tel: Tedburn St. Mary
(064 76) 236

Kings Arms (P)
Tel: Tedburn St. Mary
(064 76) 224
Bromell (PC)
Old coaching inn at centre of
village. Meals;
accommodation.

TEIGNMOUTH

Dawlish Inn (P)
Regent Street
Tel: Teignmouth
(062 67) 2200
Local cider (H)
Meals 12-2 and 7.30-9.30; live
music.

Golden Lion (P)
85 Bitton Park Road
Tel: Teignmouth
(062 67) 6442
Bulmer (P)
Snacks all sessions except
Sunday; garden; childrens'
room; pool; snooker; euchre.

Kings Arms (P)
Regent Gardens, off Regent
Street
Tel: Teignmouth
(062 67) 5268
Taunton (PC)
Snacks all sessions.

King William IV (P)
Northumberland Place
Tel: Teignmouth
(062 67) 3988
Inch (PC)

Ship Inn (P)
Queen Street
Tel: Teignmouth
(062 67) 2674
Bulmer (H)
Snacks 11-2.15; meals
5-10.30; outdoor drinking
area; childrens' room.

Teign Wines (OL)
Clarendon House, 19 Orchard
Gardens

Tel: Teignmouth
(062 67) 5651
Inch (BB)
Moores (PL)
Reddaway (PL)
Vinecombe Wines (OL)
37 Northumberland Place
Tel: Teignmouth
(062 67) 2485
Local cider (PC) (BB) (PL)

THELBRIDGE
Thelbridge Cross Inn (P)
on B3042
Tel: Tiverton (0884) 860316
Inch (PP) (BB)
18th century country inn.
Snacks 11.30-2.30 and
6.30-11 (Sunday 12-2 and
7-10.30); meals 11.45-2.30 and
6.30-11 (Sunday 12-30-2 and
7-10.30); restaurant; garden;
children's room.

THROWLEIGH
Forge Stores (OL)
Tel: Whiddon Down
(064 723) 366
Bromell (PL)

TIVERTON
APT Stores (OL)
4 New Parade, Anstey
Crescent
Tel: Tiverton (0884) 254238
Inch (BB) (J)

Banner Wines (OL)
23 West Exe North
Tel: Tiverton (0884) 255644
Yearlstone (B)
Yearlstone Wine (B)

Cross Keys (P)
Gold Street
Tel: Tiverton (0884) 3185
Bulmer (PC) (E)
Snacks lunchtime and
evening; pool table; pin table;
skittles.

Delicatessen (OL)
West Exe
Yearlstone (B)
Yearlstone Wine (B)

Devon Foods (OL)
Bampton Street
Inch ((BB) (J)
Yearlstone (B)
Yearlstone Wine (B)

Hare & Hounds (P)
Chapel Street
Tel: Tiverton (0884) 252013
Bulmer (H)
Meals and snacks all sessions;
large skittle alley.

Knighthayes Court (P)
Bolham
Tel: Tiverton (0884) 254665
Local cider (PC)
National Trust mansion
housing fine art collection,
with gardens; open daily from
April to October. Restaurant
(separate entrance) open
11-5.30.

TOPSHAM
Exeter (P)
68 High Street
Tel: Topsham (039 287) 3131
Taunton (H)
Meals lunchtime and
evening.

Kings Head (P)
22 Higher Shapter Street
Tel: Topsham (039 287) 3321
Local cider (PC)
Peaceful and pleasant side
street pub. Snacks all
sessions.

London & South Western (P)
14 Fore Street
Tel: Topsham (039 287) 3542
Local cider (H)
Taunton H)
Snacks 11-2 and 5-10.

TORBRYAN
Church House Inn (P)
Tel: Ipplepen (0803) 812372
Local cider (PC)
14th century pub. Meals;
garden.

TORCROSS
Village Inn (P)
Tel: Kingsbridge
(0548) 580206
Inch (PC)

TORQUAY
Ashley Rise Hotel (P)
18 Babbacombe Road
Tel: Torquay (0803) 37282
Teignhead (PL)

Brunswick Inn (P)
217 Union Street
Tel: Torquay (0803) 22518
Bulmer (H)

Dartmoor Maiden Restaurant (P)
Teignmouth Road,
Maidencombe
Tel: Torquay (0803) 38760
Teignhead (PL)

Foresters Arms (P)
1-2 Queen Street
Tel: Torquay (0803) 23056

Local cider (PC)
Snacks lunchtime.

Fortune (P)
St. Marychurch Road
Tel: Torquay (0803) 36272
Churchward (PC)

Intercounty Wines (OL)
5-7 East Street, Torre
Tel: Torquay (0803) 22731
Coates (PL)
Inch (BB)

PEPE & SON▲
Torquay Winery & Vineyard,
Newton Road (near Scotts
Bridge)

Sportsman's Inn (P)
15 Laburnham Street
Tel: Torquay (0803) 27739
Churchward (H)

Tolchard & Son (OL)
Woodland Road
Tel: Torquay (0803) 62844
Local cider

Westward Wines (OL)
Old Mill Road, Chelston
Local cider

TORRINGTON
Tuck Shop (OL)
Inch (BB) (J)

TOTNES
Albert Inn (P)
32 Bridgetown
Tel: Totnes (0803) 863214
Local cider (PC)
Bar meals 12-2 and 6-8.30
(not Sunday); garden;
childrens' area; blue grass
first Friday in month; folk
Sunday evenings; pool room.

Castle Inn (P)
Castle Street
Tel: Totnes (0803) 863274
Bulmer (E)
Meals and snacks 11.30-1.50;
outdoor drinking area.

Globe (P)
Castle Hill
Tel: Totnes (0803) 862145
Local cider (H)
Between town and station.
Snacks 12-2; outdoor
drinking area;
accommodation.

Happy Apple (OL)
High Street
Tel: Totnes (0803) 866261
Beenleigh (PL)

Rumour (P)
Churchward (PC)

Watermans Arms (P)
Victoria Street
Bulmer (H)

WEMBWORTHY

Lymington Arms (P)
Lama Cross (near A377)
Tel: Winkleigh (083 783) 572
Taunton (PC)
Meals and snacks all sessions;
garden; pool; skittles;
accommodation.

WEST CHARLETON

Ashburton Arms (P)
on A379
Tel: Frogmore (054 853) 242
Local cider (PC)
Snacks.

WESTWARD HO

Westward Wines (OL)
Inch (BB) (J)

WHIMPLE

Paddock Inn (P)
on A30
Tel: Whimple (0404) 822356
Bromell (PC)

Thirsty Farmer (P)
near railway station
Tel: Whimple (0404) 822287
Bulmer (PC)
In the midst of Whiteways
cider works. Snacks; garden.

WIDECOMBE-IN-THE-MOOR

Old Inn (P)
Tel: Widecombe (036 42) 207

Local cider (PC)
The famous Widecombe Fair
is in September. Meals;
garden.

WINKLEIGH

INCH'S CIDER▲
Western Barn, Hatherleigh
Road
Tel: Winkleigh (083 783) 363

Kings Arms (P)
The Square
Tel: Winkleigh (083 783) 384
Inch (PC)
Tasteful pub cum restaurant
in village centre. Snacks all
sessions; full meals
lunchtime and early evening
(please book); holiday
apartments.

Winkleigh Hotel (P)
The Square
Tel: Winkleigh (083 783) 247
Inch (PC)
Snacks lunchtime and
evening.

WOODBURY SALTERTON

The Diggers Rest (P)
Tel: Woodbury (0395) 32375
Local cider (PL)
Old world village pub with
oak beams, and open fires.
Meals and snacks 12-1.45 and
7-10; Sunday 12-1.30 and
7-9.45; garden.

WOOLACOMBE

Leisureware Shopping Centre (OL)
4/5 West Road
Tel: Woolacombe
(0271) 870872
Inch (BB) (J)

Woolacombe Bay Hotel (P)
Tel: Woolacombe
(0271) 870388
Hancock (F)

WOOLFARDIS-WORTHY

Farmers Arms (P)
near Clovelly
Tel: Clovelly (023 73) 467

Inch (PC)
14th century thatched roof
pub in village pronounced,
should you get lost and need
to ask, "Woolsery". Snacks
12-2 and 7-9.30; meals
7.30-10; restaurant; garden;
children's room.

YEALMPTON

National Shire Horse Centre (P)
Dunstone
Tel: Plymouth (0752) 880268
Addlestones (H)
Bulmer (H)
Coates (H)
Haymakers (H)
Inch (H)
Merrydown (H)
One of the most popular
attractions in the south west,
a day out for the whole family.
Meals and snacks 10-5;
garden; children's room.

YELVERTON

Who'd A Thought It Inn (P)
Tel: Yelverton (0822) 853313
Inch (PC)

ZEAL MONACHORUM

Waie Inn (P)
Inch (PC)

Thelbridge Cross Inn

Dorset

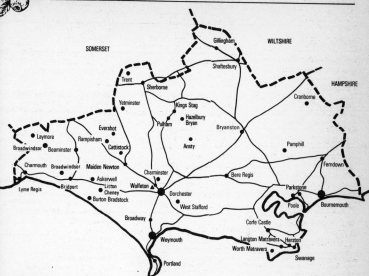

ANSTY

Fox (P)
Tel: Milton Abbas
(0258) 880328
Bulmer (E)
In Hardy Country, far from
the madding crowd; a solid
brick and flint pub in an
unspoilt farming village.
Known for its excellent food.
Snacks lunchtime; full meals
lunchtime and 7-10pm;
restaurant; garden;
children's room,
accommodation.

ASKERWELL

Spyway Inn (P)
off A35 on far side of village
Tel: Powerstock
(030 885) 250
Bulmer (H)
Country pub with marvellous
views. Meals lunchtime and
evening; garden; children's
room; facilities for disabled.

BEAMINSTER

Knapp Inn (P)
Perry (PC)

BERE REGIS

Morse Butchers (OL)
West Street
Rosies (BB) (PL)

BOURNEMOUTH

Night Caps (OL)
Holdenhurst Road
Inch

BRIDPORT

Inter Wines (OL)
South Street
Tel: Bridport (0308) 24971
Inch

Kings Arms (P)
46 North Allington (B3162)
Tel: Bridport (0308) 22833
Coates (PC)
Meals and snacks lunchtime.

Lord Nelson (P)
52 East Street (A35)
Tel: Bridport (0308) 22437
Coates (PC)

Oddfellows Arms (P)
172 North Allington (B3162)
Tel: Bridport (0308) 22665
Coates (PC)

BROADWAY

Railway (P)
Dorchester Road
Tel: Upwey (030 581) 2096
Taunton (PC)
Bar food.

BROADWINDSOR

White Lion (P)
The Square
Tel: Broadwindsor
(0308) 68855
Coates (PC)
Meals lunchtime and
evening.

BRYANSTON

Post Office (OL)
4 Bryanston
Tel: Blandford (0258) 52027
Rosies (BB) (PL)

BURTON BRADSTOCK

Anchor (P)
High Street
Tel: Burton Bradstock
(0308) 897228
Coates (PC)
Village pub built in 1560.
Meals lunchtime and
evening; children's room;
accommodation; camping
nearby.

CATTISTOCK

Fox & Hounds (P)
Tel: Maiden Newton
(0300) 20444
Taunton (H)
Opposite church. Meals
lunchtime and evening;

garden; children's room; accommodation; camping nearby.

CHARMINSTER

New Inn (P)
on A352
Tel: Dorchester (0305) 64694
Taunton (PC)
Meals lunchtime and evening; large garden.

CHARMOUTH

Coach & Horses (P)
The Street (A35)
Tel: Charmouth (0297) 60321
Coates (PC)
Meals lunchtime and evening; garden; children's room; accommodation; camping nearby.

Dampiers (OL)
Inch

CORFE CASTLE

Coopers Stores (OL)
24 West Street
Tel: Corfe Castle (0929) 480223
Cornish Scrumpy

CRANBORNE

Fleur de Lys (P)
5 Wimborne Street
Tel: Cranborne (072 54) 282
Taunton (H)
Meals and snacks every lunchtime and evening, including vegetarian dishes; own bread baking; restaurant; garden; accommodation.

DORCHESTER

Great Western Hotel (P)
Great Western Road
Tel: Dorchester (0305) 63074
Taunton (H)
Near Dorchester West Station, hence the name. Meals and snacks lunchtime and 6.30-8.30; dining room; accommodation; skittle alley.

Hodge Wines (OL)
5 Trinity Street
Tel: Dorchester (0305) 65586
Inch

New Inn (P)
27 South Street
Tel: Dorchester (0305) 62716
Town centre pub, convenient for both railway stations. Snacks lunchtime and evening.

EVERSHOT

Acorn (P)
28 Fore Street (off A37)
Tel: Evershot (093 583) 228
Burrow Hill (PC)
17th century inn mentioned in Tess of the D'Urbervilles; four poster beds in some rooms. Meals and snacks 7-10pm; restaurant; outdoor drinking area; children's room; accommodation; skittle alley.

FERNDOWN

Lambs Wines (OL)
487 Ringwood Road
Tel: Ferndown (0202) 892316
Inch

GILLINGHAM

Dolphin Inn (P)
Peacemarsh (on B 3095 about ½ mile north of town)
Tel: Gillingham (074 76) 2758
Taunton (H)
Snacks all times; garden; pool.

Queens Head (P)
Queen Street
Tel: Gillingham (074 76) 2689
Taunton (H)
Good cider pub in town centre. Meals and snacks all times; garden.

Red Lion (P)
High Street
Tel: Gillingham (074 76) 2751
Taunton (H)
Meals and snacks 12-2 and 7-10; skittle alley; pool room.

Royal Hotel (P)
Newbury
Tel: Gillingham (074 76) 2305
Taunton (H)
Convenient for Railway Station. Meals and snacks all sessions; restaurant; garden; children's room; accommodation; skittle alley.

Suttles Chemist (OL)
Rosies (BB) (PL)

HAZELBURY BRYAN

Antelope (P)
off B3143
Tel: Hazelbury Bryan (025 86) 295
Taunton (PC)
Snacks.

HERSTON

Globe (P)
Bell Street (off A351)
Tel: Swanage (0929) 423515
Bulmer (PC)
Unspoilt local with stone floor and numerous drinking spaces; cellar in thatched outbuilding. On outskirts of Swanage. Snacks all times.

Royal Oak (P)
High Street (A351)
Tel: Swanage (0929) 423303
Bulmer (H)
A short walk up from Herston Halt on the Swanage Steam Railway. Popular with campers. Snacks.

KINGS STAG

Green Man (P)
on B3143
Tel: Hazelbury Bryan (025 86) 338
Perry (PC)
Meals and snacks all sessions; garden; children's room; skittle alley.

KINGSTON

Scott Arms (P)
near Corfe Castle, on B3069
Tel: Corfe Castle (0929) 480270
Bulmer (H)
Inn dating from 1650, haunted by a lady ghost who closes doors (a useful asset). Fine hilltop views overlooking Corfe Castle and Purbecks. World famous for steak and kidney puddings. Meals 12-2 and 6.30-8.00; garden; children's room; accommodation.

LANGTON MATRAVERS

Kings Arms (P)
on B3069
Tel: Swanage (0929) 422979
Bulmer (PC)
Village local built in Purbeck style with many small interconnecting rooms. Meals lunchtime; garden; children's room; camping nearby.

Ship (P)
on B3069 just south of village
Tel: Swanage (0929) 422884
Bulmer (PC)
The pub has a grim history of death and tragedy, fully recorded in the bar, but is now a cheerful local. Snacks lunchtime and evening; garden; children's room; accommodation.

LAYMORE

Squirrel (P)
near Thorncombe (B3162)
Tel: Winsham (046 030) 298
Vickery (PC)
Meals lunchtime and evening; garden; children's room; camping nearby.

LITTON CHENEY

White Horse (P)
Tel: Long Bredy (030 83) 539
Coates (PC)
Village local with Youth
Hostel next door. Meals
lunchtime and evening;
garden; children's room;
accommodation; facilities for
disabled.

LYME REGIS

Slipway (OL)
Henrys

MAIDEN NEWTON

Brewery Inn (P)
Main Street
Tel: Maiden Newton
(0300) 20600
Taunton (PC)
Meals and snacks lunchtime,
evening in summer; garden.

White Horse (P)
57 Dorchester Road
Tel: Maiden Newton
(0300) 20208
Bulmer (PC)
Typical village pub. Snacks
12-1.45 and 7-9; garden.

PAMPHILL

Vine Inn (P)
off B3082
Tel: Wimborne (0202) 882259
Bulmer (PC)
Village cricket in summer.
Snacks lunchtime; garden
with swings and table
draughts.

PARKSTONE

Bricklayers Arms (P)
Park Street
Taunton (H)
Opposite St. Peters Church.
Fearful of being invaded by a
hoard of mindless cider
freaks! Bar food midday.

Catchpole Wines (OL)
21 Bournemouth Road
Tel: Parkstone (0202) 742902
Inch

Sweet Home Inn (P)
25 Ringwood Road
Tel: Poole (0202) 676297
Taunton (H)
Locals pub on main road into
Poole from Ringwood. Snacks
lunchtime; large garden; live
entertainment Saturday
evening.

POOLE

King Charles Inn (P)
Thames Street (off the Quay)
Tel: Poole (0202) 674950
Bulmer (H)
Features 15th century stone
and timber Grand Hall
(Kynges Halle), an upstairs
bar also with Bulmers (H).
Meals and snacks lunchtime;
outdoor drinking area;
children's rooms; showers and
victualing for boating
fraternity.

Parry & Parry (OL)
The Quay
Inch

Queen Mary (P)
68 West Street
Tel: Poole (0202) 673000
Bulmer (H)
Town Centre pub, very near
Guildhall Museum. Meals
and snacks lunchtime;
outdoor drinking area.

Swan Inn (P)
Laglands Street
Tel: Poole (0202) 673825
Bulmer (H)
Adjoins Poole Pottery, at far
end of Poole Quay. Meals and
snacks lunchtime. Poole
room.

PULHAM

Halsey Arms (P)
on B3143
Tel: Hazelbury Bryan
(025 86) 344
Taunton (H)
Village pub with good food.
Meals lunchtime and evening
garden.

RAMPISHAM

Tigers Head (P)
off A356
Tel: Evershot (093 583) 244
Perry (PC)
Meals and snacks lunchtime
and evening; garden;
children's room; facilities for
disabled.

SHAFTESBURY

Farmer Baileys Cheese Centre (OL)
54 High Street
Tel: Shaftesbury
(0747) 51288
Rosies (BB) (PL)

Half Moon (P)
Salisbury Road (A30)
Tel: Shaftesbury (0747) 2456
Taunton (E)
Meals and snacks 12-2 and
7-9.30; restaurant; garden.

Kings Arms (P)
Bleke Street
Tel: Shaftesbury (0747) 2746
Taunton (H)
Reputed highest pub in

Dorset. Snacks lunchtime;
garden; boule court.

Ship Inn (P)
Bleke Street
Tel: Shaftesbury (0747) 3219
Taunton (H)
Built in 1605, and was a
doctors surgery until
becoming a pub in 1930.
Meals and snacks 10.30-2 and
6.30-10; garden;
accommodation.

SHERBORNE

Britannia Inn (P)
Westbury Street
Tel: Sherborne (0935) 813300
Coates (PC)
18th century inn, once a
school for wayward girls!
Meals and snacks 12-2 and
7-10; restaurant;
accommodation.

Digby Tap (P)
Cooks Lane
Taunton (H)
In side street close to Abbey;
unspoilt and laid back.
Snacks lunchtime; outdoor
drinking area.

Greyhound (P)
Cheap Street
Tel: Sherborne (0935) 812785
Taunton (H)
Snacks; accommodation.

White Hart (P)
2 Cheap Street
Tel: Sherborne (0935) 814903
Taunton (H)
Snacks all sessions; full meals
12-1.45; restaurant;
accommodation.

Woolmington Hotel (P)
South Street
Tel: Sherborne (0935) 812901
Taunton (PC)
Near Railway Station;
accommodation.

SWANAGE

Red Lion (P)
High Street
Tel: Swanage (0929) 422533
Bulmer (PC)
Town centre pub. Meals
lunchtime; garden.

White Swan (P)
The Square
Tel: Swanage (0929) 423615
Bulmer (PC)
Snacks; garden; children's
room.

SYMONDSBURY

Ilchester Arms (P)
off A35
Tel: Bridport (0308) 22600
Taunton (PC)

Old beamed and thatched
village pub. Meals and snacks
all sessions; restaurant;
garden; accommodation.

TRENT

Rose & Crown (P)
Tel: Marston Magna
(0935) 332
Rosies (BB)
Meals and snacks lunchtime
and evening; garden.

WEST STAFFORD

Wise Man Inn (P)
Tel: Dorchester (0305) 63694
Taunton (H)
Winter home of Frome Valley
Morris Men. Meals lunchtime
and evening; garden;
facilities for disabled.

WEYMOUTH

Duke of Cornwall (P)
St. Edmunds Street
Tel: Weymouth
(0305) 786593
Taunton (PC)
Meals lunchtime and
evening.

Kings Arms (P)
Trinity Road
Tel: Weymouth
(0305) 770055
Taunton (PC)
Quayside local. Lunchtime
meals.

Stephen Morrison (OL)
36 Crescent Street
Tel: Weymouth
(0305) 774825
Inch
Dorset Scrumpy
Very near Railway Station
and sea front.

WOLFETON

WOLFETON CIDER▲
Wolfeton House, near
Dorchester
Tel: Dorchester (0305) 68748

WORTH MATRAVERS

Square & Compass (P)
off B3069

Tel: Worth Matravers
(092 943) 229
Bulmer (PC)
Converted stone cottages,
with superb sea views, set
high in the Purbeck Hills.
Tiny bar and small rooms off
passageway, totally unspoilt.
Snacks; garden.

YETMINSTER

Railway Inn (P)
Tel: Yetminster
(0935) 872622
Taunton (PC)
Adjacent to Yetminster
Railway Station, on Yeovil to
Weymouth line. Meals and
snacks all sessions, and for
takeaway; garden; children's
room.

White Hart (P)
High Street
Tel: Yetminster
(0935) 872338
Thatched pub in street of old
stone buildings. The Yetties
began their career here.
Meals and snacks all sessions;
garden; play area, children
welcome; pool.

Durham

(map see page 93)

BISHOP AUCKLAND

Silver Bugle (P)
68 Newgate Street
Tel: Bishop Auckland
(0388) 603252
Bulmer (H)

Sportsman (P)
Market Place
Bulmer (H)
Young persons pub.
Reputedly haunted cellar!
Meals lunchtime.

DARLINGTON

Cleveland Arms (P)

Cleveland Street
Farmhouse (H)
The brand of cider is
something of a mystery.

Falchion (P)
Blackwellgate (off Market
Place)

About the editor . . .

David Kitton first disco-
vered cider at a tender
age, when he wandered
innocently into a back street
tavern in south London one hot
summer evening and was con-
fronted by a strong cloudy yellow
liquid, after which he has never
been quite the same.

He trained as an architect, and
describes his career as a "qual-
ified success". He is trustee of a
national charity advising
churches on the use of their
resources; and devotes much

time to producing programmes
on Hospital Radio.

His other interests include
transport except the motor car;
he is proud joint owner of an
Edwardian steam locomotive;
and most of his home is dominated by railway relics. He
broadcasts on radio whenever
anyone will let him near the mic-
rophone, is a keen walker along
and user of the canal system, and
produces his own deadly cider
with the aid of net curtains – not
a sight for the squeamish!

Tel: Darlington
(0325) 462541
Weston (H)
Named after a legionary local
sword. Cider in back bar only.
Meals lunchtime.

DURHAM

**Collingwood
College (P)**
University of Durham, South

Road
Tel: Durham (0385) 67121
Bulmer (H)

Undercroft Bar (P)
Durham Cathedral
Tel: Durham (0385) 63721
Bulmer (H)

Victoria (P)
88 Hallgarth Street
Tel: Durham (0385) 65269
Bulmer (H)

Unspoilt Victorian pub.
Snacks.

FERRYHILL

Black Bull (P)
Market Place
Tel: Ferryhill (0267) 51676
Bulmer (H)
Busy pub in pit village. Meals
and snacks lunchtime;
facilities for disabled.

Essex

BATTLESBRIDGE

Barge (P)
Hawk Hill
Tel: Wickford (037 44) 2622
Bulmer (PC)
On bank of River Crouch,
near antique centre. Short
walk from station. Snacks
morning and evening; meals
lunchtime only; garden;
children's room.

BELCHAMPS WALTER

Eight Bells (P)
Tel: Sudbury (0787) 72866
Saffron Ciders (PC)
Isolated pub. Bar snacks;
garden; pool room and post
office!

BLACKMORE END

Bull (P)
Wethersfield
Tel: Great Dunmow
(0371) 850195
Saffron Ciders (PC)
Meals Wednesday to
Saturday; snacks; garden.

BRAINTREE

Fountain (P)
103 High Street
Tel: Braintree (0376) 45544
Bulmer (PC)
Old renovated pub. Meals
lunchtime; garden;
accommodation.

BRENTWOOD

Tony's Cellar (OL)
Waterloo Road
Saffron Ciders (PC) (B)

CHELMSFORD

Prince of Orange (P)
7 Hall Street (near A130)
Tel: Chelmsford (0245) 81695

James White (PC)
Meals and snacks lunchtime;
garden.

CLACTON

Imperial Hotel (P)
Rosemary Road
Bulmer (H)
Meals lunchtime, snacks
lunchtime and evening;
garden; childrens' room;
accommodation.

COLCHESTER

Amey's (OL)
6 Headgate Buildings, Sir
Isaacs Walk
Tel: Colchester (0206) 572086
Saffron Ciders (B)

Odd One Out (P)
28 Mersea Road
Local cider (PC)
Town centre pub near St.
Botolphs Station. Snacks.
Open all evenings and
Friday, Saturday and Sunday
lunchtime.

Stockwell Arms (P)
West Stockwell Street
Tel: Colchester (0206) 74957
Bulmer (H)
Part of old Dutch Quarter.
Snacks lunchtime; live music
Thursday.

DUDDENHOE END

Woodman (P)
Chrishall (near B1039)
Tel: Royston (0763) 838354
Saffron Ciders (PC)
Meals and snacks lunchtime
and evening; garden;
campsite.

DUTON HILL

**Three Horseshoes
(P)**
near B184

Tel: Great Easton
(037 184) 487
Saffron Ciders (PC)
Snacks; garden.

EARLS COLNE

Drum (P)
High Street (A604)
Saffron Ciders (H)
Many beamed rustic pub.

EASTHORPE

**House Without a
Name (P)**
1½ miles off A12
Tel: Colchester (0206) 210455
Zum (PC)
16th century beamed local.
Meals and snacks lunchtime;
garden.

EPPING

Forest Gate Inn (P)
Bell Common (off B1393)
Tel: Epping (0378) 72312
Bulmer (H)
On edge of Epping Forest.
Snacks 12-2.15 and 7-10.15;
garden.

GREAT CHESTERFORD

Lovedays (OL)
Saffron Ciders (B)

GREAT DUNMOW

**Luckins Wine Store
(OL)**
Market Place
Tel: Great Dunmow
(0371) 2839
Saffron Ciders (B)

GREAT YELDHAM

Wagon & Horses (P)
on A604

Tel: Great Yeldham
(0787) 237520
Saffron Ciders (B)
Single bar country pub.
Meals; accommodation.

GREENSTEAD GREEN

Plough (P)
Grange Hill Road
Tel: Halstead (0787) 472119
Saffron Ciders (PC)
Snacks; garden.

HADLEIGH

Tipplers (OL)
London Road
Saffron Ciders (B)

HEMPSTEAD

Rose & Crown (P)
High Street (B1054)
Tel: Radwinter (079 987) 221
Saffron Ciders (PC)
Meals and snacks lunchtime
and evening.

HIGH EASTER

Cock & Bell (P)
Tel: Good Easter
(024 531) 296
Bulmer (H)
Meals and snacks lunchtime
and evening; garden.

KELVEDEN HATCH

Village Stores (OL)
near Brentwood
Saffron Ciders (B)

KIRBY-LE-SOKEN

Red Lion (P)
The Street (B1034)
Tel: Frinton on Sea
(025 56) 4832
Bulmer (H)
14th century pub with priests
hole. Meals and snacks
lunchtime and evening;
garden.

LANGLY LOWER GREEN

Bull (P)
Tel: Brent Pelham
(027 978) 307
Saffron Ciders (PC)
Snacks lunchtime and
evening.

LITTLE WALDEN

Crown (P)
on B1052

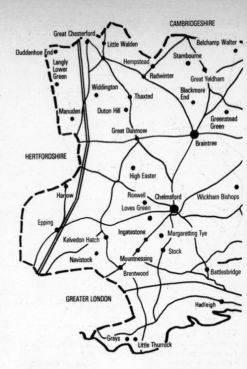

Tel: Saffron Walden
(0799) 27175
Saffron Ciders (PC)
Snacks; garden.

LOVES GREEN (HIGHWOOD)

Green Man (P)
Edney Common, Highwood
Road (near A414)
Tel: Roxwell (024 548) 256
Bulmer (H)
—winter only
In open farmland. Meals and
snacks lunchtime and
evenings except Sunday;
large garden with duckpond.

MANNINGTREE

Stour Wines (OL)
23 High Street
Tel: Colchester (0206) 395095
James White (B)

MANUDEN

Yew Tree (P)
36 The Street
Tel: Bishops Stortford
(0279) 492267
Saffron Ciders (PC)

Traditional pub in village of
thatched houses in Essex
Valley. Snacks and meals
Monday to Saturday
lunchtime and evening.

MARGARETTING TYE

White Hart (P)
Swan Lane
Tel: Ingatestone
(0277) 840478
Bulmer (PC)
Country pub with farm
animals in grounds. Meals
and snacks lunchtime and
evening; garden.

MOUNTNESSING

Prince of Wales (P)
Roman Road
Tel: Ingatestone
(0277) 353445
Bulmer (H)
Meals 10.30-2.30 and 6-11;
garden.

RADWINTER

SAFFRON CIDERS▲
4 Church Hill
Tel: Radwinter (079 987) 427

Tel: Ridgewell (044 085) 267
Saffron Ciders (PC)
15th century church house.
Meals and snacks lunchtime
and evening; restaurant;
garden. No food Sunday
morning.

STOCK

Hoop (P)
High Street (B1007)
Tel: Stock (0277) 840232
Zum (PC)

THAXTED

Cuckoo Wine Bar (P)
36 Town Street
Tel: Thaxted (0371) 830482
Saffron Ciders (PC)
—summer only
Meals and snacks 12-2 and
7-10 (10.45 Friday and
Saturday); vegetarian menu
Tuesday night; children
welcome; dogs welcome,
anything welcome!

Old Swan (P)
Newbiggin Street
Tel: Thaxted (0371) 830321
Saffron Ciders (PC)
Meals and snacks lunchtime
and evening; accommodation.

WICKHAM BISHOPS

Mitre (P)
The Street
Tel: Maldon (0621) 891378
Bulmer (H)
Meals lunchtime and
evening; garden.

WIDDINGTON

Fleur de Lys (P)
High Street
Tel: Saffron Walden
(0799) 40659
Saffron Ciders (PC)
Near wildlife park. Meals and
snacks; garden.

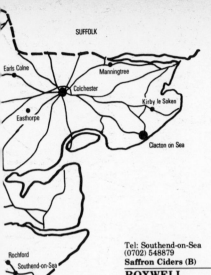

SUFFOLK

Earls Colne

Manningtree

Colchester

Kirby le Soken

Easthorpe

Clacton on Sea

Rochford

Southend-on-Sea

Village Tavern (P)
Church Hill (near B1053)
Tel: Radwinter (079 987) 207
Saffron Ciders (B)
Small local with a shop.
Meals and snacks lunchtime
and evening; children's room.

ROCHFORD

Welbeck Wines Ltd (OL)
49 Purdeys Way
Tel: Southend-on-Sea
(0702) 540611
Saffron Ciders & Perrys (B)

Woody's Wines (OL)
4 East Street

Tel: Southend-on-Sea
(0702) 548879
Saffron Ciders (B)

ROXWELL

Chequers (P)
The Street
Tel: Roxwell (024 548) 240
Bulmer (H)
Meals and snacks lunchtime
and evening except Sunday;
garden.

SOUTHEND-ON-SEA

Cliffs Pavilion (P)
Shorefields
Tel: Southend-on-Sea
(0702) 344553
Saffron Ciders (PC)

STAMBOURNE

Red Lion (P)
Church Street

Gloucestershire

ALVINGTON

Blacksmiths Arms (P)
Tel: Netherend (059 452) 657
Bulmer (H)
Meals and snacks; garden.

AMPNEY CRUCIS

Butchers Arms (P)
off A417
Tel: Poulton (028 585) 486
Weston (PC)
Old fashioned village local. Meals and snacks; garden.

ANDOVERSFORD

Andoversford Hotel (P)
off A40
Tel: Andoversford (0242) 203
Bulmer (H)
Meals and snacks; garden.

Frogmill Inn (P)
off A436
Tel: Andoversford (0242) 237
Bulmer (H)
Meals and snacks, restaurant; live music; garden; accommodation.

Kilkenny Inn (P)
Tel: Andoversford (0242) 820341
Bulmer (H)
Beautiful location with superb Cotswold views. Hot and cold snacks at lunchtime; garden; children welcome.

Royal Oak (P)
on A436
Tel: Andoversford (0242) 335
Bulmer (H)
Village local with galleried eating area. Meals and snacks; restaurant; garden.

APPERLEY

Farmers Arms (P)
on B4213
Tel: Tirley (045 278) 307
Bulmer (H)
Meals and snacks, restaurant; children's room; garden.

ASHLEWORTH

Boat Inn (P)
The Quay (off A417)
Tel: Hartpury (045 270) 272
Weston (PC)
On bank of River Severn, near ancient tithe barn. Garden.

ASTON BLANK

Plough (P)
Taunton (PC)
Stone flagged country pub with low beams. Meals and snacks; garden; children's room.

AVENING

Cross Inn (P)
on B4014
Tel: Nailsworth (045 383) 2953
Bulmer (PC)
Bar snacks.

AYLBURTON

Besum (P)
Bulmer (PC)
Bar snacks; extensive garden.

Cross Inn (P)
Tel: Dean (0594) 42823
Bulmer (H)
400 year old pub. Meals and snacks; garden; children's room.

54

BERKELEY

COUNTRY FARE CIDER▲
Berkeley Heath Farm
Tel: Dursley (0453) 810220

Bird in Hand (P)
on B4066
Tel: Dursley (0453) 811101
Bulmer (H)
Meals and snacks.

Boars Head (P)
Salter Street
Tel: Dursley (0453) 810688
Bulmer (H)
Handy if waiting for the bus.
Snacks; garden.

Mariners Arms (P)
Salter Street
Taunton (PC)
Ancient two bar pub, circa
1490.

BIRDLIP

Air Balloon (P)
on A417/A436/B4070
Junction
Tel: Gloucester
(0452) 862541
Bulmer (H)
Close to Crickley Hill
Country Park. Good views
around Cotswold escarpment
900 ft up. Meals and snacks;
garden; children's room.

Golden Heart (P)
Nettleton Bottom
Tel: Coberley (024 287) 261
Dunkerton (PC)
Weston (PC)
Isolated Cotswold pub. Meals
at lunchtime, snacks; garden;
accommodation.

Royal George (P)
Tel: Gloucester
(0452) 862506
Bulmer (H)
Hotel with Applecart Cider
Bar. Meals and snacks;
restaurant; accommodation;
garden.

BISHOPS CLEEVE

Farmers Arms (P)
Evesham Road (A435)
Tel: Bishops Cleeve
(024 267) 2772
Bulmer (H)
Just north of the village.
Snacks; garden.

BISLEY

Bear (P)
Bulmer (H)
Former court house with 17th
century fireplace. Meals and
snacks; restaurant; children's
room; accommodation;
garden.

BLEDINGTON

Kings Head (P)
Tel: Kingham (060 871) 712
Weston (PC)
Pub by the village green.
Meals and snacks;
accommodation; garden.

BLOCKLEY

Great Western Arms (P)
on B4479
Bulmer (H)
One time blacksmith's house
and shop, now much altered.
Meals and snacks, children's
room; garden.

BOURTON ON THE WATER

Coach & Horses (P)
Foss Way (A429)
Tel: Bourton (0451) 21064
Bulmer (H)
Meals and snacks; garden.

Mousetrap Hotel (P)
Lansdowne
Tel: Cotswold (0451) 20579
Taunton (PC)
Don't let the name put you off!
Meals and snacks;
restaurant; accommodation;
garden.

Old New Inn (P)
High Street
Tel: Bourton (0451) 20467
Bulmer (PC)
Dating from 1709. Adjacent
to model village and model
railway. Meals and snacks;
restaurant; children's room;
accommodation; garden.

BREAM

Cross Keys (P)
Bulmer (E)
Meals and snacks; garden.

Rising Sun (P)
Tel: Dean (0594) 562374
Bulmer (H)
Well known Forest of Dean
viewpoint. Snacks; garden;
live music.

BRIMSCOMBE

Ship Inn (P)
off A419
Tel: Brimscombe
(0453) 884388
Weston (PC)
Snacks; garden.

BROAD CAMPDEN

Bakers Arms (P)
Bulmer (H)
Cotswold stone pub, former

granary. Meals and snacks;
garden; live music.

BROADWELL

Fox Inn (P)
½ mile east of A429
Tel: Cotswold (0451) 30212
Weston (H)
Weston Perry (PP)
Overlooking village green.
Meals, except Tuesdays,
snacks; restaurant;
accommodation; garden.

BROADWELL LANE END

Rising Sun (P)
Bulmer (H)
Snacks; garden.

BROCKWEIR

The Brockweir Country Inn (P)
Tel: Tintern (029 18) 548
Bulmer (H)
Unspoilt 17th century inn on
the banks of the River Wye.
Full meals evenings, snacks
lunch and evening; children's
room; accommodation;
garden.

BROOMS GREEN

The Horseshoe Inn (P)
Tel: Dymock (053 185) 385
Weston (PC)
Attractive pub with pleasant
garden. Meals and snacks all
sessions; restaurant with
supper licence.

CHARLTON KINGS

Merry Fellow Inn (P)
Church Street
Bulmer (H)
Snacks; garden; skittle alley.

Ryeworth Inn (P)
Ryeworth Road, Ryeworth
Tel: Cheltenham
(0242) 528692
Weston (H)
Meals and snacks; garden.

CHELTENHAM

Art College (P)
Dunkerton (B) (H)

Bayshill Inn (P)
St. Georges Place
Tel: Cheltenham
(0242) 524388
Bulmer (H)
Georgian building with old
stables at rear. Full meals
lunchtimes, snacks evenings;
garden; accommodation.

Brewery Tap (P)
St. Margarets Road
Weston (PC)

Coopers Arms (P)
High Street
Tel: Cheltenham
(0242) 584889
Weston (PC)
Meals and snacks; live music.

Engineers Arms (P)
St. Pauls Road
Tel: Cheltenham
(0242) 521031
Bulmer (H)

Old Swan (P)
High Street
Bulmer (H)
Outside drinking area with
dovecot. Meals and snacks.

Prince of Wales (P)
Portland Street
Bulmer (H)
Meals and snacks; outside
drinking area; childrens'
room.

The Retreat (P)
10-11 Suffolk Parade
Tel: Cheltenham
(0242) 35436
Dunkerton (B)

St. Georges Vaults (P)
53 St. Georges Place
Tel: Cheltenham
(0242) 525561
Bulmer (H)
Snacks; outdoor drinking
area.

Shakespeare (P)
386 Lower High Street
Tel: Cheltenham
(0242) 513685
Bulmer (H)
Meals and snacks.

The Shambles (OL)
Units 21-22 The Courtyard,
Montpelier Street
Tel: Cheltenham
(0242) 577458
Dunkerton (B)

Smith (OL)
Lypiatt Street
Weston (PC)
Weston Perry (F)

Somerset Arms (P)
Moorend Street
Tel: Cheltenham
(0242) 523899
Bulmer (H)
Meals and snacks; outdoor
drinking area.

Stonehouse Inn (P)
Swindon Road
Tel: Cheltenham
(0242) 525654
Bulmer (PC)
Tiny street corner local
opposite brewery.

CHILDS WICKHAM

Cotswold Orchards (OL)
Weston (PC)

CHIPPING CAMPDEN

COTSWOLD FARMHOUSE CIDER▲
Smiths Garden Centre,
Station Road
Tel: Evesham (0386) 840367

The Eight Bells (P)
Church Street
Tel: Chipping Campden
(0386) 840371
Bulmer (PP)
Chipping Campden's oldest
pub, 15th century with
cobbled courtyard and
inglenook; named after the
church's bells were stored
here before fitting. Snacks
lunchtime; outdoor drinking
area.

Lygon Arms (P)
High Street
Tel: Chipping Campden
(0386) 840318
Bulmer (PC)
Meals and snacks;
restaurant; skittle alley;
accommodation.

Volunteer (P)
High Street
Tel: Chipping Campden
(0386) 840688
Bulmer (H)
Stone built pub. Meals and
snacks; children's room;
outdoor drinking area.

CINDERFORD

Heywood Inn (P)
Heywood Road
Bulmer (E)
Snacks; garden.

Railway Hotel (P)
Station Street
Bulmer (H)
Opposite the site of the old
GWR station. Snacks.

Upper Bilson (P)
30 Valley Road
Tel: Dean (0599) 24368
Hawthorn (H)
Meals and snacks;
restaurant; garden; skittle
alley.

CIRENCESTER

Golden Cross (P)
Blackjack Street
Tel: Cirencester (0285) 2137
Bulmer (PC)
Meals and snacks; outdoor
drinking area; skittle alley.

Marlborough Arms (P)
Sheep Street
Tel: Cirencester (0285) 3926
Bulmer (H)
Meals lunchtime, snacks;
accommodation; open until
4pm on Tuesdays.

Oddfellows Arms (P)
Chester Street
Bulmer (PC)

Plume of Feathers (P)
Watermoor Road
Tel: Cirencester (0285) 2112
Bulmer (PC)
Meals and snacks.

CLEARWELL

Lamb (P)
Bulmer (H)
Meals and snacks; garden.

Wyndham Arms (P)
Tel: Dean (0594) 33666
Bland (PC)
Built in 1340. Meals and
snacks; accommodation;
garden.

COALEY

Fox & Hounds (P)
Tel: Cambridge (045 389) 366
Bulmer (PC)
Village local. Meals and
snacks; childrens' room;
garden.

COALWAY LANE END

Crown (P)
Bulmer (H)
Snacks; garden; live music.

COATES

Tunnel House Inn (P)
off A433, up side road
between Tarlton and Coates
Tel: Kemble (028 581) 280
Bulmer (H)
At entrance to Sapperton
canal tunnel, built in 1780 for
the tunnel diggers. Meals and
snacks; garden; children's
room; live music.

COBERLEY

Green Dragon (P)
Cockleford, Cowley, off A435
Tel: Coberley (024 287) 271
Bulmer (PC)
Meals and snacks; garden;
skittle alley.

COLEFORD

Feathers (P)

Market Place
Tel: Dean (0594) 33497
Bulmer (H)
Meals and snacks; outdoor
drinking area; live music.

Masons Arms (P)
Boxbush Road
Bulmer (PC)
Snacks; outdoor drinking
area.

Red Lion (P)
Cinderhill
Tel: Dean (0594) 34387
Bulmer (PC)
Meals and snacks;
accommodation.

CRANHAM

Black Horse (P)
Tel: Painswick (0452) 812217
Bulmer (PC)
Meals and snacks;
restaurant; garden.

DOWDESWELL

Reservoir Inn (P)
on A40
Tel: Cheltenham
(0242) 29671
Weston (H)
Lunchtime and evening
menu; garden and balcony;
large play area for children.

DRYBROOK

**Bowketts Off
Licence (OL)**
Weston (PP)

Hearts of Oak (P)
Bulmer (H)
Live music; garden.

DUNTISBOURNE
ABBOTS

Five Mile House
on A417
Taunton (PC)
Traditional roadside inn,
with tiny bar.

DURSLEY

**The Brewery Stores
(OL)**
26a Silver Street
Tel: Dursley (0453) 3918
Thatcher (PC)

**Carpenters Arms
(P)**
Uley Road
Tel: Dursley (0453) 2023
Bulmer (PC)
Snacks.

New Inn (P)
Woodmancote
Weston (PC)
Meals and snacks; garden.

DYMOCK

**Beauchamp Arms
(P)**
Tel: Dymock (053 185) 266
Weston (H)
Meals and snacks; garden;
children's room;
accommodation.

EASTINGTON

Victoria Inn (P)
Tel: Stonehouse
(045 382) 2892
Bulmer (H)
Lunchtime snacks except
Sunday; garden.

EBRINGTON

Three Oaks (P)
Bulmer (H)
Meals and snacks;
restaurant; accommodation;
garden.

ELDERSFIELD

**HARTLAND'S
FARMHOUSE
CIDER▲**
Flat Farm
Tel: Staunton Court
(045 284) 213

EPNEY

Anchor (P)
Tel: Gloucester
(0452) 740433
Bulmer (H)
Riverside pub with good
views across to Forest of
Dean. Meals and snacks;
garden.

FORD

Plough Inn (P)
Tel: Stanton (038 673) 215
Coates (PC)
Cellar used to be a jail. Meals
and snacks; accommodation;
garden.

FRAMILODE

Darrell Arms (P)
Framilode Passage
Tel: Gloucester
(0452) 740320
Bulmer (H)
Vantage point for watching
the Severn Bore. Meals,
snacks; children's room;
garden.

Ship Inn (P)
Tel: Gloucester
(0452) 740260
Bulmer (H)
Canalside pub. Meals and
snacks; garden; live music.

GLASSHOUSE

Glasshouse Inn (P)
May Hill (off A40)
Tel: Gloucester
(0452) 830529
Bulmer (PC)
Isolated old country pub with
stone flagged floor. Meals and
snacks; garden.

GLOUCESTER

**Baldwin Off
Licence (OL)**
Bristol Road
Weston (PC)

County Arms (P)
Millbrook Street
Coates (PC)
Taunton (PC)
At east end of city; left off
Barton Street by Vauxhall
Inn. The city's only true cider
house, a robust and down to
earth establishment.

R.A.O.B. Club (P)
Black Bull

GREAT
BARRINGTON

Fox Inn (P)
off A40
Tel: Windrush (045 14) 385
Coates (PC) (summer)

Hob Nails Cotswold Inn, Little Washbourne

57

A stone built pub by the River Windrush. Meals and snacks lunch and evening; garden; skittle alley; accommodation; live music.

GREET
Harvest Home (P)
Tel: Winchcombe
(0242) 602430
Ivy clad pub in centre of Cotswold village. Meals and snacks; garden; accommodation.

HALMORE
SUMMERS CIDER▲
Slimbridge Lane
Tel: Dursley (0453) 811218

HAM
Salutation Inn (P)
on B4509
Tel: Dursley (0453) 810284
Bulmer (H)
Near Berkeley Castle. Meals and snacks; garden.

HARDWICKE
Cross Keys (P)
on A38
Bulmer (H)
By the roundabout just off the M5. Meals and snacks; garden.

HILLERSLAND
The Rock Inn (P)
on B4063
Tel: Dean (0594) 32367
Bulmer (H)
Crumpton Oaks (PC)
17th century country inn near Symonds Yat, with superb views of Wye Valley, on edge of Forest of Dean. Snacks at most times; garden; family room.

HUCCLECOTE
Waggon & Horses (P)
Tel: Gloucester (0452) 66142
Addlestones (H)
Meals and snacks; garden; accommodation.

JOYFORD
Dog & Muffler (P)
off B4432
Tel: Dean (0594) 32444
Bulmer (H)
Meals and snacks lunchtime and evening; garden, original cider press (thought to be 17th century); barbeque; children's play area.

KILKENNY
Kilkeney Inn (P)
on A436
Bulmer (H)
Meals and snacks; restaurant; garden.

KINETON
Halfway House (P)
2 miles south of Ford (B4077)
Tel: Guiting Power
(045 15) 344
Bulmer (PC)
Country pub near Cotswold Farm Park. Meals and snacks; accommodation; garden.

KINGSCOURT
Kings Head (P)
The Street
Tel: Amberley (045 387) 2336
Bulmer (H)
Meals and snacks; garden.

LECHLADE
Crown Hotel (P)
The Square
Tel: Faringdon (0367) 52218
Weston (PC)
Meals and snacks; restaurant; garden; children's room.

LEONARD STANLEY
White Hart (P)
The Street
Tel: Stonehouse
(045 382) 2702
Bulmer (H)
Meals and snacks; garden.

LITTLE DEAN
George (P)
Tel: Dean (0594) 22319
Bulmer (H)
Snacks; garden.

Kings Head (P)
Tel: Dean (0594) 24474
Bulmer (H)

LITTLEDEAN HILL
Royal Foresters
Littledean Hill Road
Tel: Dean (0594) 22034
Bulmer (H)
A Forest local with splendid views. Snacks; garden; skittle alley.

LITTLE WASHBOURNE
Hobnails Inn (P)
on A438

Tel: Alderton (024 262) 458
Bulmer (PC)
Meals and snacks; restaurant; garden; skittle alley; children's room.

LONGBOROUGH
Coach & Horses (P)
Tel: Cotswold (0451) 30325
Coates (PC)
Live music; garden.

LONGHOPE
Farmers Boy (P)
on A40
Tel: Gloucester (0452) 830279
Hawthorn (H)
13th century inn. Meals and snacks; restaurant; live music; garden.

Nags Head (P)
Ross Road (A40)
Tel: Gloucester (0452) 830284
Bulmer (H)
Meals and snacks lunchtime and evening; restaurant; children's room; garden; holiday flat for weekly letting.

LOWER CAM
Berkeley Arms (P)
on A4135
Bulmer (H)
Meals and snacks; children's room; skittle alley; garden.

LOWER LYDBROOK
Forge Hammer (P)
on B4234
Symonds (PC)
Full of ironmaking photographs. Meals and snacks; garden.

LOWER SWELL
Golden Ball (P)
on B4068
Tel: Cotswold (0451) 30247
Bulmer (PC)
Weston (PC)
Cotswold pub with stream running close by. Meals and snacks lunchtime and evening; garden.

LYDNEY
Cross Keys (P)
Church Road
Tel: Dean (0594) 41619
Bulmer (H)
Meals and snacks; garden.

Greyhound (P)
Tel: Dean (0594) 42670

Bulmer (H)
Weston (PC)
Meals and snacks;
accommodation; garden.

MAISMORE

White Hart (P)
Bulmer (E)

MICKLETON

Butchers Arms (P)
Chapel Lane (off A46)
Tel: Mickleton (038 677) 285
Bulmer (H)
Snacks lunchtime; full meals
7-9pm; garden; skittle alley.

Kings Arms (P)
on A46
Bulmer (PC)
Meals and snacks; garden.

MINCHIN-HAMPTON

Crown (P)
Tel: Brimscombe
(0453) 882357
Bulmer (H)
Village centre hotel. Meals and
snacks; restaurant;
accommodation; garden; live
music.

MITCHELDEAN

Wellington Off
Licence (OL)
Weston (PC)

MORETON IN MARSH

Swan (P)
at junction of A429 and A44
Bulmer (PC)
Meals and snacks.

Wellington (P)
London Road (A44)
Tel: Moreton in Marsh
(0608) 50396
Bulmer (H)
Imposing stone pub at edge of
town. Snacks; garden;
childrens' room.

White Horse (P)
on A429
Bulmer (PC)
Meals and snacks; garden.

NAUNTON

Black Horse (P)
north of B4068
Tel: Guiting Power
(045 15) 378
Weston (PC)
Typical Cotswold stone pub.
Meals and snacks; garden;
accommodation.

Foxhill Inn (P)
on B4068
Tel: Guiting Power
(045 15) 323
Taunton (PC)
Snacks; garden.

NETHER WESTCOTE

New Inn (P)
off A424
Tel: Shipton under Wychwood
(0993) 830827
Bulmer (H)
Small and hidden away in north
side of village. Meals, snacks;
garden; camping site adjoining.

NEWLAND

Ostrich (P)
B4231
Tel: Dean (0594) 33260
Bulmer (PC)
Opposite church known as the
Cathedral of the Forest. Meals,
snacks; garden.

NEWNHAM

Ship Inn (P)
Bulmer (H)
Snacks; live music (piano).

NORTH CERNEY

Bathurst Arms (P)
Tel: North Cherney
(028 683) 251
Dunkerton (B)
Unspoilt pub on Cheltenham to
Cirencester road. Home cooked
soups and snacks; riverside
garden.

NORTHLEACH

Red Lion (P)
Market Square
Tel: Northleach (045 16) 251
Taunton (PC)
16th century inn in centre of
village. Morning coffee; hot and
cold meals and snacks
lunchtime and evening;
accommodation.

Sherborne Arms (P)
Market Square
Tel: Northleach (045 16) 241
Bulmer (H)
Adjacent forge now a
restaurant. Meals and snacks;
outdoor drinking area.

Union Hotel (P)
Market Square
Tel: Northleach (045 16) 259
Bulmer (H)
Meals and snacks; restaurant;
children's room; outdoor
drinking area; accommodation.

Wheatsheaf (P)
High Street
Tel: Northleach (045 16) 244
Bulmer (H)
Hot and cold snacks; a la carte
restaurant with home cooking;
accommodation, garden.

NORTH NIBLEY

New Inn (P)
Waterley Bottom
Tel: Dursley (0453) 3659
Inch (PC)
Hard to find pub in magnificent
countryside. Meals and snacks
lunchtime and evening; large
garden; children's play area;
accommodation.

ODDINGTON

Fox (P)
Lower Oddington
Tel: Cotswold (0451) 30446
Bulmer (PC)
Meals and snacks; garden;
accommodation.

Horse & Groom (P)
Upper Oddington
Tel: Cotswold (0451) 30584
Bulmer (H)
Meals and snacks lunchtime
and evening; restaurant;
garden; children's room.

PAGANHILL

Old Crown (P)
Tel: Stroud (045 36) 3288
Bulmer (PC)
Garden.

PAXFORD

Churchill (P)
B4479
Tel: Paxford (038 678) 203
Bulmer (H)
Meals and snacks lunchtime
and evening; children's room;
garden.

PILLOWELL

Swan (P)
Tel: Dean (0594) 562477
Bulmer (E)
Forest local near disused
railway line. Snacks; garden.

PRESTBURY

Beehive (P)
Bouncers Lane
Tel: Cheltenham
(0242) 521000
Bulmer (H)
Snacks; children's room; skittle
alley.

Royal Oak (P)
The Burgage
Tel: Cheltenham (0242) 22344
Bulmer (E) (H)
Home made meals lunchtime;
snacks; garden; skittle alley.

PUESDOWN

Puesdown Inn (P)
Tel: Cotswold (0451) 60262
Bulmer (H)

PURTON

Berkeley Hunt (P)
off A38
Tel: Dursley (0453) 811217
Bulmer (PC)
Thatcher (PC)
On the bank of the Sharpness &
Gloucester canal. Snacks;
garden; children's room.

QUENINGTON

Keepers Arms (P)
Tel: Coln St. Aldwyns
(028 575) 349
Bulmer (PC)
Former gamekeepers' cottages.
Meals and snacks; restaurant;
accommodation; garden.

RED MARLEY

Rose & Crown (P)
Weston (PC)

RUARDEAN

Malt Shovel (P)
off B4227
Tel: Dean (0594) 543028
Bulmer (E)
Meals and snacks; garden;
skittle alley.

RUARDEAN WOODSIDE

Roebuck (P)
Bulmer (H)

RUSPIDGE

New Inn (P)
Tel: Dean (0594) 24508
Bulmer (H)
Garden.

Rising Sun (P)
Bulmer (E)
Snacks.

ST. BRIAVELS

Crown (P)
Pistol Lane
Tel: Dean (0594) 530205
Bulmer (H)
Snacks; garden; live music.

SHARPNESS

Severn Bridge & Railway Hotel (P)
Tel: Dursley (0453) 811347
Bulmer (H)
The title is a reminder of the old
railway bridge over the Severn,
demolished by an oil tanker!
Near the docks, and a haunt for
seamen from far off parts.
Meals and snacks; garden;
children's room.

SLIMBRIDGE

Tudor Arms (P)
Shepherds Patch
Tel: Cambridge (045 389) 306
Andrews (PC)
Old pub on the bank of
Sharpness canal, near Wildfowl
Trust reserve. Snacks
lunchtime and evening; full
meals evening; restaurant;
garden; children's room.

SLING

Miners Arms (P)
Bulmer (H)
Snacks; garden.

SOUTHROP

Swan (P)
Tel: Southrop (036 785) 205
Weston (PP)
Meals and snacks lunchtime
and 7-9.30pm; restaurant;
children accepted; garden;
skittle alley.

STANTON

Mount Inn (P)
Black Bull (PC)
Bulmer (PC)
Meals and snacks; garden.

STAUNTON

White Horse (P)
near Coleford
Tel: Dean (0594) 33387
Bulmer (H)
Meals and snacks lunchtime
and 7-10pm; restaurant;
garden; accommodation.

STAVERTON

House in the Tree (P)
Haydens Elm (on B4063)
Tel: Coombe Hill
(024 268) 241
Bulmer (E)
Snacks; garden.

Plough (P)
Staverton Bridge
Bulmer (H)
Close to caravan sites and
airport. Snacks; garden.

STINCHCOMBE

Yew Tree (P)
Bulmer (H)
Meals and snacks; garden.

STONEHOUSE

Brewers Arms (P)
Gloucester Road
Tel: Stonehouse
(045 382) 2621
Local (H)
Snacks; garden; children's
room.

Royal Arms (P)
Bath Road
Tel: Stonehouse
(045 382) 2718
Bulmer (H)
Snacks lunchtime.

Woolpack (P)
4 High Street
Tel: Stonehouse
(045 382) 2542
Weston (PC)
Unusual Cotswold building;
cellar visible from public bar.
Snacks, garden.

STOW ON THE WOLD

Bell (P)
Park Street
Tel: Cotswold (0451) 30663
Bulmer (PC)
Overlooking small green.
Snacks; garden; live music.

Buffery & Sons (OL)
Digbeth Street
Tel: Cotswold (0451) 30667
Weston (PL)

Farmers Arms (P)
A429/A424 junction
Tel: Cotswold (0451) 30330
Bulmer (H)
Good food, not including the
stuffed parrot. Meals and
snacks; outdoor drinking area;
accommodation.

Queens Head (P)
The Square
Tel: Cotswold (0451) 30563
Weston (H)
Fine old Cotswold town centre
pub. Meals and snacks;
outdoor drinking area;
accommodation.

Royalist Hotel Tavern (P)
Digbeth Street
Tel: Cotswold (0451) 30670
Bulmer (E)

STROUD

Victoria (P)
Gloucester Street
Tel: Stroud (045 36) 5250
Dunkerton (B)
Snacks lunchtime.

TEDDINGTON

Teddington Hands (P)
Teddington Hands
Bulmer (H)
Meals and snacks; garden; live music; skittle alley; children's room.

TETBURY

Royal Oak (P)
Cirencester Road
Tel: Tetbury (0666) 52570
Taunton (PC)
Meals and snacks; restaurant; outdoor drinking area; accommodation; children's room; skittle alley.

TEWKESBURY

Anchor (P)
High Street
Tel: Tewkesbury (0684) 296614
Bulmer (PC)
Weston (PC)
Snacks lunch and evening; full meals lunch; coffee room; accommodation.

Berkeley Arms (P)
Church Street
Tel: Tewkesbury (0684) 293034
Bulmer (PC) (PL)
Taunton (PC) (PL)
17th Century inn, with access via alley way. Snacks lunchtime; accommodation.

Sports & Social Club (P)
Black Bull (PC)

TIRLEY

Haw Bridge Inn (P)
on B4213
Tel: Tirley (045 278) 316
Weston (H)
On the bank of River Severn. Snacks; garden.

TODENHAM

Farriers Arms (P)
Tel: Moreton (0608) 50901
Bulmer (H)
Formerly a blacksmith's shop. Meals and snacks; restaurant; garden; live music.

TWYNING GREEN

Fleet Inn (P)
Tel: Tewkesbury (0684) 292561
Bulmer (PC)
On bank of River Avon, with mooring. Snacks; large garden; skittle alley.

Village Inn (P)
Tel: Tewkesbury (0684) 293500
Bulmer (PC)
On Village Green. Meals and snacks; garden; live music; skittle alley.

UPPER LYDBROOK

Masons Arms (P)
Hawsley
Bulmer (H)
An isolated pub. Garden.

UPPER SOUDLEY

White Horse (P)
Tel: Dean (0594) 22380
Bulmer (H)
Meals and snacks; restaurant; garden; live music.

UPTON ST. LEONARDS

Kings Head (P)
on B4073
Weston (H)
Meals and snacks; garden.

WAINLODES

Red Lion (P)
Tel: Gloucester (0452) 730251
Weston (H) (PP)
On the bank of the River Severn, with caravan and camping park, excellent fishing. Snacks lunchtime and 7-10pm; garden; holiday cottage and chalet to let; children's room.

WANSWELL

Salmon Inn (P)
between Berkeley and Sharpness
Tel: Dursley (0453) 811306
Bulmer (PC)
Convenient for Berkeley Castle, Slimbridge Wildfowl Trust, and Sharpness Marina. Meals and snacks lunchtime and 7.30-10pm; children's room and large children's lawn.

WHITECROFT

Miners Arms (P)
Bulmer (H)
Snacks; skittle alley.

WHITESHILL

Star Inn (P)
Bulmer (H)
Live Music

WINCHCOMBE

Corner Cupboard (P)
Gloucester Street
Tel: Winchcombe (0242) 602303
Bulmer (H)
Old stone built inn in Cotswold town. Snacks lunchtime; full meals Tuesday-Saturday 7.15-8.30pm; restaurant.

White Hart (P)
High Street
Tel: Winchcombe (0242) 602359
Bulmer (PC)
Meals and snacks; restaurant; children's room; accommodation.

WITHINGTON

Kings Head (P)
Weston (PC)
Snacks; garden.

Mill Inn (P)
Tel: Withington (024 289) 204
Dunkerton (B) (H)
Popular brookside inn. Meals and snacks; garden; childrens' room.

WOODCROFT

Rising Sun (P)
on B4228
Taunton (H)
Meals and snacks; garden.

YORKLEY

Bailey (P)
Bulmer (H)
Village crossroads pub. Snacks; skittles.

YORKLEY SLADE

Nags Head (P)
Tel: Dean (0594) 562592
Bulmer (H)
Snacks; garden.

Your recommendations are welcomed for future editions of the Guide Please use the inspection form at the back

61

Hampshire

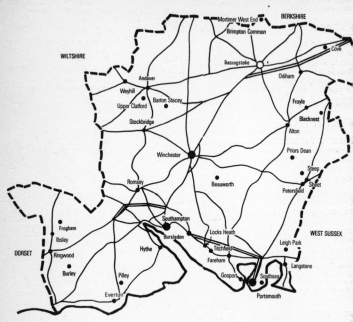

ALTON

Eight Bells (P)
Church Street
Tel: Alton (0420) 82417
Selborne Gold (PC)
Snacks 12-2; full meals
6-8.30.

SELBORNE GOLD CIDER
Hampshire Cider Company,
4 Manor Cottages, Neatham
Tel: Alton (0420) 86759

ANDOVER

Bottoms Up (OL)
63 Charlton Road
Tel: Andover (0264) 59022
Zum (PC)

BARTON STACEY

Swan (P)
Tel: Winchester
(0962) 760470
Bulmer (H)
Snacks; garden; camping
nearby.

BEAUWORTH

Milburys (P)
Tel: Bramdean (096 279) 248
Dunkerton (B)
Remote old inn with huge
treadmill and 300 ft well in
bar. Meals lunchtime and
evening; garden; children's
room; accommodation.

BLACKNEST

Jolly Farmer (P)
off A325
Tel: Bentley (0420) 22244
Bulmer (H)
Roadside pub about 1 mile
from Bentley Station;
attractive walks in nearby
Alice Holt Forest. Meals and
snacks all sessions; Sunday
lunches; restaurant; garden;
skittle alley.

BRIMPTON COMMON

Pineapple (P)
on B3051
Tel: Tadley (073 56) 4376

Bulmer (H)
Ancient thatched pub on
Berkshire border. Home
made meals 12-2 except
Sunday; garden.

BURSLEDON

Jolly Sailor (P)
Lands End Road, Old
Bursledon
Tel: Bursledon
(042 121) 3787
Bulmer (PC)
Waterfront pub used in
"Howards Way" series.
Meals, snacks; restaurant;
garden.

BURLEY

**White Hart at
Burley (P)**
Bisterne Close
Tel: Burley (042 53) 2264
Taunton (H)

COVE

**Crown & Cushion
(P)**

Minley Road
Tel: Farnborough
(0252) 542564
Bulmer (H)
Old wayside pub with huge
raftered "Meade Hall". Meals
and snacks; garden.

EVERTON

Crown Inn (P)
Old Christchurch Road
Tel: Lymington (0590) 42655
Bulmer (H)
Old village pub east of
Lymington. Meals 11-1.45
and 7.30-9.45; garden;
children's room.

FAREHAM

Bird in Hand (P)
Gosport Road
Tel: Gosport (0705) 280841
Coates (H)
Meals and snacks lunchtime.

FROGMORE

Foresters Arms (P)
Tel: Fordingbridge
(0425) 52294
Perry (H)
Thatched pub 2 miles east of
Fordingbridge, on edge of
New Forest; start of many
walks and pony treks. Meals
and snacks 12-2 and 7-10
except Sunday; large garden;
children's room.

GOSPORT

Naval & Military Arms (P)
Elson Road, Elson
Bulmer (H)
Meals and snacks lunchtime.

Park Hotel (P)
Park Road, Alverstoke
Tel: Gosport (0705) 58374
Bulmer (H)
Snacks; garden; live music;
children's room.

Robin Hood (P)
Mayfield Road
Tel: Gosport (0705) 585349
Bulmer (H)
Small corner local. Meals and
snacks.

Royal Arms (P)
Stoke Road
Bulmer (H)

HYTHE

Lord Nelson (P)
High Street
Tel: Hythe (0703) 842169
Bulmer (PC)
Waterfront pub. Meals
lunchtime; garden; facilities
for disabled.

IBSLEY

Old Beams (P)
on A338 (near Ringwood)
Tel: Ringwood (042 54) 3387
Bulmer (H)
Ancient inn with cruck beams
in end wall. Meals and
snacks; garden; children's
room.

LANGSTONE

Royal Oak (P)
19 High Street
Tel: Havant (0705) 483125
Bulmer (H)
Picturesque waterside pub.
Meals and snacks lunchtime
and evening; garden.

LEIGH PARK

Swallow (P)
500 Dunsbury Way
Tel: Havant (0705) 476334
Coates (H)
On the largest housing estate
in the country. Leigh Park
Gardens and Farm Trail
nearby.

LOCKS HEATH

Sir Joseph Paxton (P)
Titchfield Common
Tel: Locks Heath
(048 95) 2125
Bulmer (H)
Snacks; garden.

MARTIN

Coote Arms (P)
Martin Drove End (on A354)
Tel: Martin Cross
(072 589) 220
Bulmer (H)
Roadside inn with free range
eggs for sale. Pool; garden.

MORTIMER WEST END

Red Lion (P)
Church Road
Tel: Silchester (0734) 700169
Taunton (H)
On Berkshire border, 16th
century country inn. Meals
and snacks except Sunday
evening; restaurant; garden.

ODIHAM

Waterwitch (P)
Colt Hill, London Road
Tel: Odiham (025 671) 2778
Bulmer (H)
16th century pub on bank of
restored Basingstoke Canal;
trips available nearby. Meals
and snacks; large garden

PETERSFIELD

Market Inn (P)
Tel: Petersfield (0730) 63723
Bulmer (H)
Dates back 300 years. Meals
and snacks all sessions.

PILLEY

Fleur de Lys (P)
High Street
Tel: Lymington (0590) 72158
Bulmer (PC) summer
Very old thatched pub,
originally a pair of foresters
cottages. Garden; children's
room.

PORTSMOUTH

Brewery Tap (P)
17 London Road, North End
Tel: Portsmouth
(0705) 699943
Taunton (H)
Shopping centre pub. Meals
lunchtime and evening
Monday to Friday; facilities
for disabled.

Bottoms Up (OL)
7 Kingston Road
Tel: Portsmouth
(0705) 830760
Zum (PC)

Hornpipe Bar (P)
Kingston Road, Buckland
Tel: Portsmouth
(0705) 862812
Taunton (PC)
Theatre bar in Art Decco
style, part of Hornpipe
Theatre, opens only in
evening.

PRIORS DEAN

White Horse (P)
Merrydown (H)
Remote pub in middle of field
off A32; no sign! Garden.
camping.

RINGWOOD

Elm Tree (P)
Hightown (east of town)
Tel: Ringwood (042 54) 2516
Bulmer (H)
Home made food; garden;
children's room.

ROMSEY

Dolphin Hotel (P)
The Cornmarket
Tel: Romsey (0794) 512171
Coates (H)
Cider in Market Bar. Meals
and snacks except Sunday
evening; pool;
accommodation.

SHEET

Half Moon (P)
on A3 near Petersfield
Tel: Petersfield (0730) 63859
Bulmer (H)
Meals and snacks;
restaurant; garden.

SOUTHAMPTON

Cliff (P)
Portsmouth Road, Woolston
Tel: Southampton
(0703) 448547
Bulmer (H)
Overlooking River Itchen.
Meals and snacks; garden;
skittle alley.

Crown & Sceptre (P)
Burgess Road, Bassett
Tel: Southampton
(0703) 768414
Bulmer (H)
Meals and snacks; garden.

Glasgow (P)
Bernard Street
Tel: Southampton
(0703) 28387
Bulmer (H)
Meals and snacks lunchtime;
garden.

Mount Hotel (P)
Winchester Road
Tel: Southampton
(0703) 60666
Bulmer (H)
Berni Inn with separate bar.
Meals; restaurant.

North Star (P)
St. Marys Street
Tel: Southampton
(0703) 229789
Bulmer (H)
Meals

Oddbins (OL)
83 Queensway
Tel: Southampton
(0703) 38010
Weston (J)

Rover Inn (P)
Shirley Road, Freemantle
Tel: Southampton
(0703) 772882
Bulmer (H)

Ship (P)
Woolston
Bulmer (H)

Sun Hotel (P)
Weston Lane, Woolston
Tel: Southampton
(0703) 448339
Bulmer (H)

SOUTHSEA

Bold Forester (P)
Albert Road
Tel: Portsmouth
(0705) 823609
Bulmer (H)
Meals except Sunday.

Conbeni Market (OL)
95 Fawcett Road
Cornish Scrumpy (B)

Eastney Cellars (P)
Cromwell Road, Eastney
Tel: Portsmouth
(0705) 826249
Bulmer (H)

Nell Gwynne (P)
Jessie Road
Tel: Portsmouth
(0705) 826508
Bulmer (H)
Turreted street corner house.
Meals except Sunday.

Pompey Beer Shop (OL)
62 Elm Grove
Tel: Portsmouth
(0705) 756118
Rich (PC)

RMA Tavern (P)
58 Cromwell Road, Eastney
Tel: Portsmouth
(0705) 820896

Bulmer (PC)
Opposite Royal Marines
Museum. Meals 12 noon to
2pm; children's room.

STEEP

Harrow Inn (P)
Tel: Petersfield (0730) 62685
Bulmer (PC)
Unspoilt pub near
Petersfield. Snacks
lunchtime and evening;
garden.

STOCKBRIDGE

White Hart (P)
Tel: Andover (0264) 810475
Taunton (H)
Meals and snacks;
accommodation.

TITCHFIELD

Wheatsheaf (P)
East Street
Tel: Titchfield (0329) 42965
Bulmer (H)
Mentioned in Doomsday
Book. Meals and snacks
lunchtime and evening;
restaurant; garden.

UPPER CLATFORD

Crook & Shears (P)
Tel: Andover (0264) 61543
Bulmer (H)
Thatched village local.
Snacks; garden; skittle alley

WEYHILL

Weyhill Fair (P)
on A303
Tel: Weyhill (026 477) 3631
Weston (H)
Zum (PC)
Meals lunchtime and
evening; garden; children's
room.

WINCHESTER

Royal Oak (P)
Royal Oak Passage, High
Street
Tel: Winchester (0962) 6113
Bulmer (H)
Medieval pub with oldest bar
in England. Meals and snack
lunchtime.

The Harrow at Steep, an unspoilt rural gem

Herefordshire

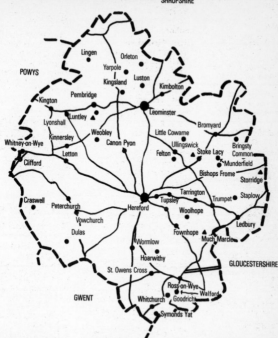

SHROPSHIRE

POWYS

Lingen · Orleton · Yarpole · Kingsland · Luston · Kimbolton · Pembridge · Kington · Leominster · Luntley · Lyonshall · Weobley · Bromyard · Kinnersley · Little Cowarne · Whitney-on-Wye · Canon Pyon · Ullingswick · Bringsty Common · Letton · Felton · Stoke Lacy · Munderfield · Clifford · Bishops Frome · Storridge · Craswell · Peterchurch · Tarrington · Trumpet · Staplow · Hereford · Tupsley · Woolhope · Vowchurch · Dulas · Fownhope · Ledbury · Wormlow · Much Marcle · Hoarwithy · St. Owens Cross · GLOUCESTERSHIRE · Ross-on-Wye · Walford · GWENT · Whitchurch · Goodrich · Symonds Yat

BISHOPS FROME

Green Dragon (P)

west 50 yards along Burley
Gate Road by village green
Tel: Mundersfield
(088 53) 607

Weston (H) ·

17th century village pub.
Meals and snacks 12-2 and
7-10, including children's
menu; patio and garden.

BRIDGE
SOLLARS

Nelson (P)

on A438
Tel: Bridge Sollars
(098 122) 208

Weston (PC)

In pretty Wye Valley village.
Meals and snacks; garden and
patio; children's room.

Nelson Farm (OL)

Weston (PL) (PP)

BRINGSTY
COMMON

Live & Let Live (P)

ust off A44

Tel: Knightwick
(0886) 21462
Bulmer (PC)
Remarkably remote pub,
some 500 years old, in the
midst of the common. Turn
down a rough track off the
road and persevere! Garden;
and whole common!

BROMYARD

Pullens Farm Shop
(OL)

Ridgeway Cross
Dunkerton (B) (PC)

Royal Oak (P)

Norton Downs
Tel: Bromyard (0885) 82234
Black Bull (PC)

White Horse (P)

Old Road
Tel: Bromyard (0885) 82279
Weston (PC)
Old town pub. Snacks.

CANON PYON

Plough (P)

Tel: Canon Pyon
(043 271) 577

Bulmer (PC)
Meals and snacks all sessions;
restaurant; garden; pool.

CLIFFORD

Castlefield Inn (P)

Tel: Clifford (049 73) 345
Weston (PC)
Snacks all sessions; garden;
caravan club site and
camping.

CRASWELL

Bulls Head (P)

Weston (PC)
Old pub with beamed ceiling
and stone floor, in hilly
country at end of Monnow
valley.

DULAS

Trout Found Out (P)

off B4347
Tel: Golden Valley
(0981) 240356
Bulmer (H)
Isolated and unspoilt. Meals
lunchtime and evening;
garden; camping.

FELTON

Crozens Arms (P)
Tel: Burley Gate
(043 278) 213
Weston (H)
Georgian pub with accent on
food and sport. Meals and
snacks all sessions; children's
room; sports pitch.

FOWNHOPE

Forge & Ferry (P)
Ferry Lane (off B4224)
Tel: Fownhope (043 277) 391
Weston (PC)
Meals and snacks all sessions;
garden; children's room.

Green Man (P)
on B4224
Tel: Fownhope (043 277) 243
Weston (PC)
Dating from 1485, timber
fronted bar. Meals and snacks
lunchtime and evening;
garden; accommodation.

GOODRICH

Cross Keys (P)
just off A40
Tel: Symonds Yat
(0600) 890203
Bulmer (H)
Near Goodrich Castle. Meals
and snacks; garden.

HEREFORD

Brewers Arms (P)
Eign Road (B4224)
Tel: Hereford (0432) 273746
Bulmer (E)
Local with good company and
good cider. Bar snacks;
morning coffee, garden.

Bricklayers Arms (P)
St. Owen Street
Tel: Hereford (0432) 274998
Weston (PC)
Snacks all sessions.

BULMER'S TRADITIONAL DRAUGHT CIDERS
H.P. Bulmer Limited, UK
Drinks Division. The Cider
Mills, Plough Lane;
Tel: Hereford (0432) 270622

The Cider Museum (OL)
Pomona Place, off Whitecross
Road
Tel: Hereford (0432) 54207
King Offa (B)

Crown Inn (P)
St. Martins (by Greyfriars
Bridge roundabout)
Tel: Hereford (0432) 51227

Bulmer (H)
Unspoilt pub. Snacks;
outdoor drinking area,
children's room.

Cheng Off Licence (OL)
The Quay, Belmont
Weston (PL) (PP)

Delicatessen (OL)
Dunkerton (B)

Dickinsons (OL)
14 Bridge Street
Tel: Hereford (0432) 53720
Dunkerton (B)
Symonds (PL)
Weston (PL) (PP)

Peter Dominic (OL)
56 Broad Street
Tel: Hereford (0432) 269150
Dunkerton (B)

Effys Restaurant
96 East Street
Tel: Hereford (0432) 59754
Dunkerton (B)

Ford (OL)
Westfields
Weston (PL)

Goslings General Store (OL)
Green Lane
Weston (PL)

Half Crown (P)
Commercial Road
Tel: Hereford (0432) 272379
Bulmer (H)
Weston (PC)
Near railway station,
opposite bus station, an
unspoilt pub with a cider
following. Snacks; outdoor
drinking area;
accommodation.

Heart of Oak (P)
Newton Road
Tel: Hereford (0432) 276056
Bulmer (E)
Meals lunchtime; garden;
childrens' room.

Horse & Groom (P)
Eign Street
Tel: Hereford (0432) 55026
Bulmer (E)
Snacks lunchtime; garden;
live music Friday and
Saturday night.

KING OFFA CIDER▲
The Cider Museum, Pomona
Place, off Whitecross Road
Tel: Hereford (0432) 54207

Lamb (P)
St. Owen Street
Tel: Hereford (0432) 274968
Bulmer (PC)
Originally a coaching inn,
now a locals' pub. Snacks all
sessions; children's room.

Moss Cottage (P)
Foley Street (off Ledbury
Road)
Tel: Hereford (0432) 276188
Bulmer (E)
A pub which merges into the
rest of the Victorian terrace
Garden.

Old Harp (P)
Widemarsh Street (north)
Tel: Hereford (0432) 56531
Weston (PC)
Near the market. Meals
lunchtime, snacks all
sessions; childrens' room.

Quinsey Off Licence (OL)
St. Martins
Weston (PL) (PP)

Saracens Head (P)
St. Martins Street
Tel: Hereford (0432) 275480
Bulmer (H)
Dunkerton (PC)
Black Bull
Weston (H)
Adjacent to Old Wye Bridge
One of Hereford's oldest
buildings. Meals lunchtime
and evening; garden.

Shop Under the Clock (OL)
11 Commercial Road
Tel: Hereford (0432) 268279
Bulmer (J)
Dunkerton (B) (J)
Black Bull (J)
Weston (PL)

Sun (P)
St. Owen Street
Tel: Hereford (0432) 266403
Bulmer (W)
Enthusiastic cider pub.
Snacks all sessions.

Volunteers Arms (P)
21 Harold Street
Tel: Hereford (0432) 276189
Bulmer (H)
Weston (H)
Home cooking, meals and
snacks all sessions;
restaurant; garden; pool;
skittle alley.

HOARWITHY

Harp (P)
Tel: Carey (043 270) 213
Bulmer (H)
Meals all sessions; garden;
childrens' room.

KIMBOLTON

Stockton Cross (P)
on A4112
Bulmer (H)
Old timber framed village
local from 15th century.
Garden; children's room.

KINGLAND

Corners Inn (P)
on B4360 off A4110
Tel: Kingsland (056 881) 385
Weston (PC)
17th century pub, which used to have its own cider press. Snacks; children's room.

KINGTON

Husseys Off Licence (OL)
High Street
Dunkerton (B)

Kington Off Licence (OL)
15 High Street
Tel: Kington (0544) 230987
Dunkerton (B)
Symonds (PC)

Youngs Off Licence (OL)
High Street
Weston (PL) (PP)

KINNERSLEY

Kinnersley Arms (P)
on Letton road out of Kinnersley
Tel: Eardisley (054 46) 240
Bulmer (H)
Dunkerton (H)
Weston (H)
Do not confuse with the Kinnersley in Worcestershire! Meals and snacks Monday to Saturday 11-2.30 and 7-11; Sunday 12-2 and 7-10.30; restaurant; garden; children's room; accommodation.

LEDBURY

Brewery Inn (P)
Bye Street
Tel: Ledbury (0531) 4272
Weston (H)
Unspoilt pub with two rooms served from a unique small corner bar—more like a bar in the living room! Dates from the 15th century. Meals and snacks lunchtime; garden; children's room.

Hereford Bull (P)
High Street
Tel: Ledbury (0531) 2766
Weston (H)
Town centre steak bar. Meals all sessions

Hope End Country House Hotel (P)
Wellington Heath
Tel: Ledbury (0531) 3613
Dunkerton (B)

Plough Hotel (P)
Homend
Tel: Ledbury (0531) 2911
Bulmer (H)

Old coaching inn, and still residential. Meals and snacks all sessions; restaurant; accommodation; skittle alley.

Prince of Wales (P)
Church Lane
Tel: Ledbury (0531) 2250
Bulmer (H)
16th century pub in picturesque cobbled street, once the Grammar School. Meals all sessions, choice limited in evening; childrens' room.

Seven Stars (P)
The Homend
Tel: Ledbury (0531) 2824
Weston (PC)
16th century inn with display of corn grinders. Morning coffee; snacks lunchtime and evening; garden; accommodation.

Spar Off Licence (OL)
Weston (P) (PP)

Vine Off Licence (OL)
11 High Street
Tel: Ledbury (0531) 2665
Weston (PL) (PP)

White Hart (P)
Church Street
Weston (PC)
Good value local.

LEOMINSTER

Black Horse (P)
South Street
Tel: Leominster (0568) 611946
Dunkerton (B)

Bodega Wines (OL)
28 High Street
Tel: Leominster (0568) 2003
Weston (PC)

Dukes Arms (P)
Etnam Street
Tel: Leominster (0568) 2681
Bulmer (H)
On road to the station. Snacks; garden; children's room.

The Red Lion in ancient Weobley

Henpen Restaurant (P)
3 High Street
Tel: Leominster (0568) 4194
Dunkerton (B)

Hop Pole (P)
Bridge Street
Tel: Leominster (0568) 2779
Bulmer (E)
Very busy cider house at edge of town, a friendly mix of town and country folk.

Royal Oak (P)
South Street
Tel: Leominster (0568) 2610
Bulmer (H)
Dunkerton (B)
Old coaching inn with original panelling, beams and open fires. Meals and snacks, including Sunday lunches; accommodation.

LETTON

Swan (P)
on A438
Tel: Eardisley (054 46) 304
Dunkerton (B)
Roadside pub near River Wye. Meals and snacks; 2 acres of garden.

LINGEN

Royal George (P)
Tel: Presteigne (0544) 267322
Weston (PC)
Remote 17th century pub, which serves as post office and shop—one of only three in the country. Snacks; meals by arrangement; garden; children's room.

LITTLE COWARNE

Three Horseshoes (P)
Tel: Pencombe (088 55) 276
Symonds (PC)
The pub was the village blacksmiths till 1900. Meals and snacks all sessions; garden.

LUNTELY

DUNKERTON'S CIDER CO. ▲
Hays Head, near Pembridge
Tel: Pembridge (054 47) 653

LUSTON

Balance Inn (P)
on B4361
Tel: Leominster (0568) 5757
Bulmer (H)
Originally a wool weighing station. Watch out for Bessie the Ghost! Meals and snacks; restaurant; garden.

LYONSHALL

Penrhos Court Restaurant (P)
Tel: Kington (0544) 230 720
Dunkerton (PC)

Royal George Inn (P)
on A480
Tel: Lyonshall (054 48) 210
Bulmer (E)
16th century timber framed inn which was once a cider mill with its own orchard. Meals and snacks; restaurant; garden; games room; accommodation.

MUCH MARCLE

WESTON'S CIDER AND PERRY ▲
Bounds
Tel: Much Marcle (053 184) 233

MUNDERFIELD

Hollybush Inn (P)
Munderfield Row (B4214)
Tel: Munderfield (088 53) 394
Bulmer (H)
Snacks all sessions; meals evening; garden; children's room; camp site with view of Malverns; folk evening every Sunday; accommodation.

ORLETON

Boot Inn (P)
off B4361
Tel: Yarpole (056885) 228
Dunkerton (B)
Once a butchers shop with slaughter house at back, then became a pub cum small holding selling rough cider. Meals and snacks; garden.

PEMBRIDGE

Greyhound (P)
Tel: Pembridge (054 47) 322
Bulmer (H)
Once a coaching inn on the London to Aberystwyth road; with 14th century exterior. Meals and snacks; garden; accommodation.

House of Steps (OL)
Dunkerton (B)

New Inn (P)
Market Square
Tel: Pembridge (054 47) 427
Bulmer (H)
Actually *older* than the Greyhound, dating from 1311, and dominating this picture book village. Meals and snacks; restaurant; garden; accommodation.

PETERCHURCH

Boughton Arms Hotel (P)
on B4348
Tel: Peterchurch (098 16) 208
Weston (PC)
Nearby is the well preserved Norman church (with fibreglass spire!) Snacks all sessions; meals 7.30-10.30; restaurant; garden; accommodation; a "clean air pub".

Nags Head (P)
Tel: Peterchurch (098 16) 271
Weston (PC)

ROSS ON WYE

Corkscrew (OL)
Dunkerton (B)

Horse & Jockey (P)
New Street
Tel: Ross-on-Wye (0989) 62168
Bulmer (PC)
Quiet back street local. Snacks lunchtime; skittle alley.

Man of Ross (P)
Wye Street
Tel: Ross-on-Wye (0989) 64597
Weston (PC)
Jacobean inn in town centre. Snacks 12-2 and 7-9.30; speciality homemade steak and kidney pies.

Meaders Restaurant (P)
1 Copse Cross Street
Tel: Ross-on-Wye (0989) 62803
Dunkerton (B)

Patio Restaurant (P)
45 High Street
Tel: Ross-on-Wye (0989) 62217
Dunkerton (B)

Royal Hotel (P)
Tel: Ross-on-Wye (0989) 65105
Dunkerton (B)
Accommodation.

Ryefield House Hotel (P)
Gloucester Road
Tel: Ross-on-Wye (0989) 63030
Dunkerton (B)
Accommodation.

Stag (P)
5 Henry Street
Tel: Ross-on-Wye (0989) 62893
Bulmer (W)
Enthusiastic cider pub near main bus stop – use it while you wait!

ST. OWENS CROSS

The New Inn (P)
at crossroads of A4137 and B4521
Tel: Harewood End (0989 87) 274
Weston (PC)
The pub was actually "new" in 1540; it was a posting inn the great half timbered bar serving for stabling and changing the horses. Meals and snacks; garden; children's room.

STAPLOW

Oak Inn (P)
on B4214
Tel: Bosbury (053 186) 621
Bulmer (PC)
Pleasant 17th century country pub; forge 100 yards along road, visitors welcome. Snacks all sessions; garden

STOKE LACY

SYMONDS CIDER ▲
Symonds Cider and English Wine Company, Cider Mill and Winery
Tel: Munderfield (088 53) 21

STORRIDGE

KNIGHT'S CRUMPTON OAK CIDER ▲
Crumpton Oaks Fruit Farm
Tel: Malvern (068 45) 4594

SYMONDS YAT

Saracens Head (P)
Tel: Symonds Yat (0600) 890435
Bulmer (H)
On bank of River Wye, with passenger ferry. Ideal area for canoeing, camping, walking and fishing. Meals and snacks 12-2 and 7-10.30; restaurant; garden; children's room; accommodation.

Woodlea Guest House (P)
Dunkerton (B)

Ye Olde Ferrie Inne (P)
just off B4164
Tel: Symonds Yat (0600) 890232
Bulmer (PC)
Riverside setting, ferry crossing. Meals and snacks 11-2 and 7-10; restaurant; riverside patio and picnic area; accommodation; cream teas; gift shop; boat hire.

TARRINGTON

Foley Arms (P)
on A438
Tel: Tarrington (043 279) 217
Weston (H)
Georgian red brick hotel in village surrounded by hop fields. Fine Norman church. Snacks lunchtime and Monday to Thursday evening; large garden; accommodation.

TRUMPET

Trumpet Inn (P)
at crossroads of A438 and A417
Tel: Trumpet (053 183) 277
Weston (H)
400 year old timber framed pub in small hamlet. Snacks all times; garden.

TUPSLEY

Rose & Crown (P)
Tel: Hereford (0432) 273272
Weston (H)

ULLINGSWICK

Three Crowns (P)
Bleak Acre
Tel: Burley Gate (043 278) 279
Bulmer (H)
Unspoilt country pub with emphasis on food. Meals lunchtime and evening; garden.

VOWCHURCH

Sun (P)
St. Margarets
Tel: Michaelchurch (098 123) 223
Dunkerton (PC) (B)

WALFORD

Kerne Bridge Inn (P)
Tel: Symonds Yat (0600) 890495
Bulmer (H)

Views over River Wye to Goodrich Castle. Meals and snacks all sessions; garden; children's room.

WEOBLEY

Cafe Jules (P)
Dunkerton (B)

Red Lion (P)
off A4112
Tel: Weobley (0544) 318220
Bulmer (E)
In charming village of 14th century black and white buildings; 13th century church. The cottage at the Red Lion is reputed to be the oldest in the country. Until recently the pub was owned by Bulmers. Snacks lunchtime; meals lunchtime and 7-9.30; garden; accommodation.

Williams Butchers (OL)
Dunkerton (B)

WHITCHURCH

Crown (P)
just off A40
Tel: Symonds Yat (0600) 890234
Weston (H)
16th century village local, an old coaching inn. Meals and snacks; childrens' play area; accommodation.

Gallery Restaurant (P)
Wayside
Tel: Symonds Yat (0600) 890408
Weston (PC)

WHITNEY-ON-WYE

Rhydspence Inn (P)
A438 on Welsh border
Tel: Clifford (049 73) 262
Dunkerton (H)
Timber framed 14th century inn with homely atmosphere in Kilvert Country.

Interesting bar snacks and a la carte menu, lunchtime and evening; 12-1.45 and 7-9.30; restaurant; large gardens with super views; family room lunchtime and evening discretionary; accommodation.

WOOLHOPE

Butchers Arms (P)
Tel: Fownhope (043 277) 281
Weston (PC)
Black and white with low beamed bars, in a rural setting amid wooded country, fine views. Bar meals and snacks 11.30-2.15 and 7-10, Monday to Saturday, 12-1.45 and 7-10 Sunday; restaurant 7.30-9 Wednesday to Saturday evening; garden; accommodation.

Crown (P)
Tel: Fownhope (043 277) 468
Bulmer (H)
300 year old village local. Full bar menu; restaurant; children's garden; accommodation.

WORMELOW

The Tump Inn (P)
Tel: Golden Valley (0981) 540233
Bulmer (H)
18th century inn between the Wye Valley and the Black Mountains. Meals and snacks; pool room; live music at weekends.

YARPOLE

Bell Inn (P)
off B4361
Tel: Yarpole (056 885) 359
Bulmer (H)
17th century pub in beautiful surroundings. Meals and snacks lunchtime and evening all week; garden; games room; accommodation.

Tump Inn Wormelow, named after a Celtic burial mound

Hertfordshire

ALDBURY

Valiant Trooper (P)
Trooper Lane (off A41)
Tel: Aldbury Common
(044 285) 203
Bulmer (H)
Meals lunchtime and
evening; garden.

ALDENHAM

**Church Farm Shop
(OL)**
Old Radlett Road
Tel: Radlett (092 76) 7443
Weston (PC) (PL)
Also sell real ale, bread,
cheese and homemade pies,
plus full range of farm
produce. Snacks and tea room
in summer; garden; children's
room; accommodation.

AYOT ST.
LAWRENCE

Brocket Arms (P)
Shaws Corner
Tel: Stevenage (0438) 820250
Lanes (PC)
15th century country inn
near George Bernard Shaw's
home, now owned by National
Trust. Meals and snacks;
garden.

BARLEY

Fox & Hounds (P)
High Street
Tel: Barkway (076 384) 459
Bulmer (H)
300 year old inn with gallows
sign over road, ancient
windmill just down the street.
Meals and snacks all sessions;
restaurant; garden.

BASSINGBOURNE

Blakey's Stores (OL)
High Street
Saffron Ciders (B)

BISHOPS
STORTFORD

Fox (P)
Rye Street (B1004)
Tel: Bishops Stortford
(0279) 488222
Saffron Ciders (H)
Meals and snacks lunchtime
and evening; riverside
garden.

Jug & Bottle (OL)
8 Stanstead Road

Tel: Bishops Stortford
(0279) 507177
**Saffron Ciders & Perrys
(B) (PC)**

BRAUGHING

Golden Fleece (P)
22 Green End (B1368)
Tel: Ware (0920) 821200
Saffron Ciders (PC)
Meals and snacks; garden.

BUNTINGFORD

Bensons (OL)
14a High Street
**Saffron Ciders and Perrys
(B)**

BUSHEY

King Stag (P)
Bournehall Road
Tel: 01-950 2988
Bulmer (H)
Meals and snacks; garden.

CHANDLERS
CROSS

Clarendon Arms (P)
Tel: Kings Langley
(092 77) 62924

70

Bulmer (H)
Meals, snacks; garden.

HERTFORD

White Horse (P)
8 Castle Street (off A414)
Zum (PC)
Tiny town centre pub.
Snacks.

LITLINGTON

**Post Office Stores
(OL)**
Saffron Ciders (B)

OFFLEY

Red Lion (P)
Kings Walden Road
Tel: Offley (046 276) 281
Bulmer (H)
Old farmhouse pub. Meals
and snacks 12.30-2 and
7.30-10; restaurant and
carvery.

REED

Cabinet (P)
High Street (off A10)
Tel: Barkway (076 384) 366
Saffron Ciders (PC)
Weatherboarded cottage.
Meals lunchtime and evening
(not Monday and Tuesday);
large garden.

ROYSTON

Old Bull Inn (P)
56 High Street
Tel: Royston (0763) 42003
Saffron Ciders (PC)
A former coaching inn, dating
from 1520. Meals and snacks;
accommodation.

ST. ALBANS

Rose & Crown (P)
St. Michaels Street
Tel: St. Albans (0727) 51903
House ciders (PC)
About a mile from city centre,
but worth the walk! A
Georgian pub behind a brick
facade. Also visit the
Kingsbury Elizabethan
Water Mill Museum nearby.
Snacks lunchtime; garden;
folk music Thursday.

STEVENAGE

Jug & Firkin (OL)
67 Albert Street
Tel: Stevenage (0438) 726093
Saffron Ciders (B) (PC)

TRING

King Street
Tel: Tring (044 282) 3318
House Cider (PC) (not
always available)
Unspoilt back street pub
(turn down Queen Street off
main road). Snacks all
sessions, even "breakfast" on
Saturday! garden.

**Tring Wine Shop
(OL)**
19 High Street
Tel: Tring (044 282) 3211
Bulmer (PC)
Rich (PC)

WALLINGTON

Plough (P)
7 The Street
Tel: Broadfield (076 388) 397

Saffron Ciders (H) (PC)
Saffron Perrys (PC)
Small cottage style pub.
Snacks; garden.

WALTHAM CROSS

**Melbourne Off
Licence (OL)**
192 Eleanor Cross Road
Saffron Ciders (B)

WATFORD

Blakes (P)
94-96 Queens Road
Tel: Watford (0923) 47697
Weston (H)
Meals and snacks all sessions;
outdoor drinking area.

WHEATHAMP-
STEAD

Bull (P)
11 High Street
Tel: Wheathampstead
(058 283) 3379
Bulmer (H)
Beefeater Inn. Snacks 12-2
and 7-9.30; full meals 12-2
and 6-10.30 (11 on Friday and
Saturday); garden; children's
room.

Wicked Lady (P)
Normansland Common
Tel: Wheathampstead
(058 283) 2128
Harvest Scrumpy (PC)
Named after a local
highwaywoman. The origin of
the cider is uncertain. Meals
and snacks all sessions except
Sunday night; restaurant;
garden; children's room.

The Fox and Hounds, Barley, with gallows inn sign

Humberside

BRIGG

Larry Arnold (OL)
4 Queens Street
Merrydown (BB)

CLEETHORPES

Small Beer (OL)
199 Grimsby Road
Tel: Cleethorpes
(0472) 699234
Symonds (PC)
Cider wholesaler with wide
range of bottled ciders in
stock.

Willy's (P)
17 High Cliff Road
Tel: Cleethorpes
(0472) 602145
Symonds (PC)
Views across Humber estuary
to Spurn Head. Meals and
snacks 11-3pm; outdoor
drinking area.

Acknowledgements

I should like to thank the following for their help and encouragement during research for this Guide: the many cider makers and cider brokers for their hospitality, and information about their products and outlets; individual branches of the Campaign for Real Ale, in particular Gloucestershire, Bath & Borders, and Norwich & Norfolk, for details of pubs in their local area; readers of the first edition who sent in updates on the original text; other useful contacts and information given, usually over a pint or two; landlords and proprietors who took the trouble to fill in my irritating little forms; and last but not least Mr. John Hawkins, who contributed the home spun cider technique.

D.K.

Isle of Wight

APSE HEATH

Apse Heath Stores (OL)
Godshill (B) (PP)

BRADING

Anglers Inn (P)
Yar Cross
Bulmer (H)
Meals: garden.

CALBOURNE

Sun Inn (P)
Tel: Calbourne (098 378) 231
Bulmer (H)

COWES

Britannia (P)
The Arcade
Tel: Cowes (0983) 296577
Bulmer (H)
Adjacent to ferry terminal.
Meals and snacks lunchtime;
garden.

GODSHILL

GODSHILL CIDER CO.▲
The Cider Barn

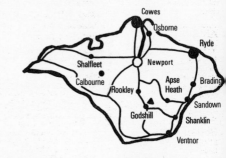

Tel: Isle of Wight
(0983) 840680

OSBORNE

Prince of Wales (P)
Whinningham Road
Bulmer (H)
Opposite entrance to Osborne
House. Meals lunchtime and
evening; garden; children's
room; accommodation.

ROOKLEY

Harts Farm Foodstore (OL)
Main Road

Tel: Chilerton (098 370) 326
Godshill (B)

RYDE

The Wine Cellar (P)
Lind Street/St. Thomas
Street
Tel: Isle of Wight
(0983) 67721
Godshill (PC)
Godshill Apple Wine (B)
Godshill Mead (B)
Closed on Sunday

SANDOWN

Prince of Wales (P)

72

Avenue Road
Tel: Isle of Wight
(0983) 403453
Bulmer (H)
At east end of town, with
holiday caravan trade.
Snacks.

SHALLFLEET

New Inn (P)
Yarmouth Road (A3054)
Tel: Calbourne (098 378) 314

Bulmer (H)
A gathering place for
yachtsmen. Specialises in
fresh fish. Meals and snacks
all sessions; terrace.

SHANKLIN

Newnham Bros (OL)
26 High Street
Tel: Shanklin (098 386) 2122
Godshill (B)
Godshill Mead (B)

The Chine Inn (P)
Chine Hill
Tel: Isle of Wight
(0983) 864612
Merrydown (H)

VENTNOR

Blenheim (P)
High Street
Tel: Isle of Wight
(0983) 853633
Bulmer (H)

Kent

ALDINGTON

**Post Office Stores
(OL)**
Tel: Aldington (023 372) 246
Biddenden (B)

APPLEDORE
HEATH

Victoria Arms (P)
Tel: Appledore (023 383) 359
Biddenden (PL)
About a mile outside
Appledore. Snacks
10.30-2pm; garden. Try also
the cheese straws, ideal with
cider.

ASH

Volunteer (P)
43 Guilton (A257)
Tel: Ash (0304) 812506
Pippin (PC)
Meals lunchtime and
evening; garden.

ASHFORD

Bottles (OL)
31 Court Wurtin, Beaver
Lane
Tel: Ashford (0233) 28660
Biddenden (PC)

**Bungalow Stores
(OL)**
212 Kingsnorth Road
Biddenden (B)

**Corkers Wine Bar
(P)**
30 Bank Street
Tel: Ashford (0233) 32566
Weston (PC)

BARFRESTON

Yew Tree (P)
Tel: Shepherdswell
(0304) 830288

Theobald (PL)
Meals and snacks.

BENENDEN

Rollings Stores (OL)
Biddenden (B)

BIDDENDEN

**BIDDENDEN
CIDER▲**
Biddenden Vineyards,
Little Whatmans
Tel: Biddenden
(0580) 291726

Post Office (OL)
Biddenden (B)

Red Lion (P)
High Street
Tel: Biddenden
(0580) 291347
Biddenden (B)
15th century inn at heart of
medieval village. The sign on
the village green opposite
commemorates the famous
Siamese twins who lived in
the village in the 16th
century. Meals and snacks
11.30-1.30 and 7.00-9.30;
restaurant; garden;
accommodation.

Three Chimneys (P)
Tel: Biddenden
(0580) 291472
Biddenden (PC)
French prisoners of war in the
nearby Sissinghurst Castle
during the Seven Years War
are said have given the pub
its name, a corruption of
"trois chemins", or "three
ways", after the adjacent road
junction. Meals and snacks
11.30-2 & 6.30-10:
restaurant; garden;
children's room.

**Woodlands Filling
Station (OL)**
Tenterden Road (B2082)

Tel: Biddenden
(0580) 291473
Biddenden (B)

BIGGIN HILL

**Valley Wine Co.
(OL)**
Nor Heads Lane
Tel: Biggin Hill (0959) 73019
Inch (PC)

BODSHAM GREEN

Timber Batts Inn (P)
Tel: Elmstead (023 375) 237
Biddenden (PC)
Meals; restaurant; garden.

BRENCHLEY

Bournes Stores (OL)
High Street
Tel: Brenchley
(089 272) 2066
Biddenden (B)

Rose & Crown (P)
High Street
Tel: Brenchley
(089 272) 2107
Biddenden (PC)
14th century half timbered
inn, originally the admin
block to the Old Palace
opposite. Meals and snacks
every session; restaurant;
garden; accommodation;
children's room.

BROADSTAIRS

**Cartons Off Licence
(OL)**
22 St. Peters Park Road
Tel: Thanet (0843) 64032
Theobald (PC)
Theobald Perry (B)

BROMPTON

Cannon (P)
Bulmer

Two Sawyers (P)
High Street
Tel: Medway (0634) 44929
Bulmer (H)

BURHAM

Toastmasters Inn (P)
Church Street
Tel: Medway (0634) 61299
Weston (PC)
Zum (PC)
Meals 11.30-2 & 7.30-10.30;
restaurant.

CANTERBURY

Cherry Tree (P)
Whitehorse Lane
Tel: Canterbury
(0227) 451266
Biddenden (H)
Snacks lunchtime and
evening.

Falstaff Tap (P)
North Lane
Tel: Canterbury (0227) 64267
Near Westgate, adjoining
Falstaff Hotel. Snacks.

New Inn (P)
Havelock Street
Tel: Canterbury (0227) 46584
Zum (PC)

Rose & Crown (P)
76 St. Dunstans Street
Tel: Canterbury
(0227) 463583
Bulmer (H)

Tascolls Wine Bar (P)
49 Castle Street
Tel: Canterbury (0227) 60381
Biddenden (PC)

CHARING

Charing Stores (OL)
High Street
Biddenden (B)

Gillards Stores
Biddenden (B)

CHATHAM

Case Rate (OL)
3 Watling Street
Biddenden (B)

CHIDDING-STONE

Castle Inn (P)
Tel: Penshurst (0892) 870247
Taunton (PC)
Ancient pub in preserved
village, an ideal place to wait
for the *other* castle to open.
Snacks 10-2.15 & 6-10.15;
meals 12-2 & 7.30-9.30;
restaurant; garden;
children's room.

CHILHAM

Browns Kitchen Shop (OL)
High Street
Tel: Canterbury
(0227) 730597
Theobald (PC)

COURT AT STREET

Welcome Stranger (P)
on B2067
Tel: Aldington (023 372) 400
Biddenden (PC)
On the hills above Romney
Marsh, near Port Lymne Zoo
Park and Gardens. Snacks.

CRANBROOK

Perfect Partners (OL)
7 Stone Street
Tel: Cranbrook
(0580) 712633
Biddenden (B)

Prince of Wales (P)
High Street
Tel: Cranbrook
(0580) 713058
Biddenden (PC)
Snacks all sessions; children's
room.

CRAYFORD

Real Ale Shop (OL)
14 Princesses Parade,
Waterside
Tel: Crayford (0322) 526512
Zum (PC)

CRUNDALE

Compasses (P)
Sole Street
Tel: Petham (022 770) 300
Biddenden (PC)
On the North Downs above
Wye. Meals except Sunday
night, garden; children's
room.

CUXTON

Broad Oak Wines (OL)
Owlet (B)

DOVER

Park Inn (P)
Ladywell
Merrydown (H)

The Wine Seller (OL)
13 Worthington Street
Tel: Dover (0304) 201406
Biddenden (PL)
Inch (PP)
Open till 10pm every night.

DYMCHURCH

Tappit Hen (OL)
67 High Street
Tel: Dymchurch
(0303) 873883
Biddenden (B)

EAST STOURMOUTH

Rising Sun (P)
The Street (B2046)
Tel: Preston (022 781) 220

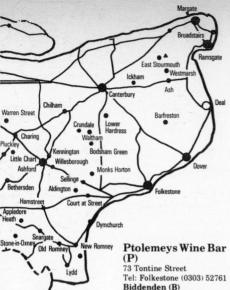

Theobald (PC)
Good fishing in River Stour.
Meals and snacks 12-2 and
7-10 weekdays, 12-1.30 and
7-10 Sunday; garden;
children welcome if taking
meals.

FAVERSHAM

Shipwrights Arms (P)
Hollowshore
Biddenden (PC)
Cade (PC)
Cade Apple Wine
One mile across marshes
along unmade road at
confluence of two creeks, fine
river panorama and yachting
centre. Snacks lunchtime and
evening; garden; children's
room.

FOLKESTONE

Alexandra Wines (OL)
39 Canterbury Road
Biddenden (B)

Coolinge Stores (OL)
Alton House,
Shorncliffe Road
Tel: Folkestone (0303) 54977
Biddenden (B)

Grape Vine (OL)
34 The Old High Street
Tel: Folkestone (0303) 44497
Biddenden (B)

Ptolemeys Wine Bar (P)
73 Tontine Street
Tel: Folkestone (0303) 52761
Biddenden (B)

GOUDHURST

Burgess Stores (OL)
High Street
Tel: Goudhurst
(0580) 211206
Biddenden (B)

HAM STREET

VG Stores (OL)
Falstead House
Tel: Ham Street
(023 373) 2206
Biddenden (B)

HARRIETSHAM

Ringlestone Inn (P)
Tel: Maidstone (0622) 859207
Pippin (B)
Sams (PC)
Guest ciders
High on the North Downs
north of the village, an
unspoilt medieval tavern
with oak beams and log fires.
Famous for its food, available
lunchtime and evening, 12-2
& 7-10; restaurant. The
ciders are all local pressings.

HAWKHURST

Tudor Arms Hotel (P)
Rye Road (A268)
Tel: Hawkhurst
(058 05) 2312 & 2577
Owlet (B)
Meals; restaurant; garden;
accommodation.

HEADCORN

Ferndale Stores (OL)
Biddenden (B)

Village Shop (OL)
7 High Street
Biddenden (B)

ICKHAM

Duke William (P)
The Street
Tel: Canterbury
(0227) 721308
Biddenden (PC)
Near Howletts Zoo Park. In
centre of village. Meals and
snacks all sessions;
restaurant; garden;
children's room.

IDEN GREEN

Iden Green Stores (OL)
Tel: Cranbrook
(0580) 240668
Biddenden (PL)

KENNINGTON

Knotts Off Licence (OL)
Faversham Road
Biddenden (B)

KILNDOWN

Globe & Rainbow (P)
Rogers Rough Road
Tel: Lamberhurst
(0892) 890283
Biddenden (PC)
Meals; restaurant; garden;
accommodation; children's
room.

LAMBERHURST

OWLET CIDER▲
Owl House Fruit Farm
Tel: Lamberhurst
(0892) 890553

Victoria House Stores (OL)
Biddenden (B)
Owlet (B)

LENHAM

Lurcocks Off Licence (OL)
The Square
Biddenden (B)

LITTLE CHART

Post Office (OL)
Tel: Pluckley (023 384) 262
Biddenden (B)

Swan Inn (P)
Tel: Pluckley (023 384) 248
Biddenden (F)
Hot and cold food all sessions.

LONGFIELD

Railway (P)
2 Station Road (off B260)
Tel: Longfield (047 47) 2217
Bulmer (H)
Snacks lunchtime Monday to
Saturday.

LOOSE

Linton Road Stores (OL)
48 Salts Avenue
Tel: Maidstone (0622) 43481
Biddenden (B)

LOWER HARDRES

Three Horseshoes (P)
Catts Wood Road
Tel: Petham (022 770) 333
Lane (PC)
Zum (PC)
Snacks lunchtime;
dinner/lunch parties by
arrangement; garden;
vintage buses; occasional jazz
festivals; ciders may vary. If
lost ask for "Lower Hards"

LYDD

Corner Stores (OL)
1 Dengemarsh Road
Biddenden (B)

West End Stores (OL)
84 High Street
Tel: Lydd (0679) 20493
Biddenden (B)

MAIDSTONE

Jones Off Licence (OL)
46 Mote Road
Cornish Scrumpy

MARGATE

Benjamin Beale (P)
10 Fort Hill
Tel: Thanet (0843) 223997
Theobald (PC)

The Cottage (P)
19 High Street
Tel: Thanet (0843) 291452
Weston (PC)
Town centre free house.
Meals and snacks lunchtime
and evening except Sunday;
restaurant; separate family
room.

MARSH GREEN

Wheatsheaf Inn (P)
Marsh Green Road
Tel: Edenbridge (0732) 86438
Biddenden (F)
Snacks 12-2 and 7.30-9.30;
meals 7.30-10; restaurant;
garden; accommodation.

MONKS HORTON

Black Horse Inn (P)
Biddenden (PC)

NEW ROMNEY

Ship Hotel (P)
High Street
Tel: New Romney
(0679) 2776
Biddenden (PC)

OLD GROOMBRIDGE

Crown Inn (P)
Groombridge Hill
Tel: Groombridge
(089 276) 742/361
Biddenden (PC)
16th century brick and
weather boarded inn
overlooking the green. Bar
snacks to a la carte menu;
restaurant; garden;
accommodation.

OLD ROMNEY

Rose & Crown (P)
off A259
Tel: New Romney
(0679) 2270
Biddenden (PC)
Free house on Romney
Marsh. Meals lunchtime and
evening; garden;
accommodation.

PADDOCK WOOD

Davisons (OL)
Commercial Road
Pippin (B)

PEMBURY

Black Horse (P)
12 High Street (A21)
Tel: Pembury (089 282) 2141
Pippin (H)
Meals.

Gurners (OL)
101 Hastings Road
Biddenden (B)
Pippin (B)

PIPPINS CIDER▲
Pippins Farm,
Stone Court Lane
Tel: Pembury (089 282) 4624

PLUCKLEY

Dering Arms (P)
Station Road

Tel: Pluckley (023 384) 371
Biddenden (F)
Former hunting lodge of
Dering Estate, adjoining
Pluckley Station. Bar food.

Heasmans Stores (OL)
Tel: Pluckley (023 384) 372
Biddenden (B)

PLAXTOL

Golding Hop (P)
Sheet Hill
Tel: Borough Green
(0732) 882150
Weston (PC)
Surrounded by orchards in a
small, hard to find valley. It
became famous for its home
made cider from a secret
recipe. Snacks and meals
lunchtime and evening; large
garden opposite.

RAMSGATE

Square Dozen (OL)
144 Grange Road
Tel: Thanet (0843) 592419
Biddenden (B)
Inch (B)
Pilgrim (B)

ROCHESTER

Broad Oak Wines (OL)
5 Victoria Street
Tel: Medway (0634) 827518
Owlet (B)

Who'd A Tho't It (P)
Baker Street
Tel: Medway (0634) 41131
Weston (PL)
Meals lunchtime and
evening; garden.

ROLVENDEN LAYNE

Layne Stores (OL)
Biddenden (B)

SANDHURST

Johnsons (OL)
Tel: Sandhurst (058 085) 227
Biddenden (B)

SELLINGE

Sellinge Stores (OL)
Tel: Sellinge (030 381) 2102
Biddenden (B)

SHOREHAM

Royal Oak (P)
2 High Street (off A225)
Tel: Otford (095 92) 2319
Scrumpy (J)

The centre of the village community. Snacks lunchtime and evening during week.

SISSINGHURST

D. C. Hemsted (OL)
Biddenden (B)
Owlet (B)

SITTINGBOURNE

Case Rate (OL)
Biddenden (B)

Wine Market (OL)
Biddenden (B)

SMARDEN

The Bell (P)
Bell Lane
Tel: Smarden (023 377) 283
Biddenden (PP)
Ancient inn with oak beams and inglenook fireplaces, between Smarden and Headcorn in typical orchard and oast country. Good choice of meals and snacks 12-2 and 6.30-10.30 all sessions; garden; accommodation; children's room.

SNARGATE

Red Lion (P)
on B2080
Biddenden (PC)
A tiny isolated free house which doubles as the village shop, all a pub should be.

SNODLAND

Papermakers Arms (P)
Biddenden (PC)

SPELDHURST

George & Dragon (P)
Tel: Langton (089 286) 3125
Bulmer (H)
Medieval timber framed inn with stone flagged floors. Good range of meals lunchtime and evening; restaurant; garden.

STONE IN OXNEY

Crown Inn (P)
The Street
Tel: Appledore (0233 83) 267
Biddenden (PP)
Delightfully remote on the edge of Romney Marsh; Rye, Military Canal, and RHD Railway in the vicinity. Meals and snacks all sessions except Sunday evening, when

there is live jazz. Traditional roasts Sunday lunch.

STROOD

Glanville Off Licence (OL)
Biddenden (B)

SWANLEY

Real Ale Shop (OL)
31 Azealia Drive
Tel: Swanley (0322) 63221
Zum (PC)

TENTERDEN

Brookways Stores (OL)
High Street
Biddenden (B)

TONBRIDGE

Constitutional Club (P)
3 Barden Road
Tel: Tonbridge (0732) 350086
Merrydown (H)

Plough (P)
Powder Mills Lane
Tel: Hildenborough (07320) 832149
Merrydown (H)
Between Tonbridge and Leigh, a series of footpaths lead west across the fields from the town. Hot and cold buffet.

Priory Wine (OL)
64 Priory Street
Tel: Tonbridge (0732) 359784
Pippin (B)

TUNBRIDGE WELLS

Booker Cash & Carry (OL)
North Farm Road, North Farm Industrial Estate
Merrydown (BB)

Deli Delicious (OL)
28 Camden Road
Tel: Tunbridge Wells (0892) 44522
Pippin (B)

Dowlings Stores (OL)
81 Forest Road
Tel: Tunbridge Wells (0892) 34975
Biddenden (B)

Grape Vine (P)
8 Chapel Place
Tel: Tunbridge Wells (0892) 34219
Merrydown (H)
Meals; outdoor drinking area; restaurant.

WALTHAM

Lord Nelson (P)
Church Lane
Tel: Petham (022 770) 628
Biddenden (PC)
High in the Kentish hills, good walking country. Meals and snacks all sessions except Tuesdays; 12-2 and 7-9.30; large garden with glorious views.

WARREN STREET

Harrow Inn (P)
Tel: Maidstone (0622) 858727
Biddenden (PC)
On the North Downs, once the forge and rest house for travellers on the nearby Pilgrims Way. Snacks 12-1.45 & 7-9.45; meals 7.30-9; restaurant; garden; accommodation.

WESTMARSH

Way Out Inn (P)
Tel: Ash (0304) 812899
Theobald (PC)

WILLES-BOROUGH

Willesborough Wines (OL)
139 Church Road
Tel: Ashford (0233) 24128
Biddenden (B)

YALDING

Beauchamps (OL)
The Swan Fruit Shop, High Street
Tel: Maidstone (0622) 814486
Biddenden (B)

Your recommendations are welcomed for future editions of the Guide Please use the inspection form at the back

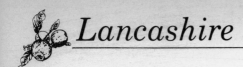

Lancashire

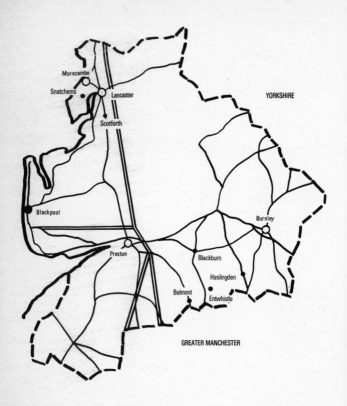

BELMONT

Black Dog (P)
2 Church Street (A675)
Bulmer (H)
Traditional village pub in popular rambling and climbing area. Meals lunchtime.

BLACKBURN

Flanagans (P)
Darwen Street
Bulmer (H)
Fine 1896 exterior, small bar, with viewing panel to cellar. Meals lunchtime; live music.

BLACKPOOL

Simpsons Off Licence (OL)
8 Dickson Road
Cornish Scrumpy

ENTWISTLE

Strawberry Duck (P)
Hob Lane
Bulmer (H)
Remote pub next to station, near Wayoh reservoir; popular with walkers. Meals lunchtime and evening; garden; live music; accommodation.

HASLINGDEN

Woolpack (P)
Manchester Road, Bentgate (A680)
Bulmer (H)
Next to cricket ground. Meals lunchtimes.

SNATCHEMS

Golden Ball (P)
Lancaster Road (on riverbank between Lancaster and Overton)
Bulmer (PC)
Tiny bar serving three low beamed rooms. Once frequented by Press Gang, hence "snatch'em". Cut off by highest tides. Meals lunchtime and evening; garden; children's room.

Leicestershire

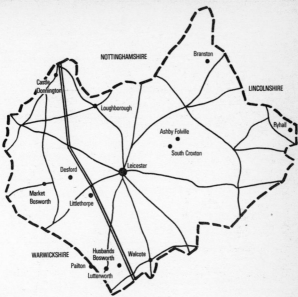

ASHBY FOLVILLE

Carington Arms (P)
Folville Street (B674)
Tel: Melton Mowbray
(0664) 840228
Bulmer (H)
Tudor style pub in attractive hunting area, described as "probably the prettiest pub in Leicestershire". Meals Monday to Saturday 12-2 and 7-10; garden/play area; skittle alley; petanque pitch.

BRANSTON

Wheel Inn (P)
Bulmer (H)

CASTLE DONNINGTON

Priest House Inn (P)
Kings Mills
Tel: Derby (0332) 810649
Bulmer (H)
On the bank of the Trent at Kings Mills, which date from the Doomsday Book. Relics of the mill wheels can be seen in the grounds. Snacks at all times; full meals evenings

and Sunday lunch; restaurant; garden; accommodation; four poster bed; clay pigeon shoots; fishing.

DESFORD

Olde Lancaster Inn (P)
Station Road
Tel: Desford (045 57) 2589
Bulmer (H)
Four roomed, oak beamed, country inn. Meals lunchtime and evening; garden.

HUSBANDS BOSWORTH

Cherry Tree (P)
8 High Street
Tel: Market Harborough
(0858) 880369
Bulmer (H)
Near Grand Union Canal's Leicester Arm. Meals lunchtime and evening.

LEICESTER

Black Horse (P)
Narrow Lane, Aylestone
Tel: Leicester (0533) 832811

Bulmer (H)
Close to Grand Union Canal and Great Central Way footpath. Meals lunchtime; garden.

Brewers Arms (P)
Belgrave Gate
Bulmer (H)
Down alley by Royal Oak PH. A select house with something of a "cult" reputation.

Bricklayers Arms (P)
Welford Road (A50)
Tel: Leicester (0533) 540687
Bulmer (H)

Globe (P)
Silver Street
Tel: Leicester (0533) 28918
Bulmer (H)
One of the city's oldest pubs. Meals lunchtime and evening; children's room; accommodation; live entertainment most nights.

LITTLETHORPE

Plough (P)
Station Road
Tel: Leicester (0533) 862383
Bulmer (H)
Thatched local. Meals

lunchtime and evening; garden; long alley skittles.

LOUGHBOROUGH

Jug & Bottle (OL)
16 Albert Promenade
Tel: Loughborough
(0509) 261174
Lloyds: Weston (PC)
Wide range of ciders in bottles and jars.

LUTTERWORTH

Fox (P)
Rugby Road (A426)
Weston (H)
Meals and snacks lunchtime and evening.

MARKET BOSWORTH

Old Red Lion (P)
Park Street

Tel: Market Bosworth
(0455) 290214
Farmhouse (PC)
Old town centre pub, near site of Battle of Bosworth Field. Bar meals.

PAILTON

White Lion (P)
on A427
Bulmer (H)
Large restaurant style pub. Meals and snacks lunchtime and evening; garden.

RYHALL

Green Dragon (P)
The Square
Tel: Stamford (0780) 5308
Bulmer (H)
11th century building, wooden beams, inglenook fireplace. Meals and snacks 12-2.30 and 7-10.

SOUTH CROXTON

Golden Fleece (P)
Main Street
Tel: Melton Mowbray
(0664) 840275
Bulmer (H)
Built in 1740, once a Blacksmiths and Methodist school. Meals lunchtime and evening; garden.

WALCOTE

Black Horse Inn (P)
Lutterworth Road (A427 near M1 junction 20)
Tel: Lutterworth
(045 55) 2684
Lanes (PC)
Rich (PC)
Specialises in Thai food. Near Foxton Locks and Stanton Hall. Bar meals lunchtime and evening; garden; children's room.

Lincolnshire

BOSTON

Carpenters Arms (P)
Witham Street
Tel: Boston (0205) 62840
Merrydown (E)
Meals and snacks 11.30-2.30; restaurant; outdoor drinking area; accommodation.

COLEBY

Bell Inn (P)
Far Lane
Tel: Lincoln (0522) 810240
Bulmer (H)
Modernised village pub. Meals lunchtime and evening; garden; children's room.

GRANTHAM

Chequers (P)

Butchers Row, Market Place
Tel: Grantham (0476) 76383
Bulmer (H)
Town centre pub.

LINCOLN

Jolly Brewer (P)
Broadgate
Tel: Lincoln (0522) 28583
Bulmer (H)
1930s Art Deco style pub in easy reach of city centre. Meals lunchtime; garden.

Small Beer (OL)
9 Newland Street West
Tel: Lincoln (0522) 28628
Symonds (PC)
Cider wholesaler with wide range of bottled ciders stocked in shop.

Victoria (P)
6 Union Road
Tel: Lincoln (0522) 36248

Bulmer (H)
Symonds (PC)
Meals and snacks lunchtime; outdoor drinking area.

SUTTON BRIDGE

Peacock Inn (P)
126 Bridge Road
Tel: Holbeach (0406) 350324
Merrydown (H)

WADDINGHAM

Anchor Inn (P)
Brandy Wharf
Tel: North Kelsey
(065 27) 364
Addlestones (H)
Inch (BB)
Merrydown (BB)
Weston (PC) (H)
Weston Perry (PC)
Virtually a cider centre on the River Ancholme.

Anchor Inn, Waddingham, with 50 ciders, meals and moorings

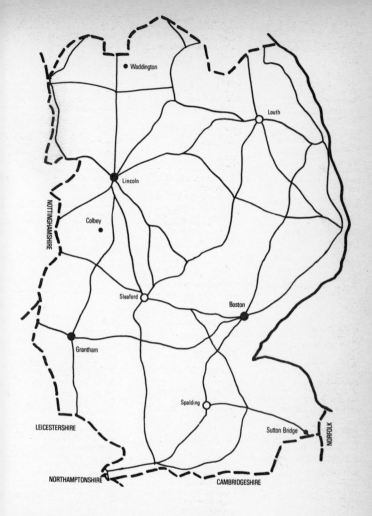

Greater London

W1 – West End

Cranks (P)
8 Marshall Street
Tel: (01) 580 6214
Aspall (B)

Glassblowers (P)
42 Glasshouse Street
Bulmer (H)
Bare boards and sawdust a
hundred yards from
Piccadilly Circus. Bar food.

George (P)
55 Great Portland Street
Tel: (01) 636 0863
Bulmer (H)
Victorian corner pub within
stone's throw of Oxford
Circus; tends to be the club
room for Broadcasting House!
Snacks lunchtime and
evening.

Grafton Arms (P)
72 Grafton Way
Tel: (01) 387 7923
Bulmer (H)
Meals lunchtime; outdoor
drinking area.

Kings Arms (P)
2 Shepherd Market
Tel: (01) 629 0083
Bulmer (H)
Off the beaten track in the
heart of Mayfair, just off
Piccadilly. Medieval
atmosphere. Hot lunches on

first floor, snacks on ground
floor, on weekdays.

Oodles Restaurant (P)
128 Edgware Road
Tel: (01) 723 7548
Aspall (B)

Wholefood (OL)
24 Paddington Street
Tel: (01) 935 3924
Aspall (B)
Retail shop selling
organically grown produce,
including wine.

WC1

Oddbins (OL)
318a High Holborn
Tel: (01) 405 0071
Weston (J)

Oodles Restaurant (P)
42 New Oxford Street
Tel: (01) 580 9521
Aspall (B)

Oodles Restaurant (P)
113 High Holborn
Tel: (01) 405 3838
Aspall (B)

Queens Larder (P)
1 Queen Square
Tel: (01) 837 5627

Bulmer (H) (PC)
Pub with an interesting 250
year history; near British
Museum. Extensive menu;
Meals 12-2.15 and 6.30-9.30;
intimate restaurant; outdoor
drinking area.

Sun Freehouse (P)
63 Lambs Conduit Street
Tel: (01) 405 8278
Jumpy Scrap (H)
Zum (H)
Popular venue for London
University students; vast real
ale selection; cellar tours
most nights – a notorious den
of iniquity! Snacks and meals
all sessions; outdoor drinking
area.

WC2

Cranks (P)
11 The Market,
Covent Garden
Tel: (01) 379 6508
Aspall (B)

Oddbins (OL)
Covent Garden,
23 Earlham Street
Tel: (01) 836 6331
Weston (J)

Porters English Restaurant (P)
17 Henrietta Street
Tel: (01) 836 6466
Weston (PC)

EC1

Pheasant & Firkin (P)
166 Goswell Road
Tel: (01) 253 7429
Weston (H)
David Bruce home brewery pub.

Three Compasses (P)
66 Cowcross Street
Tel: (01) 253 3368
Bulmer (H)
Snacks 11-3 and 5.30-11; meals 12.15-3; restaurant; jazz piano Tuesday evening and Sunday lunchtime.

EC4

Ludgate Cellars (P)
Apothecary Lane
Tel: (01) 236 6808
Bulmer (H)
Busy city pub under the railway arches near Blackfriars Station; closes early in evening and all weekend except Saturday lunchtime. Bar food lunchtime.

Oddbins (OL)
41a Farringdon Street
Tel: (01) 236 7721
Weston (J)

Oddbins (OL)
London Bridge,
42 King William Street
Tel: (01) 623 1406
Weston (J)

E1 – Stepney

Dickens Inn (P)
St. Katherines Way,
St. Katherines Dock
Tel: (01) 488 2208
Taunton (H)
Part of the imaginative rehabilitation of the old commercial basin. The pub is an 18th century warehouse, reconstructed in the style of a three storied inn of the same period with ground floor bar and restaurants on upper levels, overlooking a marina. Dickensiana is on sale, Meals lunchtime and evening; snacks.

Prospect of Whitby (P)
57 Wapping Wall, Wapping
Tel: office (01) 481 1317
     restaurant (01) 481 1095
Bulmer (H)
Legendary Thames side inn. Snacks 12-3; meals 5.30-10.15; restaurant and food bar over looking the river; open riverside terrace; children welcome in food bar and restaurant.

E9 – Homerton

Falcon & Firkin (P)
274 Victoria Park Road
Tel: (01) 985 0693
Weston (H)
David Bruce home brew pub.

BARKING

Spotted Dog (P)
15a Longbridge Road
Weston (PC)
Attractive timbered building, interior with old gas lights, Meals lunchtime and evening; restaurant.

HORNCHURCH

Queens Theatre (P)
Billet Lane
Tel: Hornchurch
(040 24) 56118
Bulmer (PC)
Bar within theatre. Restaurant.

ILFORD

Oddbins (OL)
65 Cranbrook Road
Weston (J)

N1 – Islington

Oddbins (OL)
64 Upper Street
Tel: (01) 226 2200
Weston (J)

The Beer Shop (OL)
8 Pitfield Street
Tel: (01) 739 3701
Dunkerton (B) (PC)
Inch (BB) (PL)
Weston (PC)

N2 – East Finchley

Welch Bros. (P)
130 High Road
Tel: (01) 444 7444
Zum (PC)
Snacks all sessions; meals 12-2.30.

N4 – Hornsey

John's Real Ales (OL)
41 Quernmore Road
Tel: (01) 348 8270
Saffron Ciders (PC) (B)

N7 – Holloway

Flounder & Firkin (P)
54 Holloway Road
Tel: (01) 609 9574
Weston (H)

N8 – Hornsey

The Palace (P)
22 Topfield Parade,
Tottenham Lane
Tel: (01) 340 3677
Weston (PC)

N12 – North Finchley

Oddbins (OL)
822 High Road
Tel: (01) 446 3697
Weston (J)

N16 – Stoke Newington

Marlers (P)
178 High Street
Weston (PC)

Rose & Crown (P)
199 Stoke Newington Church Street (B104)
Tel: (01) 254 7497
Bulmer (PC)
Attractive period interior. Meals lunchtime and evening.

Barrels (OL)
54 Hermon Hill
Tel: (01) 530 4358
Saffron Ciders (PC) (B)
Saffron Perrys (PC)

N19 – Upper Holloway

J. J. Moons (P)
37 Landseer Road
Tel: (01) 263 4658
Weston (H)
Snacks 12-2; outdoor drinking area.

ENFIELD

Enfield Wines (OL)
34 Southbury Road
Saffron Ciders (B)

HIGH BARNET

The Alexandra (P)
Wood Street
Saffron Ciders (PC)
Near Barnet General Hospital. Meals lunchtime; garden.

PONDERS END

Lincoln Stores (OL)
330 Lincoln Road
Cornish Scrumpy

NW1 – Camden Town

Camden Home Brew (OL)

4 Ferdinand Street
Tel: (01) 482 2186
Dunkerton (B)
Zum (PC)

Victoria (P)
2 Mornington Terrace
Tel: (01) 387 3804
Zum (PC)
Snacks, including vegetarian
dishes, lunchtime and
evening.

NW3 – Hampstead

King of Bohemia (P)
10 Hampstead High Street
Bulmer (PC)

NW6 – West Hampstead

Grogblossom (OL)
3 West End Lane
Tel: (01) 794 7808
Saffron Ciders
James White (PC)
Weston (H)
Zum (PC)
Also over 30 different bottled
ciders including large French
selection.

HARROW ON THE HILL

88 High Street
Tel: (01) 422 5541
Weston (PC) (PL)
Meals and snacks 11-2.30;
restaurant; garden;
children's room;
accommodation.

SE1 – Southwark

George Inn (P)
77 Borough High Street
Tel: (01) 407 2056
Bulmer (H)
The only remaining galleried
inn left in London, rebuilt in
1676; frequented by Charles
Dickens, mentioned in his
"Little Dorrit": now a
National Trust property.
Snacks 12-2.30 and 6-9.30;
meals 12.15-2 and 6-9;
restaurant; outdoor drinking
area; accommodation.

Goose & Firkin (P)
47 Borough Road
Tel: (01) 403 3590
James White (H)
Weston (H)
Bruce home brew pub. Snacks
all sessions; live music every
night, usually piano.

SE5 – Denmark Hill

Phoenix & Firkin (P)
Windsor Walk
Tel: (01) 701 8282

Weston (H)
In reconstruction of the old
Denmark Hill railway
station, full of railway
exhibits. Bruce home brew
pub. Snacks all sessions.

SE10 – Greenwich

Bottoms Up (OL)
249 Greenwich High Road
Tel: (01) 853 4877
Weston (J)

Richard I (P)
52-54 Royal Hill
Bulmer (PC)
Snacks 11-2; meals 12-2.15.

SE13 – Lewisham

Fox & Firkin (P)
316 Lewisham High Street
Tel: (01) 690 8925
James White (H)
Weston (H)
Bruce home brew pub. Meals
and snacks all sessions: live
music.

SE18 – Woolwich

Village Blacksmith (P)
4-5 Hillreach
Tel: (01) 855 2829
Weston (PC)
Snacks all sessions.

SE23 – Forest Hill

Two Brewers (OL)
97 Dartmouth Road
Tel: (01) 699 1326
Bulmer (PC)
Symonds (PC)
Weston (PC)

BROMLEY

Bitter End (OL)
139 Masons Hill
Tel: (01) 466 6083
Weston (PC)
Open Monday 5-9; Tuesday to
Friday 12-3 and 5-10;
Saturday 11-3 and 5-10;
Sunday 12-2 and 7-9.

Bromley Wine Centre (OL)
50 Widmore Road
Tel: (01) 466 6679

Oddbins (OL)
26 High Street
Tel: (01) 290 1382
Weston (J)

CARSHALTON

Cottage of Content (P)
Bulmer (PC)

CROYDON

Oddbins (OL)
10 London Road
Tel: (01) 686 4811
Weston (J)

Windsor Stores (OL)
3 Lower Coombe Street
Tel: (01) 688 2945
Bulmer (H)

W2 – Bayswater

Chimes (P)
5-6 Wellington Terrace,
Bayswater Road
Tel: (01) 229 3553
Aspall (F)
Merrydown (BB)
Weston (H) cider and perry
English restaurant and
cider/wine bar. Meals
lunchtime and evening
throughout week.

Oddbins (OL)
12 Westbourne Grove
Tel: (01) 727 4356
Weston (J)

W4 – Chiswick

Hannison Wines (OL)
392a Chiswick High Road
Saffron Ciders (B)
Saffron Perrys (B)

W6 – Hammersmith

Rutland Ale House (P)
15 Lower Mall
Tel: (01) 748 5586
Bulmer (H)
Recently converted to a
traditional ale house,
riverside pub overlooking
Hammersmith Bridge.
Function room available for
bookings; bar snacks Monday
to Saturday; traditional roast
dinner Sunday lunchtime;
outside terrace on river
embankment.

W9 – Maida Vale

Truscott Arms (P)
55 Shirland Road
Tel: (01) 286 0310
Bulmer (H)

W11 – Notting Hill

Frog & Firkin (P)
41 Tavistock Crescent
Tel: (01) 727 9250
James White (PP)
Weston (H)
David Bruce home brew pub.
Meals and snacks lunchtime
and evening all sessions; live
sessions.

SW1 – Victoria

Chimes (P)
29 Churton Street, Pimlico
Tel: (01) 821 7456
Aspall (F)
Merrydown (BB)
Weston (H) cider and perry
English restaurant and
cider/wine bar, the nearest
thing to a cider house in
central London. Restaurant
downstairs, snacks and cider
ground floor.

SW3 – Chelsea

Builders Arms (P)
13 Britten Street
Bulmer (H)
Two bar back street local.

SW5 – Earls Court

La Vigneronne (OL)
105 Old Brompton Road
Tel: (01) 589 6113
Yearlstone (B)
Yearlstone Wine (B)

SW7 – South Kensington

Ennismore Arms (P)
2 Ennismore Mews.
Brompton
Tel: (01) 584 0440
Bulmer (H)
At rear of Brompton Oratory.
Snacks lunchtime; meals
evening; outdoor drinking
area.

Gloucester Arms (P)
34 Gloucester Road
Tel: (01) 584 0020
Bulmer (H)
Number of separate bars on
split levels; lively and mixed

clientele. Meals and snacks
lunchtime and evening;
outdoor drinking area.

Gloucester Hotel (P)
Courtfield Road
Merrydown (H)

Hereford Arms (P)
127 Gloucester Road
Tel: (01) 370 4988
Bulmer (H)
Recreating the atmosphere of
an old English country tavern
in the heart of London; gas
lights, bare sawdust floors,
and serving wenches. Meals
and snacks 11.30-3 and
5.30-11.

SW10 – West Brompton

Ferret & Firkin in the Balloon up the Creek (P)
114 Lots Road
Tel: (01) 352 6645
Inch (H)
Weston (H)
David Bruce home brew pub.
Snacks 12-3 and 5.30-11;
meals 12-3; live music.

Oddbins (OL)
531 Kings Road
Tel: (01) 351 1536
Weston (J)

Oddbins (OL)
142 Fulham Road
Tel: (01) 373 5715

SW11 – Battersea

Di's Larder (OL)
62 Lavender Hill
Tel: (01) 233 4618
James White (B)

NEW MALDEN

Wine Cask (OL)
South Lane
Zum (PC)

SURBITON

Oddbins (OL)
58a Victoria Road
Tel: (01) 399 2305
Weston (J)

Southampton (P)
Station Approach
Bulmer (H)
At bottom of office block
beside station. Snacks
lunchtime and evening;
meals lunchtime; live music.

HOUNSLOW

Cross Lances (P)
Bulmer (H)

Royal Albion (P)
58 Hibernia Road
Tel: (01) 572 8461
Taunton (H)
Friendly side street local.
Meals all sessions; garden;
lending library; pool; quiz
night Thursday.

TWICKENHAM

Chimes (P)
21 York Street
Tel: (01) 892 4794
Aspall (F)
Merrydown (BB)
Weston (H) cider and perry
English restaurant and
cider-wine bar. Meals
lunchtime and evening all
sessions.

ZUM ZIDER
West Country Products,
Lyon House, 51 Lion Road
Tel: (01) 892 4114

*Sawdust and serving wenches in the Hereford Arms,
SW7*

Greater Manchester

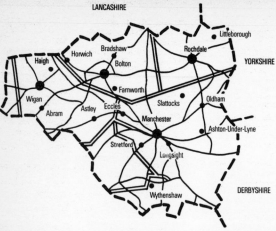

ABRAM

Bucks Head (P)
Warrington Road
Addlestones (H)

ASHTON-UNDER-LYNE

Gamecock (P)
152 Old Street
Tel: 061-344 0321
Guest Ciders (H)
Meals and snacks lunchtime;
live jazz and folk; facilities for
disabled.

ASTLEY

Miners Arms (P)
Manchester Road (A572)
Tel: 061-884060
Addlestones (H)
Meals and snacks 11.30-2.00;
outdoor drinking area.

BOLTON

Ainsworth Arms (P)
606 Halliwell Road (A6099)
Tel: Bolton (0204) 40671
Addlestones (H)
Snacks lunchtime.

Hare & Hounds (P)
531 Bury Road
Tel: Bolton (0204) 21337
Addlestones (H)

Howcroft (P)
36 Pool Street, off Topp Way
Tel: Bolton (0204) 26814
Addlestones (H)
Winner of CAMRA Pub

Preservation award. Meals
lunchtime and evening;
garden.

Man & Scythe (P)
6-8 Churchgate
Bulmer (H)

Old Three Crowns (P)
14 Deansgate
Tel: Bolton (0204) 26485
Bulmer (H)

Wilton Arms (P)
885 Belmont Road
Tel: Bolton (0204) 53307
Bulmer (H)

BRADSHAW

Lamb Inn (P)
Bradshaw Road
Bulmer (H)

ECCLES

Duke of York Hotel (P)
89 Church Street
Tel: 061-707 5409
Bulmer (H)
Holds annual Farm Cider
Event for 2 weeks in June; up
to 20 different ciders are
featured. Snacks all sessions;
full meals 7.30-2.30pm
Monday to Friday; 10-2.30pm
Saturday; outdoor drinking
area; accommodation; no
smoking lounge.

FARNWORTH

Market Inn (P)
11 Brackley Street

Tel: Farnworth (0204) 72888
Addlestones (H)
Meals and snacks 11-3pm;
outdoor drinking area.

HAIGH

Red Lion (P)
Haigh Road
Bulmer (E)
Meals lunchtime and
evening.

HORWICH

Old Original Bay Horse (P)
206 Lee Lane
Tel: Horwich (0204) 66231
Bulmer (H)

LITTLEBOROUGH

Red Lion (P)
6 Halifax Road (under the
arches)
Tel: Littleborough
(0706) 78195
Bulmer (H) (PC)
Traditional, West Country
Dry and Extra Dry, number 7;
1080 – 3 hand pumps. Follow
footpath to canal and Red
Lion is next to Railway
Station. Snacks 12-2 and 5-7;
garden; live music
Wednesday, Friday,
Saturday, Sunday.

LONGSIGHT

Waggon & Horses (P)
Stockport Road

Tel: 061-225 2649
Bulmer (H)
Snacks 11.30-3 and 5.30-11
all week; outdoor drinking
area; large games room.

MANCHESTER CITY CENTRE

Chesters Pie & Ale House (P)
Cateaton Street
Bulmer (H)
The street name does not
imply the contents of the pies!
Meals lunchtime.

Crown & Anchor (P)
41 Hilton Street (between A6
and A665)
Tel: 061-236 7683
Bulmer (H)
Meals lunchtime; children's
room.

Lass O'Gowrie (P)
36 Charles Street

Tel: 061-273 6932
Bulmer (H)
Brewhouse on view from bar;
naked gas flame lights. Meals
lunchtime; outdoor drinking
area. .

Marble Arch (P)
73 Rochdale Road (A664)
Bulmer (H)
Opens 12 noon, closed Sunday
lunch. Victorian pub with
unique barrel vaulted tiled
ceiling and frieze. Meals
lunchtime.

Salisbury (P)
Wakefield Street
Bulmer (H)
Meals lunchtime

OLDHAM

Spinners (P)
Lees Road, Clarkesfield
Bulmer (PC)
Meals lunchtime.

SLATTOCKS

Hopwood Arms (P)
Manchester Road
Bulmer (H)

STETFORD

Quadrant (P)
Great Stone Road
Bulmer (H)

WIGAN

Raven (P)
Wallgate (A49)
Tel: Wigan (0942) 43865
Addlestones (H)
Victorian town centre pub.
Opens 12 noon, closed Sunday
lunch. Meals lunchtime.

WYTHENSHAWE

Portway Wines (OL)
Westrays (F)

West Midlands

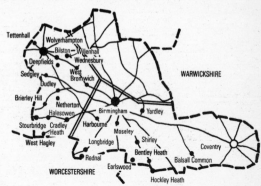

BALSALL COMMON

Grape Villa Farm Supplies (OL)
170 Kenilworth Road
Tel: Berkswell (0676) 33536
Symonds (PC)

BIRMINGHAM CITY CENTRE

Woodman (P)
106 Albert Street (corner of
New Canal Street – ¼ mile
east of Moor Street Station)
Tel: 021-643 2324

Coates (PC)
Opposite the Curzon Street
Arch, the original terminus of
the London & Birmingham
Railway, matching the late
lamented Euston Arch at the
London end of the line. Pub is
unspoilt, with original
windows, glazed tiling and
fittings. Snacks lunchtime
and evening. Saturday
evening opening 7pm.

BILLESLEY

Cellar 5 Off Licence (OL)
298 Haunch Lane
Langdon (PC)

BILSTON

Trumpet (P)
High Street
Bulmer (H)

BRIERLEY HILL

New Inn (P)
Dudley Road (A461)
Tel: Brierley Hill
(0384) 73792
Weston (H)
Near town centre.

Robin Hood (P)
Merry Hill, Quarry Park

Tel: Brierley Hill
(0384) 77224
Weston (PC)

Royal Oak (P)
258 Stourbridge Road,
Holly Hall
Tel: Brierley Hill
(0384) 75950
Weston (PC)

Waterloo Inn (P)
Mill Street
Tel: Brierley Hill
(0384) 79281
Weston (PC)

COVENTRY

Broomfield Tavern (P)
14–16 Broomfield Place,
Spon End
Tel: Coventry (0203) 28506
Bulmer (H)
Meals lunchtime and
evening; garden; regular folk
sessions.

Deedmore Off Licence (OL)
Deedmore Lane
Langdon (PC)

Gosford Wines (OL)
153 Far Gosford Street
Tel: Coventry (0203) 57828
Rich (PC
Symonds (PC)

CRADLEY HEATH

Wharf (P)
Station Road
Weston (H)

DARLESTON

K. K. Patel (OL)
144 Wolverhampton Street
Langdon (PC)

DEEPFIELDS

Boat Inn (P)
Haveacre Lane (near
Crossley)
Tel: Bilston (0902) 42993
Weston (PC)

DUDLEY

British Oak (P)
Salop Street
Tel: Dudley (0384) 236297
Bulmer (H)
Meals lunchtime and
evening.

Empire Tavern (P)
Trindle Road
Tel: Dudley (0384) 54337
Bulmer (H) (PC)
Snacks all sessions; meals
lunchtime including Sunday,
evening please book.

Lamp Tavern (P)
High Street (A459)
Bulmer (H)
Just off Town centre. Meals
lunchtime.

King & Queen (P)
Strafford Street
Weston (PC)

Smiling Man (P)
Hall Street
Tel: Dudley (0354) 53268
Weston (PC)

Ye Olde Struggling Man (P)
95 Wolverhampton Street
Tel: Dudley (0384) 58764
Weston (PC)

EARLSWOOD

Bulls Head (P)
Limekiln Lane, Salter Street
(off B4102)
Tel: Earlswood (056 46) 2335
Coates (PC)
Near Earlswood Lakes. You
need to ask for "the scrumpy".
Meals and snacks lunchtime
and evening to 8pm (not
Sundays); outdoor patio.

GOSTA GREEN

Old Union Mill (P)
Holt Street/Heneage Street
Tel: 021-359 1716
Coates (PC)
Meals and snacks lunchtime
and evening.

HALESOWEN

Pardoes (OL)
Peckingham Street
Weston (H)

HOCKLEY HEATH

Blue Bell Cider House (P)
Warings Green Road
Tel: Earlswood (056 46) 3607
Bulmer (E)
On the Stratford Canal, a pub
where cider comes first. A
relaxed atmosphere,
especially after a few pints.
Meals and snacks 12-2
Monday to Saturday; garden;
mooring for canal boats. Don't
miss it!

LONGBRIDGE

Patricks Real Ale (OL)
129 Longbridge Lane
Tel: 021-476 1588
Weston (PC

LYE

Windmill (P)
90 Dudley Road
Tel: Lye (038 482) 3313
Weston (PC)

MOSELEY

Mr. Booze (OL)
School Road
Tel: 021-772 5368
Weston (PC)
Wonnacott (PC)

NETHERTON

Hope Tavern (P)
Cinder Bank
Tel: Dudley (0384) 59021
Weston (PC)
Meals and snacks lunchtime.

Old Swan (P)
Halesowen Road (A459)
Bulmer (H)
Famous old home brew house.

REDNAL

Da Costa Wines (OL)
Weston (PC)

SEDGLEY

Grand Junction (P)
High Holborn
Tel: Sedgley (090 73) 2980
Weston (PC)

SHIRLEY

Bernies Real Ale Off Licence (OL)
266 Cranmore Boulevard (off
A34)
Tel: 021-744 2827
Somerset Scrumpy (E) (H)
Closed Monday; open
Tuesday to Friday 12-2 and
5.30-10; Saturday 11-3.30
and 5.30-10; Sunday 7-10.

STOURBRIDGE

Moorings (P)
78 Lower High Street,
Amblecote
Tel: Stourbridge
(0384) 374124
Weston (H)

Swan Hotel (P)
157 Hagley Road, Old
Swinford
Tel: Stourbridge
(0384) 396290
Weston (PC)

TETTENHALL

Mitre (P)
Lower Green
Tel: Wolverhampton
(0902) 753487
Weston (PC)

WARDEND

Gaybell Wines (OL)
101 Glenpark Road
Langdon (PC)

WEDNESBURY

Horse & Jockey (P)
Wood Green Road (A461)
Tel: 021-566 0464
Bulmer (PC)
Meals lunchtime and
evening; restaurant.

Turks Head (P)
Lower High Street
Weston (PC)

WEST BROMWICH

**Odd Fellows Arms
(P)**
Bulmer (H)

Sow & Pigs (P)
Hill Top
Tel: 021-553 3127
Bulmer (H)

Wheatsheaf (P)
Bulmer (H)

WEST HAGLEY

Cross Keys (P)
Worcester Road
Tel: Hagley (0562) 882812
Weston (PC)

WILLENHALL

Tiger Inn (P)
Stafford Street
Tel: Willenhall (0902) 65356
Bulmer (H)
Meals and snacks lunchtime;
garden; accommodation.

WOLVER-HAMPTON

Alexandra (P)
Chapel Ash (A41)
Bulmer (PC)

Builders Arms (P)
Derry Street
Tel: Wolverhampton
(0902) 57117
Bulmer (PC)

**Combermere Arms
(P)**
Chapel Ash (A41)
Tel: Wolverhampton
(0902) 21880
Bulmer (PC)
Charming little pub, looks
more like a terrace house.

Feathers (P)
Molineux Street
Tel: Wolverhampton
(0902) 26924
Weston (PC)
Meals and snacks lunchtime;
garden.

Newbridge (P)

Tettenhall Road
Tel: Wolverhampton
(0902) 754911
Bulmer (PC)

Sunbeam (P)
Penn Road
Weston (PC)

Talbot (P)
Princes Street
Bulmer (PC
Weston (PC)

YARDLEY

**Clay Lane Stores
(OL)**
Weston (PC)

MERSEYSIDE

LIVERPOOL

**Everyman Bistro
(P)**
9 Hope Street
Tel: 051-708 9545
Bulmer (H)
Open all day from 12 noon to
11.30pm (midnight on Friday
and Saturday); full meals.

Swan (P)
86 Wood Street
Tel: 051-709 5281
Thatcher (PP)
Snacks 11.30-2; outdoor
drinking area.

Norfolk

ATTLEBOROUGH

**Peatling and
Cawdron (OL)**
High Street
Merrydown (BB)

BANHAM

**Ye Olde Garden
House (Banham
Cider House) (P)**
Greyhound Lane
Tel: Attleborough
(0953) 860437
**Bulmer
Local Draught Cider
Local Extra Strong Cider
Local Scrumpy**
A well-known local
institution, about a mile west
of the village. The origin of
the local ciders is uncertain.
Meals at lunchtime,
including Sunday; garden;
camping.

BAWSEY

Sandboy (P)
Bulmer

BERNEY ARMS

Berney Arms (P)
River Tare
Tel: Great Yarmouth
(0493) 700303
James White (PC)
Popular Broadland pub at
entrance to Breydon Water,
accessible only by boat or
train! Meals lunchtime and
evening; garden; children's
room.

BILLINGFORD

Forge (P)
Bintree Road (off B1145)
Tel: Elmham (036 281) 486
James White (PC)
The old village smithy, now

converted into a pub. Meals
lunchtime and evening;
garden; children's room.

BROCKDISH

**Ye Olde Kings Head
(P)**
James White (PC)

CLEY

Picnic Fare (OL)
James White Cider (B)
**James White Apple Wine
(B)**

GELDESTON

Locks Inn (P)
Station Road
Tel: Kirby Cane
(050 845) 414
James White
At the upper limit of
navigation on the River
Waveney. A beamed riverside

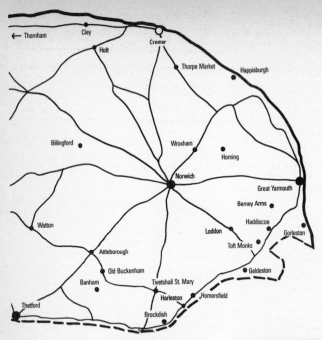

← Thornham · Cley · Holt · Cromer · Thorpe Market · Happisburgh · Billingford · Wroxham · Horning · Norwich · Great Yarmouth · Berney Arms · Watton · Haddiscoe · Loddon · Gorleston · Toft Monks · Attleborough · Old Buckenham · Geldeston · Banham · Tivetshall St. Mary · Harleston · Homersfield · Thetford · Brockdish

building dating from 1680.
Meals lunchtime and
evening; Sunday lunch;
children's room; garden;
accommodation; camping.

Wherry (P)
The Street
Tel: Kirby Cane
(050 845) 371
Bulmer
Meals lunchtime and
evening; Sunday lunch;
children's room; garden;
accommodation.

GREAT YARMOUTH

Back to Backs (P)
Market Row
Tel: Great Yarmouth
(0493) 53045
James White (PC)
Old pub with beamed ceiling.
Meals lunchtime.

Colonel H (P)
Nelson Road Central
Tel: Great Yarmouth
(0493) 857366
James White
Single bar pub with war
theme. Meals lunchtime.

Flints (P)
46 St. Georges Road
James White (PC)
Pool table.

GORLESTON

Odd Bottle (OL)
James White

Val Cole Wines (OL)
1 Marine Close,
Tel: Great Yarmouth
(0493) 662362
James White

HAPPISBURGH

Hill House (P)
The Hill
Tel: Walcott (0692) 650004
James White
In coastal village, behind
church. Meals lunchtime and
evening; garden;
accommmodation.

HARLESTON

Barwell & Jones (OL)
3 Redenhall Road
Tel: Harleston (0379) 852243
Aspall (B)
James White (B)

HOLT

Larners of Holt (OL)
Tel: Holt (0263) 712323
James White (B)

HOMERSFIELD

The Black Swan (P)
Tel: Homersfield
(098 686) 204
James White (PC)

HORNING

Main Stores (OL)
James White (B)

Val Cole Wines (OL)
James White

HADDISCOE

Pampas Lodge Caravan Site (P)
Beccles Road
Tel: Aldeby (050 277) 265
James White

NORWICH

City Wines (OL)
35 St. Benedicts
Tel: Norwich (0603) 619246
James White Cider
James White Apple Wine

The Grapevine (OL)
109 Unthank Road
Tel: Norwich (0603) 613998
James White (B)

Hangovers (OL)
5 St. Johns Close

Tel: Norwich (0603) 661517
James White Cider
James White Apple Wine

Horse and Dray (P)
137 Ber Street
Tel: Norwich (0603) 624741
Bulmer (H)
Snacks and meals lunchtime, evening meals by arrangement, parties catered for; separate restaurant; outdoor drinking area; children's room.

Kett's Corner Off Licence (OL)
20 Bishop Bridge Road
Tel: Norwich (0603) 627906
James White (B)

Mecca Wholefoods (OL)
5 Orford Hill
Tel: Norwich (0603) 614829
James White (B)

Plasterers (P)
Cowgate
"Scrumpy" (PC)
Good value pub grub lunchtime Monday to Friday.

Premises (Norwich Arts Centre) (P)
Reeves Yard, St. Benedicts
Tel: Norwich (0603) 660352
James White
Food, including vegetarian, through day; closed on Sunday.

D. J. Rees (OL)
James White (B)

Ribs of Beef (P)
Fye Bridge
Tel: Norwich (0603) 619517
James White
Inch
Riverside position with mooring. Home cooked food lunchtimes; children's room.

Rosary Tavern (P)
Rosary Road
Tel: Norwich (0603) 666287
Inch
Close to city yacht station and railway station. Meals lunchtime; garden.

Vintages Off Licence (OL)
33 Angel Road
Tel: Norwich (0603) 617887
James White (B)

White Lion (P)
73 Oak Street
Tel: Norwich (0603) 620630
James White
Lunchtime meals.

Wine Growers Association (OL)
5-6 Castle Meadow
Tel: Norwich (0603) 625128
James White (B)

Wine Warehouse (OL)
59 Dereham Road
Tel: Norwich (0603) 612839
James White (B)

OLD BUCKENHAM

White Horse (P)
On B1077
Tel: Attleborough (0953) 860397
James White (PC)
Meals lunchtime and evening, Sunday lunch; children's room; garden; accommodation; camping.

THETFORD

Central Hotel
Market Place
Tel: Thetford (0842) 2253
James White
Town centre pub, with jazz nights on second Friday of each month. Meals lunchtime and evening; accommodation; garden.

THORNHAM

Lifeboat (P)
Sea Lane
Tel: Thornham (048 526) 236
Bulmer
Ex-smugglers' inn overlooking marshes. Meals lunchtime and evening, Sunday lunch; children's room; garden.

THORPE MARKET

Suffield Arms (P)
Church Road (near Gunton Station)

Tel: Southrepps (026 479) 461
James White
Meals lunchtime and evening; garden.

TIVETSHALL ST. MARY

Old Ram (P)
Ram Lane (A140)
Tel: Pulham Market (037 976)
James White Cider
James White Apple Wine
Meals lunchtime and evening, Sunday lunch; garden.

TOFT MONKS

Post Office Stores (OL)
James White (B)

Toft Lion (P)
The Street (A143)
Tel: Aldeby (050 277) 369
James White (PC)
Meals lunchtime and evening.

WATTON

Breckland Wines (OL)
James White (B)

WROXHAM

Norfolk Fayre (OL)
James White Cider
James White Apple Wine

Cider graced the finest tables — especially when England was at war with France and wine drinking was considered unpatriotic. Here country gentlemen, plus yokel and dog, broach a cask

Northamptonshire

LEICESTERSHIRE

Harringworth

Kettering

Wellingborough

WARWICKSHIRE

Daventry

Northampton

BEDFORDSHIRE

Eydon

Towcester

BUCKINGHAMSHIRE

Weston

Cosgrove

Charlton

Aynho

OXFORDSHIRE

CAMBRIDGESHIRE

AYNHO

Great Western Arms (P)
Station Road (B4031)
Tel: Deddington (0869) 38288
Bulmer (H)
Between a disused station,
after which the pub is named,
and the busier Oxford Canal.
Meals and snacks; garden;
children's room; moorings.

CHARLTON

Rose & Crown (P)
Main Street
Tel: Banbury (0295) 811317
Bulmer (H)
Village local in conservation
area, with wealth of oak
beams. Non smoking food bar.
Meals lunchtime and
evenings Tuesday to
Saturday; garden; children's
room.

COSGROVE

Navigation Inn (P)
Thrupp Wharf, Castlethorpe
Road
Tel: Yardley Gobion
(0908) 543156
James White (H)
Old canalside pub on Grand
Union Canal. Snacks 12-2
and 7-10; canalside garden;
children's room;
accommodation, moorings.

EYDON

Royal Oak (P)
Lime Avenue
Tel: Byfield (0327) 61526
Bulmer (H)
Old local, all passages and
parlours. Meals lunchtime
and evening; garden;
children's room.

HARRINGWORTH

White Swan (P)
Tel: Morcott (057 287) 543
Bulmer (PC) summer
Meals lunchtime and
evening; carvery;
accommodation.

NORTHAMPTON

King William IV (P)
Commercial Street
Tel: Northampton
(0604) 21307
Weston (H)
Town centre pub. Meals and
snacks lunchtime.

Northampton Beer Agency (OL)
34 Derby Road
Tel: Northampton
(0604) 37670
Bland (H)

WELLING-BOROUGH

Wellingborough Beer Agency (OL)
Jug & Bottle, 54 Midland
Road
Tel: Wellingborough
(0933) 71134
Bland (H)
Specialises in draught beers
and ciders. Open 9.30am to
9.30pm Monday to Saturday;
12 noon to 2pm, and 7pm to
9pm, on Sunday.

WESTON

Crown (P)
by Weedon Lois
Tel: Sulgrave (029 576) 328
Weston (PC) summer
Meals lunchtime and
evening; regular live music;
Northants skittles.

Northumberland, Tyne & Wear

BENWELL

Mitre (P)
Benwell Lane
Tel: Tyneside (091) 274 9191
Bland
Ex bishops palace, now
rambling pub. Meals
lunchtime.

BYKER

Baxters (P)
Wilfred Street
Tel: Tyneside (091) 276 2721
Bulmer
Meals evening.

Cumberland Arms (P)
Byker Buildings
Tel: Tyneside (091) 265 6151
Bland (W)
Bulmer (H)
Character local. Snacks 11-3;
children's room.

FELLING

Wheatsheaf (P)
Carlisle Street
Tel: Tyneside (091) 438 6633
Bland
Regular folk nights.

GATESHEAD

Travellers Rest (P)
Sheriff Hill
Bland
Meals lunchtime.

JARROW

Allison Arms (P)
Straker Street
Tel: Tyneside (091) 489 7342
Bulmer
On south side of Tyne Tunnel.
Meals lunchtime and
evening.

NEWCASTLE

Dog & Parrot (P)
Clayton Street West
Tel: Newcastle (0632) 616998
Bulmer
Newcastle's only own brew
pub, split level with bare
boards. Opposite
Marlborough Bus Station.
Meals lunchtime.

Barley Mow (P)
City Road
Bulmer

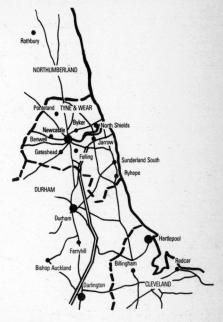

Meals lunchtime and
evening; garden

Broken Doll (P)
Blenheim Street
Tel: Newcastle (0632) 321047
Bulmer
Popular with students in
nearby Art College. Meals
lunchtime.

Cooperage (P)
32 The Close
Tel: Newcastle (0632) 328286
Coates
Beams and low ceilings; near
Swing Bridge. Meals
lunchtime.

Groat Bar (P)
Groat Market
Tel: Tyneside (091) 232 0730
Bulmer

Kings Arms (P)
Diana Street/Douglas
Terrace
Tel: Tyneside (091) 273 4105
Bulmer
Meals lunchtime.

Newcastle Poly Students Union (P)

2 Sandyford Road
Tel: Newcastle (0632) 328761
Bland
Meals lunchtime and
evening.

Percy Arms (P)
Bulmer

University of Newcastle Students Union (P)
Kings Walk
Tel: Newcastle:
(0632) 328402
Bulmer
Meals lunchtime and
evening.

NORTH SHIELDS

Tynemouth Lodge Hotel (P)
Tynemouth Road (A193)
Tel: Newcastle (0632) 577565
Bland
Meals lunchtime.

Wooden Doll (P)
Hudson Street
Tel: Newcastle (0632) 573747
Bulmer

93

Superb view over the mouth of Tyne. Meals lunchtime and evening.

PONTELAND

Blackbird Inn (P)
North Road
Tel: Ponteland (0661) 24949
Bulmer
Ancient pub which originated as a medieval Pele Tower, and later became a Manor House. Meals lunchtime.

ROTHBURY

Newcastle Hotel (P)
Tel: Rothbury (0669) 20334
Bulmer

RYHOPE

Albion Inn (P)
on A1018
Tel: Wearside (091) 521 0293
Bulmer

SUNDERLAND SOUTH

Borough (P)
Vine Place
Tel: Sunderland
(0783) 656316
Bulmer (H)
Victorian renovation, with bare boards. Meals lunchtime except Sunday.

 # Nottinghamshire

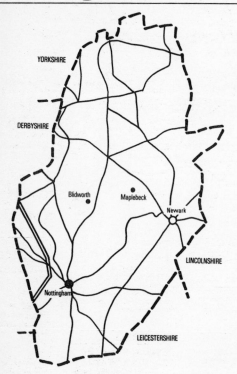

BLIDWORTH

Black Bull (P)
Field Lane/Main Street
Tel: Mansfield (0623) 792291
Bulmer (E) (H)
On edge of mining village. Meals lunchtime and evening (not Tuesday or Sunday); garden.

MAPLEBECK

Beehive (P)
off A616
Tel: Caunton (063 686) 306
Bulmer (H)
Country pub in secluded hamlet, smallest pub in the county.

NOTTINGHAM

Falcon (P)
Canning Circus
Bulmer (H)
Meals: garden.

FMC Brewhouse (P)
Canal Street
Bulmer (H)

Turf Tavern (P)
Upper Parliament Street
Bulmer (H)
Meals and snacks.

Warrows Wine Bar (P)
Fletcher Gate
Bulmer (H)

Oxfordshire

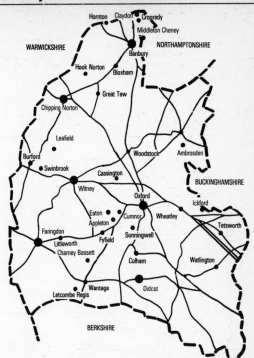

AMBROSDEN

Turner Arms (P)
Merton Road
Tel: Bicester (0869) 2468
Weston (PC)
Modernised local in ancient
village in the Ray valley.

APPLETON

Plough Inn (P)
Eaton Road (off A420)
Tel: Oxford (0865) 862441
Bulmer (PC)
17th century village inn,
head quarters of Oxford
branch of MG Owners Club.
Snacks lunchtime and
evening; garden.

BANBURY

Vitis Wines (OL)
James White (B)

BLOXHAM

Elephant & Castle
(P)

Humber Street (off A361)
Tel: Banbury (0295) 720383
Bulmer (PC)
Fine four storey mid 17th
century building in
picturesque north
Oxfordshire village. Lunches
except Sunday; garden;
children's room.

BURFORD

Masons Arms (P)
Witney Street (off A361)
Tel: Burford (099 382) 2438
Bulmer (H)
Meals lunchtime and
evening; garden; children's
room.

CASSINGTON

Chequers Inn (P)
off A40
Tel: Oxford (0865) 881390
Weston (H)
Meals lunchtime and
evening; room and garden for
children.

CHARNEY
BASSETT

Chequers (P)
off A420
Tel: West Hanney
(023 587) 642
Weston (H)
In Vale of White Horse, near
Pusey House and Gardens.
Meals and snacks all sessions;
garden.

CHIPPING
NORTON

Red Lion (P)
Albion Street
Tel: Chipping Norton
(0608) 3233
Bulmer (PC)
Backstreet pub up hill off
Market Place. Meals
lunchtime and evening;
outdoor drinking space.

CLAYDON

Sun Rising (P)

off A423
Tel: Farnborough
(029 589) 393
Bulmer (H)
—summer
Convenient overnight stop on
the Oxford Canal. Meals
lunchtime and evening;
garden.

CROPREDY

Red Lion (P)
Red Lion Street
Bulmer (PC)
15th century thatched pub
near church in village on
Oxford Canal. Meals
lunchtime and evening;
garden.

CULHAM

Jolly Porter (P)
Station Yard
Tel: Abingdon (0235) 24749
Weston (H)
Adjoining original Brunel
railway station, on Didcot to
Oxford line. Snacks
lunchtime; full meals
7-10pm; garden;
accommodation.

CUMNOR

Bear & Ragged Staff (P)
Appleton Road (off A420)
Tel: Oxford (0865) 862329
Weston (H)
Large 16th century pub first
licenced in 1555. Meals and
snacks lunchtime and
7.30-10.30pm; restaurant;
garden.

DIDCOT

Prince of Wales (P)
Station Road (off A4130)
Tel: Didcot (0235) 813027
Weston (H)
Near Didcot Steam Railway
Centre and station. Meals
lunchtime and evening;
garden; accommodation.

EATON

Eight Bells (P)
Tel: Oxford (0865) 862983
Bulmer (PC)
Small local within walking
distance of the Thames.
Meals except Sunday; garden.

FARINGDON

Crown Hotel (P)
Market Place
Tel: Faringdon (0367) 20196
Bulmer (H)
16th century coaching inn
with cobbled courtyard. Said
to be haunted by ghost from a
fatal fire. Meals and snacks
all sessions; accommodation.

FYFIELD

White Hart (P)
off A420
Tel: Frilford Heath
(0865) 390585
Weston (H)
15th century half timbered
and tiled building, originally
hospital or chantry for the
poor, leased as tavern by St.
Johns College, though they
reserve the right to reside
there "in time of pestilence".
Antiquarian bookshop in
nearby Manor House. Home
made food, lunchtime and
7-10pm; restaurant; garden;
children's room.

GOZZARDS FORD

Black Horse (P)
Tel: Frilford Heath
(0865) 390530
Weston (H)

GREAT TEW

Falkland Arms (P)
Tel: Great Tew (060 883) 653
Range of house ciders (PC)
18th century thatched pub in
heart of a Cotswold
conservation village, with
flagstone floor, lunchtime
snacks during summer except
Monday, when pub is closed
midday; barbeque during
summer (bring your own
food); folk music.

HORNTON

Dun Cow (P)
West End (near Banbury)
Tel: Edge Hill (029 587) 524
Bulmer (H)
Reputedly haunted! Meals
lunchtime and evening;
garden.

ICKFORD

Royal Oak (P)
Tel: Ickford (084 47) 633
Weston (PC)

LEAFIELD

Fox Inn (P)
Weston (PC)

LETCOMBE REGIS

Sparrow (P)
South Street
Tel: Wantage (023 57) 3228
Weston (H)
At foot of Lambourn Downs;
take narrow winding lane
south of church. Meals and
snacks lunchtime; large
garden with children's
facilities.

LITTLEWORTH

Blackwood Arms (P)
off Oxford to Swindon road
Weston (H)
In small village at Thames
end of Vale of White Horse.

MIDDLETON CHENEY

Dolphin (P)
134 Main Road. (near
Banbury)
Tel: Banbury (0295) 71314
Weston (PC)

NETHERWESTCOTE

New Inn (P)
Bulmer (H)

OXFORD

Georges Wine Bar (P)
High Street
Weston (H)

Grog Shop (OL)
13 Kingston Road
Tel: Oxford (0865) 57088
Weston (H)

Horse & Jockey (P)
69 Woodstock Road
Tel: Oxford (0865) 52719
Weston (H) & (PC)
Close to Radcliffe Hospital.
Food bar, extensive range of
hot and cold meals and snacks
all sessions; garden.

Isis (P)
near Iffley Lock
Tel: Oxford (0865) 242501
Bulmer (H)
—summer
Isolated river pub with no
road access, formerly a
farmhouse. Lunchtime
meals; riverside garden;
skittle alley.

Kings Arms (P)
40 Holywell Street
Tel: Oxford (0865) 242369
Weston (H)
Popular 17th century pub in
heart of University area,
opposite Bodleian New
Library and Sheldonian
Theatre. Hot and cold snacks
lunchtime and evening,

Oddbins (OL)
108 High Street
Tel: Oxford (0865) 725254
Weston (PC)

Oddbins (OL)
263 Banbury Road,
Summertown
Tel: Oxford (0865) 52407

Oxford Beer Shop (OL)
12 Western Road
Tel: Rich (0865) 250089
Rich (PC)
Symonds (PC)

Port Mamon (P)
St. Clements Street
Bulmer (H)

Radcliffe Arms (P)
67 Cranham Street, Jericho
Tel: Oxford (0865) 52693
Bulmer (H)
Convenient for Oxford Canal.
Snacks all sessions; garden;
live music most weekends.

Turf Tavern (P)
10 Bath Place (off Holywell
Street)
Tel: Oxford (0865) 43235
Weston (H)
Peace in the middle of the
city. Approached only by two
narrow passages from
Holywell Street and set in its
own courtyard. Good range of
hot and cold food lunchtime
and evening.

Wheatsheaf (P)
Wheatsheaf Yard (off High
Street)
Tel: Oxford (0865) 243276
Weston (H)
Meals and snacks all sessions.

SUNNINGWELL

Flowing Well Inn (P)
Tel: Oxford (0865) 735846

Weston (PC)
Attractive setting near duck
pond. Meals lunchtime and
evening; garden.

SWINBROOK

Swan Inn (P)
off A40
Tel: Burford (099 382) 2165
Weston (PC)
Bar food at lunchtime;
accommodation.

TETSWORTH

Red Lion (P)
on A40
Tel: Tetsworth (084 428) 274
Weston (H)
Village local opposite green.
Meals and snacks lunchtime
and evening; garden.

Swan Inn (P)
7 High Street (A40)
Tel: Tetsworth (084 428) 489
Weston (H)
Large 16th century coaching
inn with original panelling
and beamed ceiling, many
royal connections. Meals
lunchtime and evening;
accommodation; garden;
children's room.

WANTAGE

Kings Arms (P)
Wallingford Street
Tel: Wantage (023 57) 4272
Bulmer (H)

WATLINGTON

Hare & Hounds (P)
Couching Street (A4009)
Tel: Watlington
(049 161) 2329
Weston (PC)
Georgian coaching inn on
corner of High Street,
opposite Town Hall. Bar food
lunchtime and evening.

WHEATLEY

King & Queen (P)
High Street
Tel: Wheatley (086 77) 2701
Weston (H)
Tudor building with beamed
ceilings and open fires.

WITNEY

Royal Oak (P)
High Street
Tel: Witney (0993) 2576
Weston (PL)
In main shopping area. Meals
except Sundays; garden.

WOODSTOCK

Black Prince (P)
Manor Road (A34)
Tel: Woodstock
(0993) 811530
Bulmer (PC
Riverside pub with several
separate rooms. Meals
lunchtime and evening;
garden; children's room.

 # *Shropshire*

ASTON-ON-CLUN

Kangaroo Inn (P)
near Craven Arms
Tel: Little Brampton
(058 87) 263
Bulmer (H)
Snacks lunchtime every day;
full meals lunchtime except
Sunday; children's section;
large garden; bowling green;
Caravan Club certified site;
pool table.

BISHOPS CASTLE

Philips Wine Shop (OL)
Weston (full range)

Three Tuns (P)
Salop Street
Tel: Bishops Castle
(0588) 638797

Weston (H)
Medieval coaching inn at
centre of town. One of the
original home brew
pubs – tours available.
Snacks lunchtime; full meals
7-9; outdoor drinking area.

Vaults (P)
High Street
Weston (H)

BRIDGNORTH

Railwaymans Arms (P)
Bridgnorth Station
Tel: Bridgnorth (074 62) 4361
Bulmer (H)
The station buffet and bar of
the preserved Severn Valley
Railway Station, open only
when the trains are running.
The steam operated service
runs to Kidderminster, along
the River Severn. The

Midland Motor Museum and
Bird Garden are 2 miles from
the town. Snacks; eat and
watch the trains.

Shakespeare (P)
West Castle Street
Tel: Bridgnorth (074 62) 2403
Bulmer (H)
Take the only inland railway
in the country from the
Station up to the town and the
pub. Meals and snacks 12-2
and 6-8.30; garden; skittle
alley.

CHURCH STRETTON

Bikold Freezer Centre (OL)
10 Sandford Avenue
Tel: Church Stretton
(0694) 722081
Weston (full range)

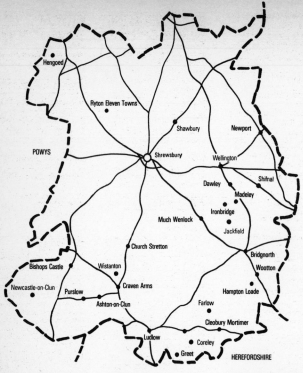

Map showing locations: Hengoed, Ryton Eleven Towns, POWYS, Shawbury, Newport, Shrewsbury, Wellington, Shifnal, Dawley, Madeley, Ironbridge, Jackfield, Much Wenlock, Church Stretton, Bridgnorth, Wootton, Bishops Castle, Wistanton, Newcastle-on-Clun, Purslow, Craven Arms, Ashton-on-Clun, Hampton Loade, Farlow, Cleobury Mortimer, Ludlow, Coreley, Greet, HEREFORDSHIRE

Malins Super Stores (OL)

Weston (full range)

CLEOBURY MORTIMER

Bell (P)
Lower Street
Tel: Cleobury Mortimer
(0299) 270305
Bulmer (H)
Unspoilt inn of character.

Lion (P)
Lower Street
Tel: Cleobury Mortimer
(0299) 270395
Weston (H) (PC)
Elizabethan pub. Meals and
snacks lunchtime; patio;
accommodation.

Three Horseshoes (P)
Tel: Cleobury Mortimer
(0299) 270494
Weston (PC)

CORELEY

Colliers Arms (P)
off A4117 near Clee Hill
Tel: Ludlow (0584) 890445

Bulmer (H) (W)
16th century inn. Snacks;
garden.

DAWLEY

Bulls Head (P)
Dawley Bank
Tel: Telford (0952) 503378
Weston (PC)

FARLOW

The Gate Hangs Well (P)
near Cleobury Mortimer
Tel: Ludlow (0584)890273
Dunkerton (PC) (B)
Snacks 12-2; full meals
7-10.30; restaurant; garden;
touring caravan site.

GREET

Harvest Home Inn (P)
Weston (PC)

HAMPTON LOADE

Unicorn (P)
Tel: Highley (0746) 861515
Weston (PC)
—summer

Near intermediate station on
Severn Valley Steam
Railway. Down the road is a
current powered ferry over
the River Severn. Out of peak
season 3 pint jars of draught
cider are sold. Meals and
snacks all sessions; terrace
within sight and sound of
railway.

HENGOED

The Last Inn (P)
Tel: Oswestry (0691) 659747
Weston (H)
Large country inn. Meals all
sessions; children's room;
regular live music.

IRONBRIDGE

Golden Ball (P)
1 Newbridge Road, Madeley
Wood
Tel: Ironbridge
(095 245) 2179
Weston (PC)

JACKFIELD

Boat Inn (P)
access by footbridge from
Coalport side of river

Tel: Telford (0952) 882178
Weston (PC)
Riverside pub in pleasant
setting. Meals lunchtime and
evening; garden; camping
site; facilities for disabled.

LUDLOW

Bull Hotel (P)
Bull Ring
Tel: Ludlow (0584) 3611
Weston (PC)
14th century timber framed
building. Snacks lunchtime
and evening; meals lunch
except Sunday; outdoor
drinking area.

Earthworks (OL)
22 Corve Street
Tel: Ludlow (0584) 2010
Dunkerton (B)

Feathers (P)
Corve Street
Tel: Ludlow (0584) 5262
Dunkerton (B)

Hardwicks Restaurant (P)
Dunkerton (B)

Stephens (OL)
3 Castle Street
Tel: Ludlow (0584) 2375
Dunkerton (B)

MADELEY

Pheasant (P)
Coalport Road
Weston (PC)

MUCH WENLOCK

Horse & Jockey (P)
Stretton Road
Tel: Much Wenlock
(0952) 727001
Weston (PC)
Near Wenlock Edge
viewpoint.

NEWCASTLE-ON-CLUN

Anchor Inn (P)
near Craven Arms
Tel: Kerry (068 688) 250
Weston (PC)
Snacks all sessions; meals
12-2 and 7-10; restaurant;
garden; accommodation.

NEWPORT

Pheasant (P)
Upper Bar
Tel: Newport (0952) 811961
Weston (PC)

RYTON ELEVEN TOWNS

Bridge (P)
Weston (PC)
The Manor once contained
eleven townships.

SHAWBURY

Pyms Stores (OL)
118 Church Street
Tel: Shawbury (0939) 250223
Weston (full range)

SHIFNAL

Burgesses Wines (OL)
Weston (full range)

WELLINGTON

Tudor Wines (OL)
15 Market Square
Tel: Telford (0952) 55297
Weston (full range)

WISTANTON

Plough Inn (P)
near Craven Arms
Tel: Craven Arms
(058 82) 3251
Weston (PC)

WOOTTON

The Cider House (P)
near Bridgnorth (off A442 at
Quatt or A458 at Broad Oak)
Tel: Quatt (0746) 780285
Bulmer (E) (H) (PC)
Until recently a Bulmer's
cider house, now
independent, and *still* a cider
house! In delightful country,
in easy reach from Severn
Valley Railway (about 2
miles from Hampton Loade
Station). Hot and cold food;
large garden; far from the
madding crowd! Wassail!

Somerset

ALHAMPTON

Alhampton Inn (P)
Tel: Ditcheat (074 986) 210
Coates (PC)

APPLEY

Globe (P)
Tel: Greenham (0823) 672327
Bulmer (PL)
Ancient village pub unspoilt
by passage of time. Snacks all
sessions; garden; children's
room (summer only).

ASHILL

ASHILL CIDER ▲
Ashill Farm (near Ilminster)
Tel: Hatch Beauchamp
(0823) 480513

Square & Compass (P)
Windmill Hill (off A358)
Local cider (PC)
Meals and snacks; garden;
camping and caravan site.

ASHCOTT

Railway Inn (P)
Wilkins (PC)
You've missed the last train –
it went in 1966 – so there's no
hurry.

BAMPTON

Bampton Stores (OL)
Inch

BARRINGTON

Royal Oak (P)
Tel: Ilminster (046 05) 3455
Taunton (PC)
Vickery (PC)
Meals and snacks 12-2 and
7-10; garden.

BAYFORD

Unicorn (P)
near Wincanton
Tel: Wincanton (0963) 32324
Taunton (H)
17th century coaching inn.
Hot and cold bar food; garden;
accommodation.

BECKINGTON

Forester Arms (P)

Goose Street (off A361)
Tel: Frome (0373) 830864
Bulmer (PC)
Snacks; meals lunchtime and
evening; live music.

Woolpack (P)
on A361
Tel: Frome (0373) 830388
Taunton (PC)
Meals and snacks lunchtime
and evening; pool.

BICKNOLLER

MEADOWSWEET
CIDER ▲
Meadowsweet Farm
Tel: Stogumber (0984 46) 409

BINEGAR

Horse & Jockey (P)
off A37
Tel: Oakhill (0749) 840537
Thatcher (PC)
Meals and snacks lunchtime
and evening (not Tuesday or
Sunday); garden with
children's pets corner.

BISHOPS
LYDEARD

Bell (P)
Tel: Bishops Lydeard
(0823) 432213
Taunton (H)
Snacks; garden; children's
room.

Lethbridge Arms
(P)
Tel: Bishops Lydeard
(0823) 432234
Taunton (H)
Small hotel with listed fives
wall. Meals and snacks;
restaurant; accommodation.

BLUE ANCHOR

Blue Anchor
Caravan Site (OL)
Tel: Dunster (064 382)
Sheppy

Blue Anchor Hotel
(P)
Tel: Washford (0984) 40239
Rich (PC)
Good views of bay from this
large pub near caravan sites.
Meals and snacks lunchtime
and evening; garden;
children's room;
accommodation.

BRADFORD-
ON-TONE

SHEPPY'S
FARMHOUSE
CIDER ▲
Three Bridges

Tel: Bradford-on-Tone
(082 346) 233

BREAN

Allens Holiday
Shop (OL)
South Road
Tel: Brean Down
(0278 75) 248
Langdon (PC)
Rich (PP)
Weston (PL)
Cider sold by the pint or in
ready filled bottles or
containers – tastings with
pleasure!

South Brean Stores
(OL)
Rich (PC)

BRIDGETOWN

Badgers Holt (P)
Tel: Winsford (064 385) 204
Taunton (PC)
Open plan Swiss style bar.
Snacks; garden; games room;
children's room.

BRIDGWATER

Andys Mini Market
(OL)
Taunton Road
Rich (PC)

Boat & Anchor (P)
Huntworth
Tel: North Petherton
(0278) 662473
Taunton (H)
On bank of Bridgwater to
Taunton Canal, south of
town. Meals; restaurant
overlooking canal; outdoor
terrace, accommodation.

Bristol & Exeter (P)
135 St. John Street
Tel: Bridgwater
(0278) 423722
Hall (PC)
Taunton (H)
Near railway station; the
name derives from the
original title of the line. A
basic cider pub.

British Railways
Club (P)
Rich (PC)

Bunch of Grapes (P)
24 St. John Street
Taunton (H)
Cold bar snacks lunchtime;
outdoor drinking area.

Crowpill Stores
(OL)
93 Chilton Street
Tel: Bridgwater
(0278) 422735
Rich (PC)

Dawes Farm Shop
(OL)
Huntworth
Lane (PC)
Rich (PC)
Sheppy

Lions Club (P)
2617 West Quay
Tel: Bridgwater
(0278) 423453
Rich (PC)

Mellors (OL)
15 North Street
Tel: Bridgwater
(0278) 423124
Rich (PC)

New Market (P)
Bath Road
Tel: Bridgwater
(0278) 422178
Bulmer (PC)

North Pole (P)
North Street
Tel: Bridgwater (0278) 51930
Taunton (H)

Stan & Cindys Store
(OL)
15 North Street
Tel: Bridgwater
(0278) 423124
Lane (PC)
Rich (BB)

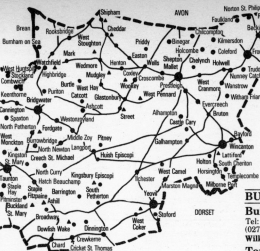

Ciders are sold in ½ and 1 gallon containers, Lanes medium and dry, Rich medium.

Taunton Road Mini Market (OL)
Rich (PC)

Wembdon Farm Shop (OL)
Cokerhurst Farm, Wembdon Hill
Tel: Bridgwater (0278) 422330
Rich (PC)

BROADWAY

Bell (P)
Tel: Ilminster (046 05) 2343
Taunton (H)
In centre of village. Meals lunchtime and evening; restaurant.

BROMPTON REGIS

George (P)
Tel: Brompton Regis (039 87) 273
Bulmer (H)
Traditional village local. Bar meals; garden; children's room; games room.

BRUTON

Castle Inn (P)
High Street
Tel: Bruton (074 981) 812211
Thatcher (PP)
Meals and snacks 11-1.45 and 5.30-8.45; garden; skittle alley.

Oak Tree (P)
Taunton (PC)
Substantial bar meals.

Sun Inn (P)
High Street
Tel: Bruton (074 981) 813493
Taunton (PC)
Meals and snacks 12-2 and 6-10; restaurant; garden.

BUCKLAND ST. MARY

VICKERY'S CIDER ▲
Hisbeers Farm, Hare Lane
Tel: Buckland St. Mary (046 034) 378

BURNHAM ON SEA

Beeline Wines (OL)
12 Regent Street
Tel: Burnham-on-Sea (0278) 786531
Sheppy

Hayes Ltd (OL)
Burnham Shopping Centre
Inch

United Services Club (P)
Victoria Street
Tel: Burnham-on-Sea (0278) 782107
Rich (PC)

BURROWBRIDGE

King Alfred Inn (P)
Tel: Burrowbridge (082 369) 379
Taunton (PC)
Snacks; garden.

BURTLE

Burtle Inn (P)
Tel: Chilton Polden (0278) 722269
Wilkins (PC)

Tom Mogg Inn (P)
Tel: Chilton Polden (0278) 722399
Rich (PC)

CANNINGTON

Kings Head (P)
High Street (A39)
Tel: Combwich (0278) 652293
Bulmer
Rich (PC)

Malt Shovel (P)
Blackmore Lane (off A39)
Tel: Spraxton (027 867) 332
Lane (PC)
Rich (PC)
Meals and snacks all sessions; restaurant; garden; children's room; accommodation.

CARHAMPTON

Butchers Arms (P)
Tel: Dunster (064 382) 333
Taunton (PC)
Wassailing still takes place in the adjoining orchard. Meals and snacks all sessions; garden; children's room; accommodation.

CASTLE CARY

Waggon & Horses (P)
Ansford (on A371)
Tel: Castle Cary (0963) 50495
Taunton (H)
Thatcher (PP)
Snacks 11-2.15 and 5.30-10.30; breakfast 8.30-10.30; lunches 12-2; evening meals 7-10.30; restaurant; garden; accommodation; snooker; bar billiards, skittle alley.

Tramps (P)
Woodcock Street
Tel: Castle Cary (0963) 51129
Rosies (BB)

White Hart (P)
Fore 'Street
Tel: Castle Cary (0963) 50255
Taunton (H)
Popular town centre pub.
Meals and snacks lunchtime
and evening; children's room;
accommodation; skittles; bar
billiards.

CATCOTT

Crown (P)
off A39
Tel: Chilton Polden
(0278) 722288
Wilkins (PC)
Popular out of town pub on
edge of moor, north of village.
Meals; garden.

King William (P)
Tel: Chilton Polden
(0278) 722374
Wilkins (PC)

CHARD

Tatworth Fruit Farm (OL)
Tel: South Chard
(0460) 20272
Sheppy

CHEDDAR

Bucklegrove Caravan Park (P)
Rodney Stoke
Tel: Wells (0749) 870261
Derrick (PC)

The Cider Shop (OL)
Derrick (B)
Rich (PC)

Cheddar Gorge Cider Co. (OL)
The Gorge
Thatcher (B)

DERRICK'S CIDERS ▲
Cheddar Valley Cheese
Depot, The Gorge
Tel: Cheddar (0934) 743079

Holly House (P)
Derrick (PC)

Kings Head (P)
Silver Street
Tel: Cheddar (0934) 742153
Bulmer (H)
15th century inn. Bar snacks;
garden; childrens' room.

Penny Farthing (OL)
The Gorge
Country Fayre (B)

Spar Shop (OL)

Union Street
Tel: Cheddar (0934) 742441
Wilkins (PC)

Tweentown Stores (OL)
Tweentown
Tel: Cheddar (0934) 742115
Wilkins (PC)

White Hart (P)
The Gorge
Taunton (PC)
Also operates an off licence
for Taunton Traditional
Draught Cider in the
adjoining outhouse.

CHELYNCH

Poachers Pocket (P)
Tel: Cranmore (074 988) 220
Wilkins (PC)
Snacks 11.30-2.30 and
6.15-9.30; full meals
6.15-9.30; restaurant;
garden; children's room.

CHILCOMPTON

Sword & Castle (P)
on B3139
Tel: Stratton on the Fosse
(0761) 232732
Taunton (PC)
Very much a locals' pub.
Garden.

COLEFORD

Anchor (P)
Highbury
Tel: Mells (0373) 812304
Bulmer (H)
Meals and snacks lunchtime
and evening; garden; pool.

Eagle (P)
Highbury
Taunton (E)
At top of village. Snacks;
garden; skittle alley, table
skittles.

Kings Head (P)
Tel: Mells (0373) 812346
Bulmer (H)
Snacks; garden; skittle alley.

COMBWICH

Harbour Garage Stores (OL)
Tel: Combwich
(0278) 652 339
Rich (PC)

Otterhampton Club (P)
Tel: Combwich (0278) 652618
Rich (PC)

COXLEY

Coxley Service Station (OL) (P)

---

near Wells
Tel: Wells (0749) 72215
Cadozebridge (PP) (PL) (W) (F)
A filling station for *you* as
well as your car! Their own
four star cider. Try to break
down nearby and spend a few
hours here. Snacks 11-2 and
6-11; restaurant; games
room; accommodation.

CREECH ST. MICHAEL

New Inn (P)
Tel: Henlade (0823) 442257
Bulmer (H)

CREWKERNE

The Castle (P)
West Street
Taunton (H)

The Railway (P)
Station Road
Taunton (H)

Spencers (OL)
3 North Street
Tel: Crewkerne (0460) 75006
Sheppy

CRICKET ST. THOMAS

Cricket St. Thomas Estate (OL)
Tel: Winsham (046 030) 755
Sheppy

CROSCOMBE

Bull Terrier (P)
Tel: Shepton Mallet
(0749) 3658
Wilkins (PC)

CROWCOMBE

Carew Arms (P)
Tel: Crowcombe (098 48) 631
Taunton (PC)
Old local in idyllic location in
Quantock foothills. Snacks;
garden; children's room;
accommodation.

DINNINGTON •

Rose & Crown (P)
near Hinton St. George
Tel: Ilminster (046 05) 2397
Taunton (H)
Vickery (PC)
Home of Dinnington Docks
and Railway Preservation
Society. Snacks 10.30-2.15
and 6.15-11.45; full meals
12-2.30 and 6.30-10.30;
children's room.

DOWLISH WAKE

New Inn (P)
Tel: Ilminster (046 05) 2413
Perry (PC)
Attractive 300 year old pub in delightful village, just down the street from Perry's Cider Mill. Snacks all sessions; full meals 12-2 and 7-10; garden.

PERRYS'S CIDER▲
The Cider Mills
Tel: Ilminster (046 05) 2681

DULVERTON

Crispins Restaurant (P)
26 High Street
Tel: Dulverton (0398) 23397
Yearlstone (B)
Yearlstone Wine (B)

Lamb Hotel (P)
Tel: Dulverton (0398) 23340
Taunton (H)
Smart town hotel. Meals and snacks; restaurant; children's room; accommodation.

Rock House Inn (P)
1 Jury Road
Tel: Dulverton (0398) 23340
Taunton (H)
Meals and snacks 12-2 and 6-10.30; restaurant; outdoor drinking area; accommodation.

Tom Tavey (OL)
Inch

DUNSTER

Castle Hotel (P)
High Street
Tel: Dunster (0643) 821445
Taunton (PC)
Busy hotel with ballroom, interesting ceiling in public bar. Meals and snacks; restaurant; outdoor drinking area; accommodation; children's room.

Foresters Arms (P)
Tel: Dunster (0643) 821313
Bulmer (H)
Interior features thatched bar. Bar meals; outdoor drinking area; accommodation.

Parhams (OL)
Church Street
Tel: Dunster (0643) 821361
Inch
Perry (PC)

Stags Head
Tel: Dunster (0643) 821229
Taunton (PC)
15th century pub with deer on walls. Snacks; garden; accommodation.

Tamarack Stores (OL)
Marsh Street
Sheppy

EASTON

Easton Inn (P)
Tel: Wells (0749) 870220
Wilkins (PC)

EVERCREECH

Bell Inn (P)
on B3081
Tel: Evercreech (0749) 830287
Taunton (PC)
Village inn near church. Snacks; garden; skittles.

Shapway Inn (P)
Queens Road
Tel: Evercreech (0749) 830273
Taunton (PC)
Two bar local. Skittles.

FAULKLAND

Faulkland Inn (P)
on A366
Tel: Faulkland (037 387) 312
Taunton (H)
Spacious, comfortably furnished country inn. Meals lunchtime and evening; snacks; garden; skittles; pool.

Tuckers Grave (P)
on A366
Tel: Faulkland (037 387) 230
Cheddar Valley (PC)
Traditional cider and ale house, a small farm cottage which has doubled as an inn for over 200 years. Garden.

FORDGATE

HALL'S CIDER▲
Wisteria Farm
Tel: Weston Zoyland (027 869) 568

FROME

Angel (P)
King Street
Tel: Frome (0373) 62469

The Ship Inn, Porlock

Taunton (H)
Meals and snacks 11-2.30 and 6-8.30; restaurant; outdoor drinking area; children's room; pool room; accommodation.

Crown & Sceptre (P)
38 Trinity Street
Tel: Frome (0373) 64370
Taunton (H)
Pub up the hill from town centre. Snacks all sessions; live music Saturday nights.

First & Last (P)
Wallbridge
Tel: Frome (0373) 62642
Bulmer (PC)
Near railway station. Lunches; garden; accommodation.

Globe (P)
31 Vallis Way
Tel: Frome (0373) 63603
Bulmer (E)
Games orientated local.

Griffin (P)
Milk Street
Tel: Frome (0373) 67344
Taunton (PC)
Unspoilt local in older part of town. Garden; live music.

Lamb & Fountain (P)
57 Castle Street
Tel: Frome (0373) 63414
Taunton (PC)
The cider centre of Frome; little else is drunk, and you probably will be too! Snacks lunchtime.

Victoria (P)
Christchurch Street East
Bulmer (PC)
Local with original atmosphere. Snacks.

Weaver (P)
6 The Butts
Tel: Frome (0373) 63733
Bulmer (PC)
Meals and snacks lunchtime and evening.

White Horse (P)
The Portway
Tel: Frome (0373) 63014
Bulmer (PC)
Authentic drinking house

GALHAMPTON

Harvester (P)
Tel; North Cadbury
(0963) 40430
Taunton (PC)

GLASTONBURY

Fairfield Inn (P)
31 Benedict Street
Tel: Glastonbury
(0458) 41442
Wilkins (PC)
Accommodation.

Glastonbury Football Club (P)
Gooncy Road
Tel: Glastonbury
(0458) 31460
Wilkins (PC)

Griffiths Stores (OL)
12 Market Place
Inch

Hawthorn Hotel (P)
8 Northload Street
Tel: Glastonbury
(0458) 31255
Inch

Riflemans Arms (P)
Chilkwell Street
Tel: Glastonbury
(0458) 31023
Wilkins (PC)
Several roomed pub, dating
from 13th century,
strategically placed for the
ascent of Glastonbury Tor
(and to recover afterwards).
Meals lunchtime; snacks
early evening; garden;
children's room; pool room.

Royal British Legion Club (P)
Benedict Street
Tel: Glastonbury
(0458) 31448
Wilkins (PC)

Stevens Stores (OL)
Inch

Windmill Hill Social Club (P)
Rich (PC)

HALSE

New Inn (P)
Tel: Bishops Lydeard
(0823) 43252
Taunton (H)
Compact old inn in friendly
village. Meals and snacks;
restaurant; garden;
accommodation.

HATCH BEAUCHAMP

Vincent Farm (OL)
Lower West Hatch

Tel: Hatch Beauchamp
(0823) 480320
Local cider (B) (PC)

HENTON

Post Office (OL)
Wilkins (PC)

Punchbowl (P)
on Wells – Wedmore road
Tel: Wells (0749) 72212
Wilkins (PC)

HIGHBRIDGE

Burnham Road Post Office (OL)
Rich (PC)

Pearce & Lea (OL)
Rich (PC)

Western Wines (OL)
Rich (PC)

HOLCOMBE

Ring O'Roses (P)
Tel: Stratton on the Fosse
(0761) 232478
Thatcher (H)
Snacks; lunch and evening
meals (not Sunday);
children's garden; pool.

HOLTON

Old Inn (P)
just south of A303
Rosies (BB)
Taunton (PC)
Meals and snacks lunchtime;
garden.

HOLWELL

Bear (P)
on A361
Tel: Nunney (037 384) 585
Taunton (H)
Snacks.

HORSINGTON

Half Moon (P)
off A357
Tel: Templecombe
(0963) 70140
Taunton (PC)
16th century listed building
with log fires and beamed
ceilings. Meals and snacks
12-2 and 7-10 every day;
restaurant; garden;
children's room;
accommodation.

HUISH EPISCOPI

Rose & Crown (P)
Tel: Langport (0458) 250494
Burrow Hill (W)
Known locally as "Eli's", a
unique pub with no bar, just a

stone floored room with wood
barrels linked to various
rooms; rustic and natural;
don't fall over the animals!
Hot and cold bar snacks.
Don't miss the nearby
medieval church with 100 ft
tower, featured on a 9p stamp
in 1972.

HUNGERFORD

White Horse Inn (P)
Washford Watchet (off A30)
Tel: Washford (0984) 40415
Bulmer (H)
Former coaching inn. Meals
lunchtime and evening;
garden; children's room;
outdoor play area;
accommodation; facilities for
disabled; free range eggs.

ILCHESTER

Bull (P)
Church Street
Tel: Ilchester (0935) 840318
Sheppy
Near Yeovilton Airbase.
Meals lunchtime and
evening; accommodation.

KEENTHORNE

Cottage Inn (P)
on A39
Tel: Nether Stowey
(0278) 732355
Lane (H)
Meals and snacks;
restaurant.

KILMERSDON

Jolliffe Arms (P)
Tel: Radstock (0761) 33192
Bulmer (PC)
Village local next to church.
Meals and snacks lunchtime
and evening; skittles.

KINGSBURY EPISCOPI

BURROW HILL CIDER▲
Pass Vale Farm, Burrow Hill
Tel: South Petherton
(0460) 40782

Wyndham Arms (P)
Tel: Martock (0935) 823239
Burrow Hill (PC)
Taunton (PC)
Meals and snacks all sessions;
garden; skittle alley.

KINGSTON ST. MARY

Swan Inn (P)
Tel: Kingston St. Mary
(082 345) 383

Taunton (H)
Village pub with superb outlook. Snacks; garden.

LANGLEY MARSH

Three Horseshoes (P)
Tel: Wiveliscombe (0984) 23763
Perry (PC) (W)
Traditional and vegetarian cooking; snacks 12-2; full meals 12-2 and 6-10.

LANGPORT

Langport Stores (OL)
Cheapside
Tel: Langport (0458) 250551
Sheppy

MARK

COOMBES SOMERSET GOLDEN BLEND CIDER ▲
Japonica Farm
Tel: Mark Moor (027 864) 265

Pack Horse (P)
Tel: Mark Moor (027 864) 209
Wilkins (PC)
At east end of village adjoining church. Hot meals.

MARSTON MAGNA

Marston Meats (OL)
Rosies (BB) (PL)

MIDDLE ZOY

Post Office (OL)
Rich (PC)

MILBORNE PORT

Queens Head (P)
on A30
Tel: Milborne Port (0963) 250314
Burrow Hill (PC)
Taunton (E)
Snacks 12-2; full meals 6.30-9 except Sunday; restaurant.

MILVERTON

Globe (P)
Fore Street
Tel: Milverton (0823) 400534
Taunton (H)
Snacks: accommodation.

MINEHEAD

Mini Market (OL)
Inch

Queens Head Hotel (P)
Holloway Street
Tel: Minehead (0643) 2940
Bulmer (H)
Taunton (H)
Meals and snacks; restaurant; accommodation.

Red Lion Hotel (P)
Tel: Minehead (0643) 6507
Taunton (H) (PC)
Large hotel with disco. Snacks.

Wellington Hotel (P)
Wellington Square
Tel: Minehead (0643) 4371
Taunton (PC)
Meals and snacks; restaurant; garden; accommodation.

MISTERTON

White Swan (P)
A356
Tel: Crewkerne (0460) 72592
Taunton (H)
½ mile from Station. Meals lunch and evening; children welcome.

MUDGLEY

WILKIN'S FARMHOUSE CIDER▲
Lands End Farm
Tel: Wedmore (0934) 712385

NETHER STOWEY

Cricket Malerbie Farm Shop (OL)
Tel: Nether Stowey (0278) 732084
Rich (PC)
Sheppy

NORTH CURRY

Angel Inn (P)
Tel: North Curry (0823) 490575
Rich (PC)

Bird in Hand
Tel: North Curry (0823) 490248
Lane (PC)

NORTH NEWTON

Harvest Moon (P)
off A38
Tel: North Petherton (0278) 662570
Taunton (H)
Meals and snacks.

NORTH PETHERTON

George Hotel (P)
Fore Street
Tel: North Petherton (0278) 662330
Bulmer (H)
Hot bar snacks.

Globe (P)
High Street
Tel: North Petherton (0278) 662999
Bulmer (H)
Taunton (H)
Snacks; garden; skittle alley.

Spar Stores (OL)
Fore Street
Lane (B)

NORTON FITZWARREN

Ring of Bells (P)
Tel: Taunton (0823) 75995
Taunton (H)
The local for Taunton Cider.

TAUNTON TRADITIONAL CIDER
The Taunton Cider Company, Norton Fitzwarren
Tel: Taunton (0823) 83141

NORTON ST. PHILIP

Fleur de Lys (P)
on A366
Tel: Faulkland (037 387) 333
Bulmer (PC)
Snacks.

NUNNEY CATCH

Theobalds Arms (P)
off A361
Tel: Nunney (037 384) 323
Taunton (H)
Meals and snacks.

PITMINSTER

Queens Arms (P)
off B3170
Tel: Blagdon Hill (082 342) 529
Taunton (H)
Village local. Bar meals.

PITNEY

Halfway House (P)
Taunton (PC)
Bar snacks.

PORLOCK

Royal Oak (P)
Tel: Porlock (0643) 862636
Bulmer (H)
Bar meals.

Ship Inn (P)

High Street
Tel: Porlock (0643) 862507
Perry (W)
13th century coaching inn.

PRESTLEIGH

Merry Miller (P)
on A371
Tel: Evercreech
(0749) 830174
Taunton (PC)
Roadside pub near Shepton
Mallet Showground. Lunch
and snacks.

PRIDDY

Hunters Lodge (P)
Tel: Wells (0749) 72275
Stott (PC)
High on the Mendips.
Accommodation.

PURITON

Exchange Inn (P)
off A39
Tel: Puriton (0278) 683436
Rich (PC)
Small village pub.

RODE

Bell (P)
on A361
Tel: Frome (0373) 830356
Bulmer (PC)
Meals and snacks lunchtime
and evening; restaurant;
table skittles.

Red Lion (P)
Main Street (off A361)
Bulmer (H)
Snacks; garden; table
skittles.

ROOKSBRIDGE

Wellington Arms (P)
on A38
Wilkins (PC)

SAMPFORD MOOR

Blue Ball Inn (P)
off A38
Tel: Wellington
(082 347) 3112
Bulmer (H)
Rural local. Snacks; garden.

SHEPTON MALLET

ADDLESTONES/ COATES CIDERS
Showerings Ltd., Kilver
Street
Tel: Shepton Mallet
(0749) 3333

Bell Hotel (P)
3 High Street

Tel: Shepton Mallet
(0749) 2166
Taunton (PC)
Meals and snacks lunchtime
and evening; children's room;
accommodation.

Crown (P)
Draycott Road
Taunton (H)
Pool.

Field (P)
The Field (on A371)
Tel: Shepton Mallet
(0749) 2830
Taunton (PC)
About ½ mile from town
centre. Snacks; garden.

Horseshoe (P)
Bowlish
Tel: Shepton Mallet
(0749) 2209
Wilkins (PP)
Meals and snacks all sessions;
garden; accommodation.

King William (P)
West Shepton (on B3131)
Coates (H)
Taunton (H)
Suburban cider house.
Snacks; accommodation.

Showerings Club (P)
Tel: Shepton Mallet
(0749) 2461
Wilkins (PC)
Snacks 12-2 and 7-10; full
meals by arrangement;
children's room; snooker;
skittle alley.

Victoria (P)
Broad Cross
Tel: Shepton Mallet
(0749) 2043
Taunton (H)
Back street local. Table
skittles.

SHIPHAM

LUKEE'S SOMERSET CIDER ▲
Lilypool Farm, Cheddar
Tel: Cheddar (0934) 742944

Miners Arms (P)
The Square
Tel: Winscombe
(093 484) 2146
Thatcher (H)
Snacks 12-2 all week; 7-10
Tuesday to Saturday; full
meals 12-2 Monday to
Saturday, 7-10 Tuesday to
Saturday; restaurant; games
room; pool.

SOUTH CHERITON

White Horse (P)
on A357

Tel: Templecombe
(0963) 70394
Taunton (PC)
Snacks all sessions; bar
skittles.

SOUTH PETHERTON

Wheatsheaf (P)
Burrow Hill (W)

SPAXTON

Lamb (P)
Four Forks
Tel: Spaxton (027 867) 350
Bulmer (H)
Adjacent to Agapemone
(Victorian commune).
Snacks; garden.

STAPLE FITZPAINE

Greyhound (P)
Tel: Hatch Beauchamp
(0823) 227
Local cider (PC)
Meals and snacks;
restaurant; garden;
accommodation.

STAPLE HAY

Crown (P)
Tel: Taunton (0823) 72560
Taunton (PC)
Snacks.

STOCKLAND

Stockland Club (P)
Tel: Combwich (0278) 653260
Rich (PC)

STOFORD

Royal Oak (P)
The Green
Taunton (PC)

STOGUMBER

White Horse Inn (P)
Tel: Stogumber (0984) 56277
Sheppy (W)
Village local opposite church.
Meals and snacks all sessions;
restaurant; garden;
accommodation.

STOKE SUB HAMDEN

Stoke Sub Hamden Club (P)
Tel: Martock (0935) 823297
Sheppy (PC)

STREET

British Legion Club (P)

3-5 Farm Road
Tel: Street (0458) 42873
Wilkins (PC) (PP)

HECK'S FARMHOUSE CIDER ▲
9-11 Middle Leigh
Tel: Street (0458) 42367

Street Football Club (P)
Tannery Ground, Middle Brooks
Tel: Street (0458) 45987
Wilkins (PC)

West Country Garden Supplies (OL)
39 Brooks Road
Tel: Street (0458) 45505
Rich (PC)

Unity Club (P)
Hindhayes Lane
Tel: Street (0458) 46183
Rich (PC)

TAUNTON

British Railways Club (P)
Tel: Taunton (0823) 75048
Rich (PC)

Cherry Grove (P)
40 Kingston Road
Tel: Taunton (0823) 75882
Taunton (H)
One bar pub with good atmosphere, just north of railway station.

County Stores (OL)
52 North Street
Tel: Taunton (0823) 72235
Inch
Sheppy

ESSJAYS (OL)
Priorswood
Lane (PL)

Foresters Arms (P)
93 East Reach
Tel: Taunton (0823) 75682
Taunton (H)
Small corner pub. Bar snacks.

Kings Stores (OL)
Eastleigh Road
Henrys

Myrtle Tree (P)
34 Bridge Street
Tel: Taunton (0823) 52690
Taunton (H)
Popular cider pub.

Plough (P)
Station Road
Tel: Taunton (0823) 75823
One bar local near station.

Priory Social Club (P)
Priory Bridge Road

Tel: Taunton (0823) 84656
Rich (PC)

Staple Grove Post Office (OL)
Bromell (PL)

Wheeltappers (P)
Station Road
Tel: Taunton (0823) 88557
Taunton (PC)
Adjoining railway station, ideal as a waiting room!

TEMPLECOMBE

The Royal (P)
High Street (A357)
Tel: Templecombe (0963) 70886
Taunton (H)
Adjoins Templecombe Station on Salisbury to Exeter line. Nearby St. Mary's Church contains painting of Turin Shroud from Knights Templar. Meals and snacks all sessions.

TIMBERSCOMBE

Lion Inn (P)
on A396
Tel: Timberscombe (064 384) 243
Taunton (PC)
Village local. Snacks.

TRUDOXHILL

White Hart (P)
Tel: Nunney (037 384) 324
Thatcher (PC)
Meals and snacks lunchtime and evening; restaurant; garden.

WANSTROW

King William (P)
on A359
Tel: Upton Noble (074 377) 247
Bulmer (H)
Meals and snacks lunchtime and evening; skittles.

WASHFORD

Washford Hotel (P)
Tel: Washford (0984) 40256
Taunton (H)
Next door to Washford Station on the preserved West Somerset Railway. Meals and snacks 12-2 and 7-10.30; restaurant; garden; children's room; accommodation.

WATCHET

Anchor (P)
Anchor Street
Tel: Watchet (0984) 31387
Taunton (H)
Snacks

Doniford Holiday Village (OL)
Tel: Williton (0984) 32130
Sheppy

Harbour Stores (OL)
Sheppy

Sunnybank Caravan Site (OL)
Sheppy

Warren Bay Caravan Site (OL)
Tel: Watchet (0984) 31460
Sheppy

WATCHFIELD

RICH'S CIDER ▲
Mill Farm
Tel: Burnham-on-Sea (0278) 783651

Watchfield Inn (P)
Tel: Burnham-on-Sea (0278) 783551
Bulmer (E)
Snacks lunchtime; limited range evenings; children's room.

WEDMORE

New Inn (P)
Combe Batch
Tel: Wedmore (0934) 712099
Wilkins (PC)
Meals and snacks 11-2 and 7-10 except Sunday; restaurant; garden.

WELLINGTON

Cheese & Wine Shop (OL)
South Street
Sheppy

Green Dragon (P)
Bulmer (H)

WELLS

Buses Club (P)
West Street
Stott (PC)

Cheddar Valley Inn (P)
22 Tucker Street
Tel: Wells (0749) 72807
Taunton (H)
Named after the one time nearby railway. Old fashioned traditional public bar. Snacks all sessions; outdoor drinking area.

Mermaid Hotel (P)
Tucker Street
Tel: Wells (0749) 72343
Bulmer (PC)
Taunton (H)
Hotel only 5 minutes walk from Cathedral. Snacks all

sessions; full meals
lunchtime and evenings
except Sunday; outdoor
drinking area; skittle alley,
pool room; accommodation.

New Inn (P)
St. Thomas Street
Taunton (PC)

WEST CAMEL

Globe (P)
Tel: Marston Magna
(0935) 850260
Taunton (PP)
Near Yeovilton Air Museum.
Bar snacks all sessions.

WEST COKER

Royal George (P)
Tel: West Coker
(093 586) 2334
Taunton (PC)
Meals and snacks lunchtime
and evening.

West Coker Club (P)
High Street
Tel: West Coker
(093 586) 2955
Sheppy

WEST CRANMORE

Strode Arms (P)
off A361
Tel: Cranmore (074 988) 450
Thatcher (P)
Village pub near preserved
East Somerset Railway.
Meals and snacks lunchtime
and evening; garden; pool.

WEST HAY

Bird in Hand (P)
Wilkins (PC)

WEST HUNTSPILL

Crossways Inn (P)
on A38
Tel: Burnham-on-Sea
(0278) 783756
Rich (PC)
17th century inn. Meals and
snacks; restaurant; garden.

WEST MONKTON

LANE'S CIDER ▲
Overton
Tel: West Monkton
(0823) 412345

WESTON-ZOYLAND

Sedgemoor Inn (P)
Tel: Weston Zoyland
(027869) 382
Bulmer (PC)

WEST PENNARD

NAISH'S CIDER ▲
Piltown Farm
Tel: Pilton (074 989) 260

WEST STOUGHTON

COUNTRY FAYRE CIDER
Tel: Wedmore (0934) 712801

WHEDDON CROSS

Rest & Be Thankful (P)
Tel: Timberscombe
(064 384) 222
Taunton (PC)
On edge of Exmoor. Meals
and snacks 12-2 and 7-10;
garden; childrens' play area;
children's room; skittles; pool.

WILLITON

County Stores (OL)
Fore Street
Tel: Williton (0984) 32280
Inch

Wyndham Arms (P)
High Street
Tel: Williton (0984) 32381
Taunton (H)

WINSFORD

Winsford Stores (OL)
Hancock (B)

WINCANTON

Dolphin Hotel (P)
High Street
Tel: Wincanton (0963) 32215
Bulmer (H)
Meals and snacks lunchtime
and evening; garden;
accommodation.

George (P)
Mill Street
Tel: Wincanton (0963) 32185
Taunton (H)

Railway Inn (P)
Station Road
Tel: Wincanton (0963) 32252
Taunton (H)
Don't be deceived, the last
train ran in March 1966!
Games orientated pub.
Snacks; garden; table
skittles; pool.

Uncle Toms Cabin (P)
High Street
Taunton (H)

WITHAM FRIARY

Seymour Arms (P)

Bulmer (PC)
Taunton (PC)
Locals' pub with serving
hatch. Garden; billiards;
children's room (mornings).

WITHYPOOL

Royal Oak Inn (P)
off B3223
Tel: Exford (064 383) 236
Hancock (P)
Small bar with oak beams.
Meals and snacks;
restaurant; garden;
accommodation.

WIVELISCOMBE

Royal Oak (P)
Church Street
Tel: Wiveliscombe
(0984) 23578
Taunton (PC)
Bar meals; accommodation.

WOOKEY

STOTT'S SUPERB CIDER ▲
Shotts Farm
Tel: Wells (0749) 73323

YEOVIL

Ambassador Wines (OL)
7 High Street
Tel: Yeovil (0935) 77223
Sheppy

BRYMPTON D'EVERCY CIDER ▲
Brympton d'Evercy
Tel: Yeovil (093 586) 2528

Globe & Crown (P)
South Street
Tel: Yeovil (0935) 23328
Taunton (H)
Lively town centre local with
strong cider following.
Snacks all sessions.

Great Lyde Hotel (P)
Lyde Road
Tel: Yeovil (0935) 29707
Coates (PC)

Royal Marine (P)
Great Western Terrace
Tel: Yeovil (0935) 74350
Taunton (H)
On route into town from Pen
Mill Station. Meals and
snacks lunchtime and
evening; skittle alley.

The Red House (P)
Dorchester Road (A37)
Barwick
Taunton (H)
About 1½ miles south of town.
Meals; pool tables.

Staffordshire

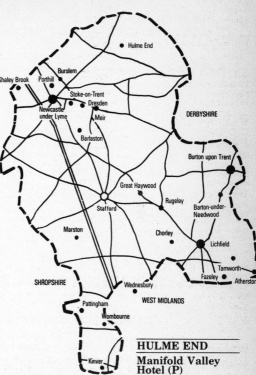

ATHERSTONE

White Hart (P)
216 Hurley Common
Tel: Tamworth (0827) 872315
Weston (PC)

AUDLEY

Audley Off Licence (The Cider Shed) (OL)
Mellord Street
Westrays (F)

Waggon & Horses (P)
Westrays (F)

BARTON-UNDER-NEEDWOOD

Barton Turns (P)
Barton Turns
Tel: Barton (028 371) 2142
Thatcher (PC)
On bank of the Trent & Mersey Canal. Snacks.

BURSLEM

Travellers Rest (P)
239 Newcastle Street, Middleport
Tel: Stoke on Trent (0782) 810418
Westrays (H)
Popular pub with own brewery.

Whisky Galore (OL)
Head Street
Westrays (F)

BURTON-ON-TRENT

Old Punch Bowl (P)
Green Street
Weston (H)

CHORLEY

Nelson (P)
Padbury Lane (near Lichfield)
Tel: Burntwood (054 36) 5084
Weston (PC)

DARLASTON

Prince of Wales (P)
Bulmer (H)

DRESDEN

Blaggs Off Licence (OL)
1 Castle Street
Tel: Stoke-on-Trent (0782) 327175
Westrays (F)

FAZELEY

Plough & Harrow (P)
south of Tamworth
Weston (PC)

GREAT HAYWOOD

Coach & Horses (P)
Weston (F) – Lloyds

HARTSHILL

Alexander Wines (OL)
472 Hartshill Road
Tel: Newcastle-under-Lyme (0782) 632996
Westrays (F)

HULME END

Manifold Valley Hotel (P)
B5054 (off B5053)
Tel: Hartington (029 884) 537
Thatcher (H)
—summer only
Meals.

KINVER

Cross (P)
Dark Lane (off High Street)
Weston (PC)
Near Staffordshire & Worcester Canal.

Plough & Harrow (P)
High Street
Tel: Kinver (0384) 872659
Weston (PC)

LICHFIELD

Duke of York (P)
Greenhill
Weston (H) (PC)
Victorian lounge, beamed bar. Meals.

MARSTON

Fox (P)
Church Eaton
Weston (PC)

MEIR

Good Cheers (OL)
Stansmore Road
Westrays (F)

NEWCASTLE-UNDER-LYME

Boat & Horses (P)
2 Stubbs Gate
Bulmer (PC)
Snacks 12-2 and 7-10; full
meals 12-2; garden.

Golfers Arms (P)
Keele Road (A525)
Bulmer (H)
2½ miles west of town.

PATTINGHAM

Pigot Arms (P)

Bulmer (PC)

PORTHILL

Tipplers (OL)
135 Watlands View
Westrays (H)

RUGELEY

Jug & Bottle (OL)
The Wharf, Bryans Lane
Weston (PC)

SHALEY BROOK

Rising Sun (P)
Knowle Bank Road (off A52)
Thatcher (PC)
Meals.

STOKE-ON-TRENT

Bull & Bush (P)
Westrays (H)

TAMWORTH

Tregaskis (OL)
Glascote
Weston (PC)

WEDNESBURY

Horse & Jockey (P)
Church Street, Bilston
Bulmer (H)

Turks Head (P)
Weston (PC)

WOMBOURNE

Mount Pleasant (P)
Ounsdale Road
Weston (PC)

Red Lion (P)
Old Stourbridge Road
Bulmer (PC)
Old coaching inn. Meals.

Vine (P)
High Street (off A449)
Weston (PC)
Meals lunchtime.

 Suffolk

BARDWELL

Six Bells (P)
Tel: Stanton (0359) 50820
Merrydown (H)

BARNBY

Swan Inn (P)
Swan Lane (off A146)
Tel: Barnby (050 276) 646
James White (PC)
Country pub tucked away
behind main road. Meals
lunchtime and evening;
garden; facilities for disabled.

BECCLES

Post Office Stores (OL)
James White (B)

St. Peters House Hotel (P)
Old Market
Tel: Beccles (0502) 713203
James White (B)

Swan House Shop (OL)
Tel: Beccles (0502) 713474
James White (B)

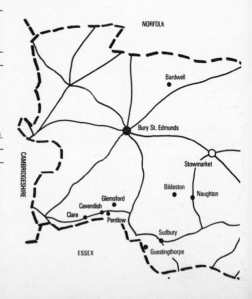

Waveney House Hotel (P)

Puddingmoor
Tel: Beccles (0502) 712270
James White (H)
Dates back to 1584. Meals & snacks lunchtime & evening; garden; children's room; accommodation.

BILDESTON

Kings Head (P)
Saffron Ciders (PC)

BLYTHBURGH

White Hart (P)
on A12
Tel: Blythburgh
(050 270) 217
Bulmer (PC)
Roadside inn, previously the village courthouse. Meals and snacks lunchtime and evening; garden.

BRANDESTON

JAMES WHITE SUFFOLK CIDER▲
The Cider House, Friday Farm
Tel: Earl Soham
(0728 82) 537

BURY ST. EDMUNDS

Abbey Wines (OL)
28 Angel Hill

Tel: Bury St. Edmunds
(0284) 704995
James White (B)

Edmunds (OL)
33 Brentgovel Street
Tel: Bury St. Edmunds
(0284) 705604
James White (B)

Goodings (OL)
31 St. Johns Street
Tel: Bury St. Edmunds
(0284) 2561
James White (B)

Hervon Wines (OL)
Angel Lane
Tel: Bury St. Edmunds
(0284) 703374
James White (B)

CAVENDISH

Bull (P)
High Street
Tel: Glemsford (0787) 280245
Bulmer (PC)
Timber framed pub built 1530, in picture book village. Meals and snacks lunchtime; garden.

CLARE

Jug & Bottle (OL)
High Street
Saffron Ciders (B)

Seafarer (P)
Nethergate Street
Tel: Sudbury (0787) 277449
Saffron Ciders (PC)
Specialises in seafood. Meals & snacks lunchtime & evening; garden; children's room.

CORTON

Corton Chalet & Holiday Camp (P)
James White (H)

CRATFIELD

Cratfield Poacher (P)
Tel: Ubbeston (038 683) 206
James White (B)
Pub including shop. Meals & snacks lunchtime & evening; garden.

CRETINGHAM

New Bell Inn (P)
Tel: Earl Soham
(072 872) 419
James White (PC)
16th century beamed pub in attractive village. Meals and snacks lunchtime and evening; garden; children's room.

DEBENHAM

ASPALL CYDER▲
The Cyder House, Aspall Hall
Tel: Debenham
(0728) 860510

H. Abbots Euromarket (OL)
Little Buck Lane
Aspall (B)

DUNWICH

Ship (P)
Tel: Westleton (072 873) 219
James White (B)
Period pub near coast. Meals lunchtime; snacks evening; garden; children's room; accommodation.

EARL SOHAM

Victoria (P)
Tel: Earl Soham
(072 882) 758
James White (B)
In attractive historical village. Snacks all sessions.

FELIXSTOWE

Grosvenor Wine Stores (OL)
Ranelagh Road

Tel: Felixstowe
(0394) 284137
James White (B)

FRAMLINGHAM

Carvey & Webb (OL)
James White (B)

GESTINGTHORPE

Pheasant (P)
Saffron Ciders (PC

GLEMSFORD

Cherry Tree (P)
Tye Green
Tel: Glemsford (0787) 280303
Saffron Ciders (PC)
Garden.

Cock (P)
27 Egremont Street (B1065)
Tel: Glemsford (0787) 280544
Saffron Ciders (PC)
Beamed pub. Meals
lunchtime and evening;
restaurant; garden.

HALESWORTH

Norris Stores (OL)
James White (B)

**Warners Wine Bar
(P)**
The Thoroughfare
Tel: Halesworth
(098 67) 282110
James White (B)

ILKETSHALL
ST. LAWRENCE

**PARADISE
CIDER▲**
Cherry Tree Farm
on A144 (Bungay to
Halesworth road)
Tel: Ilketshall (098 681) 353

IPSWICH

Barwell & Jones

(OL)
94 Russhouse Road
Tel: Ipswich (0473) 77426
James White (B)

**Barwell & Jones
(OL)**
31 Carrick Way
Tel: Ipswich (0473) 41812
James White (B)

Butts Wine Bar (P)
33 St. Nicholas Street
Tel: Ipswich (0473) 215721
James White (B)

Cossticks (OL)
20 Tackett Street
Tel: Ipswich (0473) 221210
James White (B)

LAXFIELD

Kings Head (P)
Gorams Mill Lane
Tel: Ubbeston (098 683) 395
James White (PP)
600 year old unspoilt
alehouse, otherwise known as
"The Low House". No bar, go
to the cellar door! Meals and
snacks all sessions;
restaurant; bowls green
behind pub; large meadow for
children (to safely graze?).

LEISTON

**White Horse Hotel
(P)**
Station Road
Tel: Leiston (0728) 830694
James White (H)
18th century hotel deeply
involved in smuggling in the
time. Meals and snacks
lunchtime and evening;
garden; children's room;
accommodation.

LOWESTOFT

Bottle & Basket (OL)
157 St. Peters Street
Tel: Lowestoft (0502) 64583
James White (B)

Saffron Ciders (B) (PC)
Saffron Perrys (B)

**Carlton Road
General Stores (OL)**
28 Carlton Road
Tel: Lowestoft (0502) 516285
James White (B)

Food Market (OL)
Whitton Estate
James White (B)

Jug & Bottle (OL)
161 St. Margarets Road
Tel: Lowestoft (0502) 66423
James White (B)

**Morton Road Stores
(OL)**
James White (B)

Oxford Arms (P)
Oxford Road
Tel: Lowestoft (0502) 63269
James White (PC)

Triangle Tavern (P)
St. Peters Street (A12)
Tel: Lowestoft (0502) 82711
James White (PP)
Town centre local. Meals and
snacks lunchtime and
evening; garden.

METFIELD

Duke William (P)
Tel: Fressingfield
(037 986) 371
Bulmer (PC)
Restaurant; meals and
snacks lunchtime and
evening; 2½ acre garden.

NAUGHTON

Wheelers Arms (P)
Whatfield Road
Tel: Bildeston (0449) 740496
Bulmer (PC)
12th century thatched inn.
Meals and snacks lunchtime
and evening; garden.

OULTON BROAD

Cheese Shop (OL)
James White (B)

Goodrums Off Licence (OL)
159 Victoria Road
Tel: Lowestoft (0502) 3916
Saffron Ciders (B)

PENTLOW
Pinkuah Arms (P)
Tel: Glemsford (0787) 280857
Saffron Ciders (PC)

RUMBURGH
Rumburgh Buck (P)
Tel: Linstead (098 685) 257
James White (PC)
Very traditional – once the
Priory guest house. Garden;
children's room.

SNAPE
Plough & Sail (P)
Snape Maltings
Tel: Snape (072 888) 413/303
Aspall (F)
The Malting's own pub, part
of a remarkable collection of
19th century buildings on the
bank of the River Alde,
including the world famous
concert hall, restaurants,
shops, galleries, and a centre
for activity holidays and river
trips. Meals and snacks
lunchtime and evenings in
summer.

SOMERLEYTON
Dukes Head (P)
Slugs Lane (off B1074)
Tel: Lowestoft (0502) 730281
Bulmer (H)
Family pub on the Broads
with good views. Meals
lunchtime and evening;
garden; children's room.

SOUTHWOLD
Squires of Southwold (OL)
James White (B)

STONAM ASPAL
Stonam Barns (OL)
James White (B)

STRADBROKE
Queens Head (P)
Queens Street (B1118)
Tel: Stradbroke (037 984) 681
James White (B)
Timbered 15th century inn.
Meals and snacks lunchtime
and evening; garden;
accommodation.

SUDBURY
Boat House (P)
Ballingdon Bridge (A131)
Tel: Sudbury (0787) 79090
Saffron Ciders (PC)
On river bank; boats can be
hired. Meals and snacks

lunchtime and evening;
garden; children's room;
accommodation.

WETHERINGSETT
Cat & Mouse (P)
Pages Green
Tel: Debenham
(0728) 860765
Merrydown (H)
Heavily beamed pub in rural
surroundings. Meals
lunchtime and evening;
garden; accommodation;
children's room.

WICKHAM MARKET
Taylors Superfare (OL)
66 High Street
Tel: Wickham Market
(0728) 746275
James White (B)

WOODBRIDGE
Barwell & Jones (OL)
2 Church Street
Tel: Woodbridge (0394) 3288
Aspall (B)
James White (B)

YOXFORD
Satis House Hotel (P)
Tel: Yoxford (072 877) 418
James White (B)

Surrey

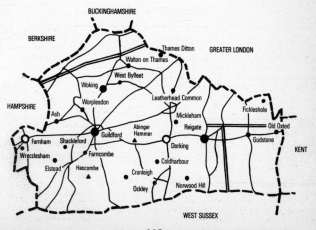

ASH

Greyhound (P)
1 Ash Street (A323)
Bulmer (PC)

Nightingale (P)
Guildford Road (A323)
Bulmer (PC)
Cosy pub with a haunted
fireplace, dating from the
1650s. Snacks; garden; near
Ash Station.

COLDHARBOUR

Plough (P)
Tel: Dorking 0306) 711793
Bulmer (H)
Old coaching inn near Leith
Hill, in good walking country.
Hot food available at most
times.

CRANLEIGH

Boy & Donkey (P)
Knowle Lane
Taunton (PC)
—summer
16th century pub with three
bars and games room. Snacks;
meals lunch and evening;
garden with swings.

Three Horseshoes (P)
High Street (B2128)
Bulmer (PC)
Meals and snacks lunchtime
and evening; garden.

ELSTEAD

Woolpack (P)
The Green (B3001)
Tel: Elstead (0252) 703106
Bulmer (F)
Dating from 1650, originally
a wool warehouse, now a
listed building. Food
lunchtime.

FARNCOMBE

Ram Cider House (P)
Catteshall Lane
Tel: Godalming
(048 68) 21093
Bulmer (E)
A must for the cider
enthusiast! A true west
country cider house which
has somehow got misplaced.
Near the River Wey, where
boats may be hired. The
"Ram", despite the sign, was
actually a pump, used for
bringing water to the farm on
the hill above. Good value
meals lunchtime and
evening; large and attractive
garden.

FICKLESHOLE

White Bear (P)
Featherbed Lane
Tel: Biggin Hill (0959) 73166
Weston (H) & (PC)
Attractive 17th century listed
inn in surprisingly remote
location considering the
nearness of New Addington
and Croydon. A Large white
bear in the forecourt, Meals
and bar snacks inside, both
lunchtime and evening;
garden.

GODSTONE

Bell Hotel (P)
120 Eastbourne Road
Somerset Scrumpy (PC)
14th century inn. Meals
lunchtime and evening;
garden.

GUILDFORD

Clavadel Hotel (P)
Epsom Road (A246)
Tel: Guildford (0483) 572064
Weston (H)

Woodbridge Hill Club (P)
29 Aldershot Road
Tel: Guildford (0483) 572919
Merrydown (H)

LEATHERHEAD COMMON

Star (P)
Kingston Road (A243)
Tel: Oxshott (037284) 2416
Bulmer (H)
Very popular main road inn
between Leatherhead and
Chessington, the Zoo is just
down the road. Good range of
hot and cold food always
available, with charcoal
grilled steaks in evenings.

MICKLEHAM

King William IV (P)
Byttom Hill (off A24)
Taunton (H)
Rural pub up a steep track.
Snacks; large garden.

NORWOOD HILL

The Orchard Shop (OL)
Norwood Hill Orchards, near
Horley
Tel: Norwood Hill
(0293) 862087
Biddenham (PC)
Bulmer (PC)
Burrow Hill (PC)
Gray (PC)

Hancock (PC)
Inch (PC)
Sheppy (PC)
Symonds (PC)
Weston (PC)
The list will tell you that here
is a veritable cider oasis! You
are encouraged to taste before
you buy: containers are
provided, or you may bring
you own. 5 Gallon polycasks
may be purchased (£6
deposit). Cider and wine
mulling spices; cans of local
apple juice; organically
grown fruit and vegetables;
general foods and plants. The
shop is 250 yards west of the
"Fox Revived" pub, 3 miles
north west of Gatwick, on the
Charlewood to Leigh road.
Open Tuesday – Friday:
10.00-4.30pm; Saturday and
Sunday: 10.00-4.00pm.
Closed on Monday.

OCKLEY

The Cricketers (P)
Stane Street (A29)
Tel: Oakwood Hill
(030 679) 205
Merrydown (H)
Fine fireplace and stone
flagged floor. Meals
lunchtime; garden.

OLD OXTED

Crown (P)
High Street (Off A25)
Merrydown (H)
Free house with wine bar
upstairs. Meals lunchtime
and evening; garden; near
Oxted Station.

REIGATE

Bottoms Up (OL)
26 Church Street
Tel: Reigate (073 72) 42373
Zum (PC)

John Landregah (OL)
46 Glovers Road
Tel: Reigate (073 72) 42317
Churchward (PC)

SHACKLEFORD

Cyder House (P)
Peperharrow Road (off A3)
Bulmer (H)
Not to be confused with the
nearby Ram at Farncombe,
this is an ordinary, but
attractive, rural pub which
sells cider! It makes a
peaceful refuge from the
nearby busy A3. Meals
lunchtime and evening;
garden; children's room;
facilities for the disabled.

THAMES DITTON

Ye Olde Swan (P)
Summer Road
Tel: 01-398 1814
Bulmer (H)
Thames side pub with moorings. Carvery restaurant; food in bar lunchtimes; garden; children's room; regular live music; accommodation.

WALTON ON THAMES

Bottoms Up (OL)

New Zealand Avenue
Zum Zider (PC)

WEST BYFLEET

Bottoms Up (OL)
Unit 3, Station Approach
Tel: Byfleet (093 23) 51084
Zum Zider (P)

WOKING

Northfleet Hotel (P)
Claremont Avenue
Tel: Woking (048 62) 22971
Merrydown (H)

WORPLESDON

F. W. Francis & Co. (OL)
School Lane, Rerry Hill
Merrydown (BB)

WRECCLESHAM

Sandrock (P)
Sandrock Hill Road, Upper Bourne (off B3384 at Shortheath crossroads)
Tel: Farnham (0252) 715865
Bulmer (H)
Meals lunchtime (not Sunday) and evening; garden, facilities for the disabled.

 East Sussex

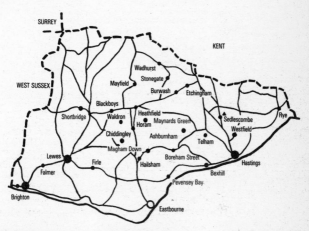

ASHBURNHAM

Ash Tree Inn (P)
Brownbread Street
Tel: Ninfield (0424) 892104
Thatcher (PC)
Oak beamed pub in peaceful surroundings. Meals; garden.

BEXHILL

Rowing Club (P)
Channel View East
Tel: Bexhill-on-Sea (0424) 210153
Merrydown (BB) & (H)

Village Mews Inn (P)
Little Common
Merrydown (BB) & (H)

BLACKBOYS

Blackboys Inn (P)
Lewes Road (on B2192)
Tel: Framfield (082 582) 283
Merrydown (BB) & (H)
14th century inn. Meals and snacks all sessions. Garden; play area for children, with animals from goats to peacocks.

BOREHAM STREET

Bulls Head (P)
near Hailsham
Tel: Herstmonceux (0323) 832143
Merrydown (BB) & (H)
Bar snacks all times; full meals lunchtime and 7-10pm; restaurant.

BRIGHTON

Albion Inn (P)
28 Albion Hill
Tel: Brighton (0273) 604439
Bulmer (H)
Snacks all sessions; outdoor drinking area; two bar billiard tables.

Bedford Hotel (P)
30 Western Street
Tel: Brighton (0273) 739495
Merrydown (BB) & (H)

Brighton Emporium (OL)
48 Warleigh Road
Tel: Brighton (0273) 602620
Bulmer (H)

Edinburgh Hotel (P)

67a Upper Gloucester Road
Tel: Brighton (0273) 27075
Long Ashton (B)
Meals and snacks all sessions.

Gatsbys (P)
Grand Parade
Tel: Brighton (0273) 681228
Merrydown (BB) & (H)

Mitre (P)
65 Queens Road
Tel: Brighton (0273) 602939
Merrydown (BB) & (H)
Near railway station.

Nobles (P)
20 New Road
Tel: Brighton (0273) 682401
Inch (PC)
Perry (PC)
Thatcher (PC)
No fruit machines, no videos, just good old fashioned real drinking bar. Meals and snacks all sessions; children's room.

Prince Albert (P)
48 Trafalgar Street
Tel: Brighton (0273) 28400
Merrydown (BB) & (H)

The Quadrant (P)
12-13 North Street
Tel: Brighton (0273) 26432
Bulmer (H)
Town centre pub; meals.

Sir Charles Napier (P)
50 Southover Street
Tel: Brighton (0273) 601413
Bulmer (H)
Snacks lunchtime.

Southover Wines (OL)
80 Southover Street
Tel: Brighton (0273) 600402
Inch (PC)
Long Ashton (B)
Perry (PC)
Thatcher (PC)
Open every night till 11pm except Sunday.

Sussex Yeoman (P)
7 Guildford Road
Tel: Brighton (0273) 27985
Long Ashton (B)
Turn sharp right out of the station, and the pub is 100 yards up Guildford Road. Snacks lunchtime.

Windsor Tavern (P)
46 Windsor Street
Tel: Brighton (0273) 23490
Burrow Hill (PC)
Town centre pub. Snacks lunchtime.

BURWASH

Bear (P)
High Street
Biddenden (PC)

CHIDDINGLY

Six Bells (P)
Tel: Chiddingly (0825) 227
Merrydown (BB) & (H)
Remote but popular village inn. Meals; gardens.

CROWBOROUGH

Half Moon Inn (P)
Friars Gate (on B2188)
Tel: Crowborough (089 26) 61276
Biddenden (PC)
Rural local on edge of Ashdown Forest. Meals; garden.

ETCHINGHAM

Etchingham Arms (P)
on A265
Tel: Etchingham (058 081) 292
Bulmer (H)
Near railway station. Meals; garden.

Etchingham Stores (OL)
Biddenden (B)

FALMER

Sussex University (P)
The Crypt Bar
Thatcher (PC)

JCR Bar
Merrydown (BB) & (H)

FIRLE

English Farm Cider Centre (OL)
Middle Farm
Tel: Ripe (032 183) 303
Aspall (B)
Biddenden (PC) (B)
Black Bull (PC) (B)
Bulmer (PC)
Burrow Hill (PC)
Churchward (PC) (J)
Coates (PC)
Country Fayre (PC) (B) (J)
Dunkerton Cider & Perry (PC) (B)
Gray (PC)
Hancock (PC) (B) (J)
Inch (PC) (B) (BB)
James White (PC) (B) (BB)
Knights Crumpton Oaks (PC)
Perry (PC)
Rich (PC)
Sellers (PC) (B)
Sheppy (PC) (B)
Symonds (PC) (B)
Taunton (PC)
Thatcher (PC) (B)

Weston Cider & Perry (PC) (B) (J)
Wilkins (PC)
Williams (PC) (B)
Almost an index for the Good Cider Guide! The Farm Shop also sells all manner of foods to go with the cider.

HAILSHAM

The George (P)
George Street
Merrydown (H)

HASTINGS

The Cheese Board (OL)
High Street, Old Town
Biddenden (B)
A comprehensive selection of cheeses to complement the cider.

Hercules Enterprises (OL)
45 Springfield Road, St. Leonards
Tel: Hastings (0424) 712272
Biddenden (B)

Mr. Cherry's (P)
42 Marina, St. Leonard's
Tel: Hastings (0424) 422705
Zum (PC)

HEATHFIELD

Crown (P)
Burwash Road (on A265)
Tel: Heathfield (043 52) 2054
Merrydown (BB) & (H)
Next to Heathfield Market (Tuesdays) for antiques and local produce. Meals and snacks all sessions; restaurant; accommodation; children's room; garden with peacocks.

HORAM

Horam Hotel (P)
Horam Road
Tel: Horam Road (043 53) 2692
Merrydown (BB)
Just down the road from the Merrydown headquarters. Meals and snacks lunchtime except Sunday; accommodation.

MERRYDOWN CIDER ▲
Merrydown Wine PLC, Horam Manor
Tel: Horam Road (043 53) 2254

LEWES

Snowdrop (P)
South Street
Tel: Lewes (0273) 472144
Bulmer (H)

MAGHAM DOWN

Red Lion (P)
on A271
Merrydown (H)

MAYFIELD

Brewers Arms (P)
South Street
Merrydown (H)

Carpenters Arms (P)
Fletching Street (near A267)
Tel: Mayfield (0435) 873294
Biddenden (BB)
Meals; garden.

Railway Inn (P)
on A267
Biddenden (PC)
You'll miss the train, the last one was over 20 years ago! Instead have another pint.

MAYNARDS GREEN

The Runt in Tun (P)
Hailsham Road
Tel: Hailsham (0323) 4284

PEVENSEY BAY

Moorings Hotel (P)
Seaville Drive
Tel: Eastbourne (0323) 761126
Merrydown (H)
Pub on the beach, the landing place of William the Conqueror in 1066. Had the pub been there then the result might have been different! Meals lunchtime and evening; large family room.

RYE

Standard Inn (P)
The Mint
Tel: Rye (0797) 3393
Merrydown (H)
Old low beamed pub. Meals

SEDLESCOMBE

BATTLE VINTAGE CYDER ▲
Garnett Brothers
Oaklands Farm, Moat Lane
Tel: Hastings (0424) 751680 or 426587

Burspin Fruit Farm Shop (OL)
Claverton Farm
Tel: Hastings (0424) 751507
Biddenden (B)

Carr Taylor English Wine Shop (OL)
on A21
Battle Vintage (B)

Harts Farm Shop (OL)
Owlett (B)

SHORTBRIDGE

Peacock Inn (P)
off A272
Tel: Uckfield (0825) 2463
Biddenden (PC)

STONEGATE

The Bridge Inn (P)
Tel: Burwash (0435) 883243
Merrydown (BB) & (H)
Adjacent to Stonegate station on Hastings to Tunbridge Wells line. Meals and snacks all times except Tuesday lunch; restaurant; children's room; one acre garden.

TELHAM

Telham Stores (OL)
Hastings Road
Tel: Battle (042 46) 3100
Biddenden (PC)
Churchward (PC)

WADHURST

Greyhound (P)
High Street (on B2099)
Tel: Wadhurst (089 288) 3224
Bulmer (H)
Meals; garden.

WALDRON

Star (P)
Tel: Horam Road
(043 53) 2495
Merrydown (H)
Meals and snacks lunchtime; garden; children's room.

WESTFIELD

Carr Taylor Vineyards (OL)
Tel: Hastings (0424) 752501
Battle Vintage (B)

West Sussex

BINSTED

Black Horse (P)
Binsted Lane (off A27/B2132)
Tel: Yapton (0243) 551213
Taunton (W)
Beautiful garden and views. Meals and snacks all sessions except Sunday evening; restaurant; accommodation.

CRAWLEY

Greenkeppers (P)
Southgate Avenue
Tel: Crawley (0293) 27146
Inch (PC)
Meals; garden

DRAGONS GREEN

George & Dragon (P)
off A272
Tel: Coolham (040 387) 230
Merrydown (BB)
Remote but popular country pub. Meals and snacks every lunchtime, Friday, Saturday and Sunday evening; large garden.

EAST GRINSTEAD

Crown (P)
High Street
Tel: East Grinstead (0342) 23117
Merrydown (H)

ELSTED

Three Horseshoes (P)
Tel: Harting (073 085) 746
Churchward (PC)
Meals; garden.

117

HANDCROSS

Royal Oak (P)
Horsham Road
Merrydown (H)

HORSHAM

Anchor (P)
East Street
Tel: Horsham (0403) 60753
Merrydown (H)

Fountain Inn (P)
Rusper Road
Tel: Horsham (0403) 2947
Merrydown (H)
Old pub, near Littlehaven
railway station.

Sun Alan Club (P)
North Heath Lane
Merrydown (H)

**Ye Olde Stout
House (P)**
29 The Carfax
Tel: Horsham (0403) 67777
Merrydown (BB)
Snacks all times.

KIRDFORD

**Kirdford Growers
Country Shop (OL)**
Pound Lane
Tel: Kirdford (040 377) 77275
Rich (W)

LINDFIELD

Snow Drop (P)
Snowdrop Lane
Bulmer (PC)
Converted farm cottage, off
the beaten track. Meals
lunchtime and evening;
garden.

MAPLEHURST

White Horse Inn (P)
Park Lane (off A272)
Tel: Horsham (0403) 76 208
Merrydown (PP)
Guest ciders (PC)
—summer
Widest bar in Sussex. Good
countryside views from
garden. Snacks lunchtime and
early evening.

NEWBRIDGE

Limeburners (P)
just off A272
Tel: Billingshurst
(040 381) 2311
Coates (PC)
About a mile out of
Billingshurst, near the
remains of the Wey & Arun
canal, now being restored.
Meals and snacks lunchtime,
garden; caravan and
campsite adjoining pub.

NORTHCHAPEL

London Road
Tel: Northchapel
(042 878) 646
Churchward (PC)
Inch (PC)
Meals and snacks all sessions;
restaurant; west
country skittle alley; floodlit
well in the bar.

OVING

Gribble Inn (P)
off A259
Tel: Chichester
(0243) 786893
Bulmer (H)
Churchward (PC)
Inch (PC)

16th century thatched house.
Meals and snacks lunchtime
and 6.30-9.30pm; large
garden; children's room.

PETWORTH

**Lurgashall Wines
(OL)**
Windfallwood
Rich (PC)

RUSPER

Plough (P)
Tel: Rusper (029 384) 312
Merrydown (BB)
Full meals lunchtime and
6.30-9pm; snacks lunchtime;
garden; children's room.

RUSTINGTON

Smugglers Rest (P)
Sea Lane
Tel: Rustington
(0903) 785714
Churchward (PC)
Various (PC)
Welcome oasis in
Littlehampton area. Meals
and snacks lunchtime and
7-9.30pm; restaurant;
garden; large children's room;
100 yards from beach.

SCAYNES HILL

Sloop Inn (P)
Freshfield Lane
Tel: Scaynes Hill
(044 486) 219
Merrydown (BB)
In fields next to a fine stretch
of the River Ouse, a
fisherman's paradise. Meals
and snacks lunchtime and
7.30-9.30pm; garden;
children's room;
accommodation.

118

SHOREHAM

Bridge (P)
87 High Street
Tel: Shoreham (079 17) 2477
Bulmer (H)
Accommodation; garden.

Red Lion (P)
Upper Shoreham Road
Merrydown (H)
Meals lunchtime and
evening; garden; no smoking
area.

Schooner (P)
Bulmer (H)

Swiss Cottage (P)
Old Shoreham Road
Merrydown (H)

TURNERS HILL

Red Lion (P)
Lion Lane (off B2028)
Tel: Copthorne (0342) 715208
Bulmer (H)
Meals lunchtime – not
Tuesday, Saturday, Sunday;
garden.

WEST ASHLING

Richmond Arms (P)
Mill Lane (¼ mile west of
B2146)
Tel: West Ashling
(024 358) 730
Selborne Gold (W)
Adjoining duck pond. Meals
and snacks lunchtimes
Monday – Saturday; garden;
children's room.

WEST CHILLINGTON

Five Bells (P)
Smock Alley (near B2139)
Tel: West Chillington
(079 83) 2143
Bulmer (H)
Hard to find but worthwhile.
Meals; garden.

WORTHING

Royal Stewart (P)
Marine Parade
Tel: Worthing (0903) 32353
Bulmer (H)

Wine Bar Rhapsody (P)
44 Portland Road
Tel: Worthing (0903) 206515
Zum (PC)

Warwickshire

ALCESTER

Cull (OL)
High Street
Langdons (PC)

ANSTY

Crown (P)
Tel: Coventry (0203) 612822
Weston (PC)
Near North Oxford Canal,
between Stretton Stop and
Hawkesbury Junction.

ARDENS GRAFTON

Golden Cross (P)
Wixford Road
near Bideford on Avon
Tel: Bideford-on-Avon
(0789) 772420
Weston (H)

AVON DASSETT

Avon Inn (P)
Weston (PC)

BEARLEY

Golden Cross (P)
Bearley Cross
Tel: Stratford-on-Avon
(0789) 731250
Weston (PC)

BULKINGTON

Chequers (P)
Chequers Street (off B4109)
Weston (H)

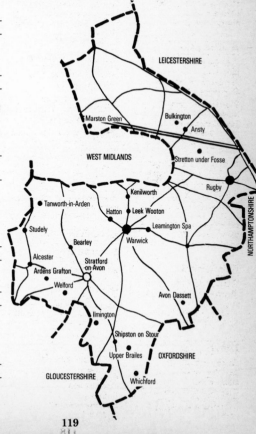

Popular 18th century 3 room pub.

Chequers Street Off Licence (OL)
Chequers Street
Weston (PC)

HATTON

Watermans Restaurant (P)
Birmingham Road (A41)
Tel: Warwick (0926) 492427
Bulmer (H)

ILMINGTON

Howard Arms (P)
Tel: Ilmington (060 882) 226
Bulmer (PC)

KENILWORTH

Royal Oak (P)
New Street (A429)
Bulmer (PC)
Meals lunchtime; garden.

KINETON

Red Lion (P)
Bridge Street (B4086)
Tel: Kineton (0926) 640240
Bulmer (H)
Old coaching inn. Meals lunchtime and evening; garden; accommodation.

LEAMINGTON SPA

Beer Engine (OL)
39 Clements Street
Tel: Leamington Spa (0926) 35758
Weston (PC)

Black Horse (P)
Bulmer (H)

LEEK WOOTON

Anchor (P)
Tel: Kenilworth (0926) 53355
Weston (PC)

MARSTON GREEN

Village Wines (OL)
Weston (PC)

RUGBY

Peacock (P)
Newbold Road
Weston (H)

SHIPSTON ON STOUR

Black Horse Inn (P)
Station Road
Tel: Shipston on Stour (0608) 61617
Bulmer (E)
16th century thatched inn. Meals and snacks 12-2.30 and 7-10.30; restaurant; garden.

STRETTON UNDER FOSSE

Union Jack (P)
on A427
Weston (PC)
Village local. Meals lunchtime and evening; garden; childrens' room.

STUDLEY

Shakespeare (P)
Bulmer (H)

TANWORTH-IN-ARDEN

Bell Inn (P)
The Green
Tel: Tanworth-in-Arden (056 44) 2212
Bulmer (PC)
Typical village pub overlooking picturesque church and village green. Meals and snacks lunchtime; restaurant.

UPPER BRAILES

Gate (P)
Bulmer (H)

WARWICK

Cape of Good Hope (P)
66 Lower Cape
Tel: Warwick (0926) 498138
Bulmer (H)

WELFORD

Bell (P)
High Street
Tel: Stratford on Avon (0789) 750353
Bulmer (H)
In village on River Avon. Meals and snacks all sessions; garden; children's room; pool room.

WHICHFORD

Norman Knight (P)
Bulmer (PC)

 # *Wiltshire*

BRADFORD ON AVON

Barge Inn (P)
17 Frome Road (B3109)
Tel: Bradford on Avon (022 16) 3403
Bulmer (PC)
Attractive 18th century inn adjacent to Bradford lock on Kennet & Avon Canal. Canal trips from lock. Meals and snacks lunchtime (not Sunday); walled garden; accommodation.

Beehive (P)
Trowbridge Road (A363)
Tel: Bradford on Avon (022 16) 3620

Bulmer (H)
Stone built pub by canal bridge. Meals and snacks 12-2 and 7-10; garden.

Canal Tavern (P)
49 Frome Road (B3109)
Tel: Bradford on Avon (022 16) 5232
Bulmer (PC)
Canalside pub. Snacks lunchtime; garden.

Dog & Fox (P)
Ashley Road
Tel: Bradford on Avon (022 16) 3257
Bulmer (PC)
Taunton (PC)
Old country pub at edge of

town, about ½ mile off Bath Road. Meals and snacks lunchtime and evening; garden.

BRADFORD LEIGH

Plough (P)
on B3109
Bulmer (PC)
Small unspoilt roadside pub. Snacks; garden.

BRATTON

Duke (P)
Tel: Bratton (0380) 830242
Bulmer (PC)

GLOUCESTERSHIRE

Crudwell
Oaksey
Minety
Pinkney
Sherston
OXFORDSHIRE
AVON
Swindon
Wanborough
Wootton Bassett
Kington Langley
Chippenham
Derry Hill
Monkton Farleigh
Lacock
Marlborough
Broughton Gifford
BERKSHIRE
Bradford Leigh
Melksham
Seend Cleeve
Devizes
Bradford on Avon
Seend
Potterne
Hilperton
Trowbridge
Bulkington
Worton
North Bradley
Bratton
Great Cheverell
Westbury
Steeple Ashton
SOMERSET
Westbury Leigh
Corsley
Ditton Marsh
Upton Scudamore
Warminster
Chittern
Shrewton
Horningsham
Heytesbury
HAMPSHIRE
Longbridge Deverill
Sutton Veny
Winterbourne Stoke
Stourhead
Porton
Mere
Fonthill Gifford
East Knoyle
Chilmark
Salisbury
Tisbury
Fovant
DORSET
Downton
Woodfalls

Meals lunchtime and evening.

BROUGHTON GIFFORD

Bell on the Common (P)
Tel: North Trowbridge (0225) 782309
Taunton (PC)
Old village pub on edge of common. Snacks lunchtime and evening.

BULKINGTON

Bell (P)
Tel: Seend (0380 82) 741
Bulmer (PC)
Snacks; garden.

CHILMARK

Black Dog (P)
Salisbury Road (B3089)
Tel: Teffont (072 276) 344

Taunton (H)
Pub dates from 1470, with inglenook fireplace with exposed bread oven, original brewhouse. Snacks 12-1.45 and 7-9.45; meals 12-1 and 7-8.45: restaurant; garden; children's room.

CHITTERN

Kings Head (P)
Tel: Warminster (0985) 50269
Bulmer (H)
Small village pub. Snacks 11-2 and 7-9; garden; pets corner.

CORSLEY

Cross Keys (P)
Lyes Green
Tel: Chapmanslade (037 388) 406
Bulmer (H)
Free house in attractive location. Garden; Skittles.

CRUDWELL

Plough Inn (P)
Tel: Crudwell (066 67) 229
Weston (H)
Bar meals.

DERRY HILL

Lansdowne Arms (P)
on A342
Tel: Calne (0249) 812422
Bulmer (PC)
Victorian Gothic pub opposite entrance to Bowood House and gardens. Meals and snacks 11-2 and 6.30-10: restaurant; garden.

DEVIZES

Nags Head (P)
New Park Street
Tel: Devizes (0380) 5363
Taunton (H)
Town centre pub specialising in discos and cabaret. Meals

121

lunchtime and evening; accommodation.

DILTON MARSH

Kings Arms (P)
High Street
Tel: Westbury (0373) 822829
Bulmer (H)
Snacks; skittle alley.

DOWNTON

Wooden Spoon (P)
High Street
Bulmer (H)
At east end of village. Meals and snacks 11.30-2 and 6.30-9; patio; children welcome.

EAST KNOYLE

Seymour Arms (P)
Tel: East Knoyle (074 783) 374
Bulmer (PC)
Meals and snacks 12-2 Monday to Saturday, 12-1.45 Sunday; evening meals 7.30-10 Friday and Saturday; restaurant; garden; accommodation.

Fox & Hounds (P)
The Green
Tel: East Knoyle (074 783) 573
Burrow Hill (PC)
Taunton (H)
Remote hillside pub with fine views; turn off A350 at Post Office and keep going! Snacks all sessions except Sunday lunch; garden; children's room.

FONTHILL GIFFORD

Beckford Arms (P)
off B3089
Tel: Tisbury (0747) 870385
Bulmer (PC)
Unspoilt 18th century rural inn on Tisbury to Hindon road; good woodland walks. Snacks up to 1 hour before last orders. garden; accommodation.

FOVANT

Poplar Inn (P)
Tel: Fovant (027 270) 658
Taunton (PC)
Meals lunchtime; garden.

GREAT CHEVERELL

Bell Inn (P)
off B3098
Tel: Lavington (038 081) 3277
Bulmer (H)

Meals and snacks lunchtime and evening; garden; childrens' room, bar billiards.

HEYTESBURY

Angel (P)
on A36
Bulmer (H)
Coates (PC)
Old low ceilinged roadhouse. Snacks lunchtime; evening meals; garden; accommodation; children's room; skittles.

HILPERTON

Lion & Fiddle (P)
Trowbridge Road (A361)
Tel: Trowbridge (022 14) 2824
Bulmer (PC)
Meals lunchtime and evening; garden; accommodation; children's room; skittles.

HORNINGSHAM

Bath Arms (P)
off B3092
Tel: Maiden Bradley (098 53) 308
Wilkins (PC)
Elegant pub in Longleat estate village. Meals and snacks lunchtime and evening; garden; accommodation, children's room.

KINGTON LANGLEY

Hit or Miss (P)
Tel: Kington Langley (024 975) 216
Bulmer (H)
Taunton (H)
Bar snacks; garden.

LACOCK

Bell Inn (P)
Bowden Hill
Tel: Lacock (024 973) 308
Taunton (PC)
In National Trust village, Fox Talbot Photographic Museum. Meals and snacks lunchtime and evening; large garden; accommodation; children's room.

George Inn (P)
4 West Street
Tel: Lacock (024 973) 263
Bulmer (PC)
Taunton (PC)
Picturesque old pub. Snacks 12-2; garden with swings and aviary.

LONGBRIDGE DEVERILL

George (P)
on A350
Tel: Warminster (0985) 40396
Taunton (PC)
Meals and snacks lunchtime and evening; garden.

MELKSHAM

Bear (P)
Bath Road
Tel: Melksham (0225) 702901
Taunton (H)
Snacks, garden; children's room.

Red Lion (P)
3 The City
Tel: Melksham (0225) 702960
Cheddar Valley (PC)
Taunton (E)
14th century pub in oldest part of town. Snacks all sessions; garden.

MERE

Butt of Sherry (P)
Castle Street (B3095)
Tel: Mere (0747) 860352
Bulmer (H)
Oak beamed pub. Meals and snacks lunchtime and evening; garden.

MINETY

White Horse (P)
Tel: Minety (066 860) 284
Bulmer (H)
Meals and snacks 12-2 and 7-11; restaurant; garden; children's room.

MONKTON FARLEIGH

Kings Arms (P)
Tel: Bath (0225) 858705
Taunton (H)
Old stone built pub with monastic connections. Meals and snacks lunchtime and evening; garden.

NORTH BRADLEY

Rising Sun (P)
61 Woodmarsh (on A363)
Tel: Trowbridge (022 14) 2453
Bulmer (PC)
Busy village pub. Snacks; pool; garden.

OAKSEY

Wheatsheaf (P)
Tel: Crudwell (066 67) 348
Bulmer (H)
16th century oak beamed pub. Hot and cold meals.

PINKNEY

Eagle (P)
Weston (PC)

PORTON

Porton Hotel (P)
off A338
Tel: Idmiston (0980) 610203
Bulmer (H)
Edwardian railway hotel.
Meals lunchtime and
evening; garden;
accommodation.

POTTERNE

Bell (P)
on A360
Tel: Devizes (0380) 3067
Bulmer (H)
Meals lunchtime and
evening.

SALISBURY

Anchor & Hope (P)
59 Winchester Street
Tel: Salisbury (0722) 27890
Taunton (H) (PC)
The city cider centre. Snacks
lunchtime and evening;
outdoor drinking area;
children's room.

Bird in Hand (P)
North Street
Tel: Salisbury (0722) 27238
Taunton (H)
Back street local near station.

Oddbins (OL)
38 High Street
Tel: Salisbury (0722) 337737
Weston (J)

Star (P)
69 Brown Street (Junction
with Ivy Street)
Tel: Salisbury (0722) 27137
Bulmer (H)
Young peoples' pub. Snacks.

Wyndham Arms (P)
27 Estcourt Street
Tel: Salisbury (0722) 28594
Broadoak (PC)
A home brew house. Snacks
all sessions; meals lunchtime
and early evening.

William IV (P)
32 Milford Street
Tel: Salisbury (0722) 21326
Bulmer (H)
Meals.

SEEND

Bell (P)
Bell Hill (on A361)
Tel: Seend (0380) 82) 338
Taunton (PC)
Pub with imposing old
brewhouse. Meals lunchtime

and evening; garden;
children's room.

SEEND CLEEVE

Brewery Inn (P)
Tel: Seend (0380 82) 463
Taunton (PC)
Near Kennett & Avon Canal.
Traditional cider press
installed on the premises.
Meals and snacks lunchtime
and evening; garden;
children's room;
accommodation.

SELLS GREEN

Three Magpies (P)
on A365
Tel: Seend (0380 82) 389
Taunton (PC)
Meals and snacks lunchtime
and evening; bar billiards;
camping.

SEMINGTON

Somerset Arms (P)
High Street (on A350)
Tel: Keevil (0380) 870067
Bulmer (H)
400 year old roadside pub,
once the property of the Duke
of Somerset. Meals and
snacks lunchtime and
evening; garden.

SHERSTON

Carpenters Arms (P)
Tel: Malmesbury (0666)
840665
Bulmer (W)
Unspoilt and natural, even to
scrubbed top tables in bar.
Meals and snacks all sessions;
garden.

SELLERS' CIDER
▲
The Vineyard
Tel: Malmesbury
(0666) 840716

SHREWTON

Royal Oak (P)
Amesbury Road
Tel: Shrewton (0980) 620260
Bulmer (H)
Meals and snacks 12-2 and
6-10; garden;
accommodation.

STEEPLE ASHTON

Longs Arms (P)
off A350
Tel: Keevil (0380) 870245
Taunton (H)
Old coaching inn in a pretty
village. Snacks; garden.

STOURHEAD

Spread Eagle (P)
Rosies (BB)

SUTTON VENY

Woolpack (P)
on B3095
Bulmer (H)
Busy pub on crossroads.
Meals lunchtime and
evening.

SWINDON

Bubbles Wine Bar (P)
Theatre Square
Tel: Swindon
(0793) 643230/643228
Bulmer (E)
Adjacent to Wyvern Theatre
and Arts Centre. Meals and
snacks lunchtime; outdoor
terrace; live music Thursday,
Friday and Saturday;
nightclub next door.

TISBURY

Cross Inn (P)
The Cross
Tel: Tisbury (0747) 870441
Taunton (H)
Snacks 10-2.30; meals 7-10;
restaurant; garden.

TROWBRIDGE

Anchor & Hope (P)
64 Frome Road (A361)
Tel: Trowbridge
(022 14) 2794
Bulmer (H)
Taunton (H)
Snacks 12-2 weekday
lunchtimes.

Black Swan (P)
1 Adcroft Street
Tel: Trowbridge
(022 14) 2600
Bulmer (H)
Taunton (H)
Meals and snacks lunchtime
and evenings; large garden
and play area.

Castle (P)
Ashton Street
Tel: Trowbridge
(022 14) 3491
Bulmer (H)
Snacks; children's play area
and garden.

Crown (P)
Timbrell Street
Tel: Trowbridge
(022 14) 3117
Bulmer (H)
Meals 10-2 and 6-9, garden;
accommodation; pool.

Greyhound (P)
61 Mortimer Street

Tel: Trowbridge
(022 14) 62135
Bulmer (H)
Taunton (H)
Meals and snacks lunchtime;
garden pool.

Stallards Inn (P)
16 Stallard Street
Tel: Trowbridge
(022 14) 4139
Bulmer (H)
Snacks all sessions; meals
lunchtime; pool.

Twelve Bells (P)
Seymour Road
Tel: Trowbridge
(022 14) 2905
Bulmer (PC)
Meals and snacks lunchtime
and evening; pool.

UPTON
SCUDAMORE

Angel (P)
off A350
Tel: Warminster
(0985) 213225
Bulmer (PC)
Meals lunchtime and
evening.

WANBOROUGH

Harrow Inn (P)
Tel: Wanbrough
(079 379) 622
Weston (H)
17th century pub. Lunchtime
meals.

WARMINSTER

Bell & Crown (P)
66 Deverill Road
Tel: Warminster
(0985) 212774
Taunton (H)

Meals and snacks all sessions;
garden; childrens' room.

Fox & Hounds (P)
Deverill Road (A350)
Tel: Warminster (0985)
216711
Cheddar Valley (PC)
Taunton (H)
Out of town on Blandford
road. Snacks all sessions;
outdoor drinking area;
lending library; skittle alley.

Globe (P)
Brook Street
Taunton (PC)
On edge of town; take A350
and turn right into Fore
Street about 1 mile from town
centre; Globe is at far end.
Meals and snacks all sessions;
garden.

WESTBURY

Castle (P)
Bratton Road
Tel: Westbury (0373) 822615
Taunton (PC)

Crown (P)
Market Place
Tel: Westbury (0373) 822828
Taunton (PC) (H)
Small town centre hotel.
Meals and snacks Monday to
Saturday, 12-2 and 7.30-10;
accommodation; pool.

Horse & Groom (P)
Alfred Street
Tel: Westbury (0373) 822854
Taunton (H)
Meals and snacks lunchtime
and evening; garden; table
skittles.

White Lion (P)
Market Place
Tel: Westbury (0373) 822700
Taunton (H)

WESTBURY
LEIGH

Phipps Arms (P)
on A3098
Tel: Westbury (0373) 822809
Bulmer (PC)
Pleasant village pub. Snacks;
garden.

WINTERBOURNE
STOKE

Bell Inn (P)
High Street
Tel: Shrewton (0980) 620445
Bulmer (H)
Snacks 11.30-2 and 7-9.30;
garden.

WOODFALLS

Bat & Ball (P)
Tel: Downton (0725) 20383
Bulmer (PC)
Drinking and talking pub.
Snacks all sessions.

WOOTTON
BASSETT

Longleaze Stores
(OL)
Longleaze
Weston (PC)

WORTON

Rose & Crown (P)
High Street
Tel: Devizes (0380) 4202
Bulmer (H)
Beamed bar in 300 year old
former forge. Meals and
snacks lunchtime and
evening; garden; children's
room; bar billiards.

Worcestershire

ARLEY

Harbour Inn (P)
Weston (PC)
The name is a reminder of
when the River Severn was
navigable up to this point.
Nowadays the best way to
reach the Harbour is by the
Severn Valley Steam
Railway.

ASHTON
UNDER HILL

Star (P)
Tel: Evesham (0386) 881325
Bulmer (H)
In the world of "soap" Ashton

is actually Ambridge, the
home of the Archers, on BBC
Radio 4, and in fact there *are* a
number of Archers in the
village – check in the church
yard and the flower rota if you
don't believe it! Presumably
the Star is the "Bull", in
which case beware of the
Grundys! Meals lunchtime
and evening; garden.

ASTLEY BURF

Hampstall Inn (P)
Tel: Stourport (029 93) 2600
Bulmer (H)
Used to be a cider house; on
the bank of the River Severn.

Meals lunchtime and
evening; moorings; private
fishing.

BADSEY

Round of Grass (P)
Tel: Evesham (0386) 830206
Bulmer (H)

Royal British
Legion Club (P)
High Street
Tel: Evesham (0386) 830200
Black Bull (PC)

Wheatsheaf (P)
Tel: Evesham (0386) 830380
Bulmer (H)

BAGGINSWOOD

Crown Inn (P)
Weston (PC)
This place could be hobbit forming.

BECKFORD

Beckford Inn (P)
Tel: Evesham (0386) 881254
Weston (H)
Accommodation.

BERROW

Duke of York (P)
Rye Cross
Weston (PC)

BEWDLEY

Bewdley Beer Agency (OL)
70 Load Street
Tel: Bewdley (0299) 402254
Black Bull (PC)
Symonds (PC)

Running Horse (P)
Long Bank
Tel: Bewdley (0299) 402161
Weston (PC)
In a small Georgian town on the Severn, with the attraction of a Steam Railway, and Safari Park, nearby.

BREDON

Royal Oak (P)
Bulmer (H)

Old coaching inn with traditional interior. Meals lunchtime; garden.

BRETFORTON

Fleece (P)
The Square
Tel: Evesham (0386) 831173
Weston (PC)
14th century farmhouse, which became a pub in 1848, and is now owned by National Trust. Snacks lunchtime; garden.

Royal British Legion Club (P)
Black Bull (PC)

Victoria Arms (P)
Bulmer (H)

BROADWAY

Arnolds (OL)
99 High Street
Tel: Broadway (0386) 852427
Black Bull (PC)

Crown & Trumpet Inn (P)
Church Street
Tel: Broadway (0386) 853202
Bulmer (H)
Cotswold stone pub in tourist centre. The locals all have their own cider mugs and cider horns which they always use. Meals and snacks all sessions; garden; accommodation.

CONDERTON

Yew Tree (P)

Black Bull (PC)
16th century village pub under Bredon Hill. Snacks lunchtime.

DEFFORD

Monkey House (P)
Tel: Evesham (0386) 750234
Bulmer Special Dry (W)
Unmarked and unspoilt; a genuine cider house. If you manage to find it you deserve a drink! Please don't invade in droves.

DRAKES BROUGHTON

Old Oak (P)
Bulmer (H)

DROITWICH

Westcroft Arms (P)
25 Ombersley Street West
Tel: Droitwich (0905) 772816
Bulmer (E)
Snacks lunchtime; Meals 6-10; garden.

ECKINGTON

Anchor (P)
Cotheridge Lane
Tel: Evesham (0386) 750356
Bulmer (PC)
Near River Avon: moor at Eckington Bridge, 10 minutes walk away. Meals and snacks 12.30-2.30 and 6.30-9.30; restaurant; garden.

Bell (P)
Tel: Evesham (0386) 750205
Bulmer (PC)
Snacks lunchtime; garden;
children welcome inside
when wet (the weather, not
the children!).

Crown (P)
Church Street
Tel: Evesham (0386) 750472
Bulmer (PC)
Cosy atmosphere, inglenook
fireplace, in village pub.
Meals and snacks 11.30-1.45
and 7.30-10.15; restaurant;
garden; children's room.

ELMLEY CASTLE
Plough (P)
Tel: Evesham (0386) 74269
Home Made (H)
A unique experience, a pub
which makes its own cider!
Beer hardly gets a look in at
the Plough, all the locals are
on the cider, which they drink
in mugs, as nature intended.
You can walk off the affects
afterwards, should you need
to, by climbing the nearby
Bredon Hill. Bar snacks
lunchtime.

EVESHAM
Angel Vaults (P)
Port Street
Tel: Evesham (0386) 2266
Bulmer (H)

Cider Mill (P)
135 Pershore Road
Tel: Evesham (0386) 2014
Weston (PC)

Corner Stores (OL)
Coronation Street
Cotswold (PC)

Crown Wines (OL)
Black Bull (PC)

Craycombe Farm Shop (OL)
Fladbury
Tel: Evesham (0386) 860732
Black Bull (PC)

Evesham Working Mens Club (P)
8 Merstow Green
Tel: Evesham (0386) 2069
Black Bull (PC)

Robbins (OL)
33/35 Port Street
Tel: Evesham (0386) 6161
Black Bull (PC)
Symonds
Weston (PC)
Licenced tea room adjacent
offers coffees, light lunches
and high teas, 9-5 Monday to
Saturday.

Royal British Legion Club (P)
Weston (PC)

Trumpet (P)
Merstow Green
Weston (PC)
Town pub, close to Market
Square. Meals lunchtime;
garden.

FERNHILL HEATH
Working Mens Club (P)
rear of Memorial Hall
Tel: Worcester (0905) 51054
Black Bull (PC)

GRIMLEY
Camp House Inn (P)
Camp Lane (off A443)
Tel: Worcester (0905) 640288
Bulmer (E)
Unspoilt pub on bank of River
Severn. Snacks 12-2 and 6-8;
garden; children's room.

HALLOW
Royal Oak (P)
Tel: Worcester (0905) 640258
Black Bull (PC)

HAMPTON
Working Mens Club (P)
Workman Road
Tel: Evesham (0386) 2719
Black Bull (PC)

HIMBLETON
Galton Arms (P)
near Droitwich
Tel: Himbleton (090 569) 672
Weston (PC)
Village local in beautiful
setting. Meals and snacks
except Monday lunchtime;
restaurant; garden.

KEMPSEY
Queens Head (P)
Main Road
Tel: Worcester (0905) 820572
Bulmer (PC)
Oak beamed bars. Snacks
lunchtime; garden with
children's play area and
patio.

KIDDERMINSTER
Coopers Arms (P)
Canterbury Road
Weston (PC)

Woodfield Tavern (P)
Woodfield Street
Tel: Kidderminster
(0562) 740173
Weston (PC)

KINLET
Eagle & Serpent (P)
Tel: Kinlet (029 924) 227
Weston (PC)

KNIGHTWICK
Talbot (P)
on A44
Tel: Knightwick
(0886) 21235
Dunkerton (B)
14th century hotel. Meals
lunchtime and evening;
garden: accommodation.

LEIGH SINTON
BLACK BULL CIDER▲
Norbury's, Crowscroft
Tel: Leigh Sinton
(0886) 32206

Somers Arms (P)
Hereford Road (A4103)
Tel: Leigh Sinton
(0886) 32343
Black Bull (H)
Knights Crumpton Oaks (H)
Home cooking and vegetarian
dishes; meals and snacks
12.30-2 and 7.30-10.30;
restaurant; garden;
childrens' room; live jazz
Tuesday to Sunday,

LITTLETON
Littleton & Cleeve Prior Royal British Legion Club (P)
School Lane, Middle Littleton
Tel: Evesham (0386) 830439

LOWER MOOR
Post Office (OL)
Tel: Evesham (0386) 860354
Black Bull

MALVERN
Davies Stores (OL)
Barnards Green
Knights Crumpton Oaks

Gordons (OL)
Barnards Green
Black Bull

Jenkins (OL)
Pickersleigh Road
Black Bull

Red Lion (P)
St. Anns Road
Tel: Malvern ((068 45) 3563
Weston (PC)
Town centre pub; lunchtime
concerts upstairs during
Malvern Festival (last 2
weeks of May). Good spot to
start or end walks in Malvern
Hills. Snacks lunchtime;
restaurant.

MARTIN HUSSINGTREE

Swan (P)
Tel: Worcester (0886) 51364
Weston (PC)

NORTON

Twyford Garden Centre (OL)
near Evesham
Tel: Evesham (0386) 40612
Cotswold (PL)

OMBERSLEY

Cross Keys (P)
Tel: Worcester (0905) 620588
Black Bull (PC)

OFFENHAM

Bridge Inn & Ferry (P)
Boat Lane
Tel: Evesham (0386) 6565
Bulmer (H)
Pub on bank of River Avon;
directly opposite is Dead
Mans Ait, an island where
Simon de Montfort's army
was slaughtered in Battle of
Evesham. Snacks lunchtime
and evening; full meals
7-8.30; riverside garden; free
mooring for customers.

Royal British Legion Club (P)
Black Bull (PC)

OVERBURY

Star Inn (P)
Tel: Overbury (038 689) 316
Bulmer (H)
Snacks (last orders half hour
before closing); garden; room
off where children can eat
with parents;
accommodation.

PENSAX

Bell (P)
B4202, 1 mile from Clows Top
Black Bull (PC)
Meals lunchtime and
evening; garden.

PERSHORE

Talbot Inn (P)
48 Newlands
Tel: Pershore (0386) 553575
Bulmer (H)
In back street near abbey.
Meals all sessions; garden.

Victoria Hotel (P)
Newland
Tel: Pershore (0386) 553662
Bulmer (E)
Near Pershore Abbey.
Snacks; garden; pool.

REDDITCH

Bell Court Wines (OL)
Black Bull

Jolly Farmer (P)
Woodrow South
Weston (PC)

SHATTERFORD

Bellman Cross (P)
Tel: Malvern (068 45) 5774
Weston (H)

SHENSTONE

Plough (P)
off A448/A450
Tel: Chaddesley Corbett
(056 283) 340
Weston (PC)
Country pub off beaten track.
Garden; facilities for
disabled.

SOUTH LYTTLETON

Edward VIII (P)
Bulmer (H)
Just the place to abdicate all
responsibility.

TENBURY WELLS

Goughs (OL)
13 Teme Street
Tel: Tenbury Wells
(0584) 810468
Weston (all range)

Old Crow (P)
Weston (PC)

Peacock (P)
Boraston
Tel: Tenbury Wells
(0584) 810506
Bulmer (H)

Rose & Crown (P)
Burford
Tel: Tenbury Wells
(0584) 810335
Weston (PC)

UPTON ON SEVERN

Ye Olde Anchor Inn (P)
5 High Street
Tel: Upton on Severn
(068 46) 2146
Weston (PC)
Near River Severn, good
overnight mooring spot.
Restaurant, buffet and
carvery all week; Saturday
and Sunday roast lunch;
homecooked dishes; outdoor
drinking area; children's
room.

WICKHAMFORD

Sandys Arms (P)
Tel: Evesham (0386) 830535
Bulmer (H)
Difficult to tell people where
you spent the evening!

WORCESTER

Brewery Tap (P)
50 Lowesmoor
Tel: Worcester (0905) 21540
Knights Crumpton Oaks (PC)
Severn Cyder (PC)
The first ever Private
Members Pub – rather a
contradiction in terms! Full
time membership £10

Cardinals Hat (P)
Friar Street
Tel: Worcester (0905) 21890
Weston (PC)
Historic half timbered pub in
old street. Snacks all times;
childrens' room.

Corner Stores (OL)
Chestnut Walk
Black Bull

Crown & Anchor (P)
Hylton Road
Tel: Worcester (0905) 421481
Bulmer (PC)
Severnside pub. Snacks
lunchtime Monday to Friday;
garden; skittle alley.

Evertons (OL)
Worcester Road
Tel: Worcester (0905) 620282
Weston (PC)

Food for Thought (OL)
20 Mealcheapen Street
Tel: Worcester (0905) 29537
Dunkerton (B)
Delicatessen and restaurant.

Melbourne Street Stores (OL)
36 Melbourne Street
Tel: Worcester (0905) 25720
Black Bull

Old Neil (OL)
Belmont Street
Symonds (PC)

Park Side Stores (OL)
9-11 Barbourne Walk
Tel: Worcester (0905) 25303
Black Bull

Slug & Lettuce (P)
12 Cornmarket
Tel: Worcester (0905) 28362
Dunkerton (B)

Wine Shop (OL)
Corn Market
Weston (PC)

Yorkshire

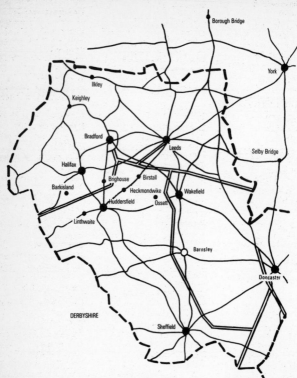

BARKISLAND

Griffin (P)
57 Stainland Road
Bulmer (PC)

BIRSTALL

Horse & Jockey (P)
Thorn Street
Bulmer (H)

BOROUGH BRIDGE

Alan Porter Provisions Ltd. (OL)
Bar Lane, Roecliffe
Tel: Borough Bridge
(090 12) 2323
Bromell (PP)

BRADFORD

Fighting Cock (P)
Preston Street (off B6145)

Westrays (H)
Meals lunchtime.

The Queens (P)
77 Listerhills Road
Tel: Bradford (0274) 731130
Bulmer (H)
Open till 1am
Thursday-Saturday nights
with disco; Saturday is Rock
n' Roll night. Snacks
Monday-Wednesday
lunchtime and evening; full
meals Friday lunchtime,
Thursday-Saturday evenings
till 12.30.

Steve Biko Bar (P)
Bradford University Link
Block, (D Floor) Great Hester
Road
Bulmer (H)

Westleigh (P)
30 Easby Road (A647)
Tel: Bradford (0274) 727089
Bulmer (H)
Meals lunchtime and

evening; accommodation;
children's room; garden.

The Wine Cellars (OL)
8 Duckworth Lane
Tel: Bradford (0274) 487135
Weston

BRIGHOUSE

The Red Rooster (P)
123 Elland Road, Brookfoot
(A6025)
Westrays (H)
Meals lunchtime; garden.

DONCASTER

The Hallcross
33-34 Hallgate
Tel: Doncaster (0302) 328213
Bulmer (H)
Home brewery, tours can be
arranged. Snacks and full
meals lunchtime; garden.

HALIFAX

The Shears (P)
Paris Gate, Boys Lane
Tel: Halifax (0422) 62936
Westrays (F)

Woodcock (P)
213 Gibbet Street
Tel: Halifax (0422) 59906
Westrays (H) (PC) (PP)
Bottle collection; live music;
snacks 11.30-3, 5-11,
including door step
sandwiches.

HECKMONDWIKE

Old Hall (P)
New North Road
Bulmer (H)

HUDDERSFIELD

**Polytechnic
Students Union (P)
Rat & Ratchet (P)**
40 Chapel Hill
Tel: Huddersfield
(0484) 516734
Westrays (PP)
Snacks and full meals
weekdays 12.00-2.00; garden.

ILKLEY

**Ilkley Wine Cellars
(OL)**
52 The Grove
Tel: Ilkley (0943) 607313
Weston (B) (PC) (PP)

KEIGHLEY

Boon's Arms (P)
Longcroft
Tel: Keighley (0535) 603102
Bulmer (H)
Snacks all times; live music
Sunday, Tuesday and
Thursday, outdoor drinking
area.

LEEDS

Ale House (OL)
79 Raglan Road,
Woodhouse Moor

Tel: Leeds (0532) 455447
Westrays (wide selection)

Duck & Drake (P)
Kirkgate
Westrays (H)

LINTHWAITE

The Sair (P)
Lane Top, Hoyle Ing
**Causeway (homemade) (H)
Westrays (H)**
Home brew pub on steep hill
overlooking Colne Valley.
Children's room.

OSSETT

Boons End
Low Mill Road, off Healey
Road (near River Calder)
Bulmer (H)
Meals lunchtime and
evening; frequent live music;
games room.

SELBY BRIDGE

The Moorings (P)
Westrays (F)

SHEFFIELD

Fat Cat (P)
23 Alma Street
Tel: Sheffield (0742) 28195
Zum (PC)
Home made food lunchtime
and 5.30-7.30,

Fox & Duck (P)
227 Fulwood Road
Tel: Sheffield (0742) 663422
Taunton (PL)
Snacks lunchtimes on
weekdays.

Frog & Parrot (P)
Division Street
Tel: Sheffield (0742) 21280
Bulmer (H)
A home brew pub with no juke
box. Snacks and full meals
weekday lunchtimes,

Small Beer (OL)
57 Archer Road
Tel: Sheffield (0742) 551356

Symonds (PC)
Open 12.00-10.30 Monday to
Friday; 10.30-10.30
Saturday; 12.00-2.00 and
7.00-10.30 Sunday.

WAKEFIELD

Henry Boons (P)
Westgate (A638/A642)
Bulmer (H)
Meals Monday to Friday
lunchtime.

WHITBY

**Shepherds Purse
(OL)**
95 Church Street
Merrydown (BB)

YORK

**Budges Off Licence
(OL)**
(near York City Football
Club)
Thatcher (PC)

John Bull (P)
Layerthorpe
Tel: York (0904) 21593
**Bulmer (H)
Thatcher (PC)**
Meals at lunchtimes; garden.

Oscars Wine Bar (P)
8 Littlestone Gate
Merrydown (H)

**St. Johns College
(P)**
Bulmer (H)

Spread Eagle (P)
98 Walmgate
Tel: York (0904) 35868
Bulmer (H)
Meals at lunchtimes;
childrens' room; garden.

**York Beer Shop
(OL)**
28 Sandringham Street,
Fishergate
Tel: York (0904) 647136
**Westrays (F)
Zum (PC)**
Guest ciders

Wales

Dyfed

ABERYSTWYTH

Boars Head (P)
Queens Road
Tel: Aberystwyth
(0970) 615220
Bulmer (H)
Comfortable bar close to sea
front. Meals lunchtime and
evening; accommodation.

LLANDRE

Felin Gyffin Watermill Restaurant (P)
Bow Street (A487)
Tel: Aberystwyth
(0970) 828852
Selborne (PC)
An 18th century watermill
with a restaurant in the mill
house. Real food – nothing
frozen, no microwave, no
chips. Open 12-2 and 7-10.30,
closed Sunday and Monday.
NB: Restaurant Licence only.

PISGAH

Halfway Inn (P)
Devils Bridge Road (A4120)
Tel: Capel Bangor
(097 084) 631
Symonds (PC)

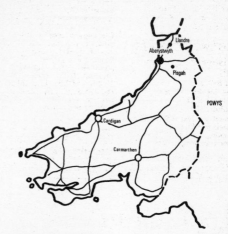

The only self service pub in
Britain; customers draw their
own drinks from casks on
stillage in beamed stone
walled room. The only cider
pub for miles; near several
tourist attractions such as
Devil's Bridge Falls and Vale
of Rheidol narrow gauge
railway (BR's only surviving
steam line). Meals and snacks
12-2 and 6-10; restaurant;
garden; childrens' room; play
area; camping; sheep
shearing contests; scenic
views; Britain's last
remaining Red Kites.

Glamorgan

BARGOED

Hanbury Arms (P)
Main Street (A469)
Bulmer (H)
Large Victorian local.
Snacks.

CARDIFF

Batemans Delicatessen (OL)
Crwys Road
Haymakers (PP)

Coles (OL)
99 Whitchurch Road
Thatcher (PC)

Oddbins (OL)
23 St. Mary Street
Tel: Cardiff (0222) 34449
Weston (full range)

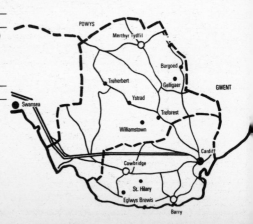

Piazzas (OL)
Cathays Terrace
Haymakers (PP)

**Plasrewydd Road
Off Licence (OL)**
Plasrewydd Road
Bulmer (H)

**Royal British
Legion Club (P)**
Penlline Road, Whitchurch
Tel: Cardiff (0222) 626015
Bulmer (E)

EGLWYS BREWIS

**Fisherbridge Inn
(P)**
off B4265
Tel: Llantwit Major
(044 65) 3921
Bulmer (H)
Country pub near RAF camp.
Meals lunchtime and
evening; garden; children's
room; camping nearby.

GELLIGAER

Harp Inn (P)

2 St. Calwgs Avenue
Tel: Bargoed (0443) 830496
Bulmer (H)

ST. HILARY

Bush Inn (P)
½ mile off A48 between Cardiff
and Cowbridge
Tel: Cowbridge (044 63) 2745
Taunton (H)
A thatched 16th century inn,
in one of the Vale of
Glamorgan's most beautiful
villages; bare stone walls,
stone flagged floors, oak
beams and plenty of
atmosphere. High quality
catering. Meals and bar food
12-2.15 and 7.30-10.30; till 2
and 9.45 Sunday (no bar food
Saturday evening);
restaurant; garden.

SWANSEA

Oddbins (OL)
223 Oxford Street
Tel: Swansea (0792) 42196
Weston (full range)

TREFOREST

Otley Arms (P)
Forest Road (A473)
Tel: Pontypridd
(0443) 402033
Langdon (PC)
Meals and snacks lunchtime
and evening; restaurant;
games area; pool room.

TREHERBERT

Baglan (P)
Bulmer (H)

Dunraven Hotel (P)
Bulmer (H)

WILLIAMSTOWN

**Glamorgan Hotel
(P)**
Brook Street (off A4119)
Bulmer (H)
Snacks,

YSTRAD

Gelligaled Inn (P)
Bulmer (H)

Gwent

CHAINBRIDGE

Bridge Inn (P)
near Usk
Tel: Abergavenny
(0873) 880243
Bulmer (H)
Weston (PC)
In good fishing and walking
country. Meals and snacks
12-2 and 7-10; restaurant;
garden; accommodation;
caravan site in grounds;
camping.

CHEPSTOW

Three Tuns (P)
Bridge Street
Tel: Chepstow (029 12) 3497
Bulmer (H)
Near castle, museum and
River Wye. Snacks 11-2; pool
table.

GROSMONT

Angel Inn (P)
Weston (PC)
In tiny village overlooking
River Monnow with remains
of 13th century castle.
Snacks.

LLANDOGO

Old Farmhouse
Hotel (P)
Tel: Dean (0594) 530303
Bulmer (H)
Features an old cider mill.
Snacks; restaurant; garden.

LLANTHONY

Abbey Hotel (P)
Tel: Crucorney (0873) 890487
**Knights Crumpton Oaks
(PC)**
In a quiet valley in the Black
Mountains; a small pub in the
cellar of the famous abbey.
Snacks lunchtime; meals
7-8.30; restaurant; garden;
accommodation.

LLANTRISANT-
ON-USK

Royal Oak (P)
Tel: Usk (029 13) 2632/2769
Bulmer (H)
15th century inn with motel
extension. Snacks; meals
evening; garden; childrens'
room; accommodation.

MONMOUTH

Bull Inn (P)
Agincourt Square
Tel: Monmouth (0600) 2226
Weston (PC)

Griffin (P)
Whitecross Street
Tel: Monmouth (0600) 3767
Weston (PC)
Snacks; accommodation.

NEWPORT

Lamb (P)
Bridge Street
Tel: Newport (0633) 66801
Taunton (H)
Meals lunchtime; snacks.

Waterloo Hotel (P)
Alexandra Road
Tel: Newport (0633) 64627
Bulmer (H)

PANDY

Pandy Hotel (P)
on A465
Tel: Crucorney (087 382) 208
Weston (H)
In small village in Monnow
Valley close to Black
Mountains; Offa's Dyke
passes one mile to the west.
Meals and snacks lunchtime
and evening; accommodation.

PENPERGWM

King of Prussia (P)
near Abergavenny
Tel: Gobion (087 385) 232
Weston (PC)

REDBROOK

Bell Inn (P)
Tel: Monmouth (0600) 3137
Weston (PC)

SHIRENEWTON

Carpenters Arms
(P)
on B4235
Tel: Shirenewton
(029 17) 231
Bulmer (H)
On outskirts of old hilltop
village. Meals and snacks
lunchtime and evening;
garden; children's room.

Tredegar Arms (P)
The Circle
Tel: Shirenewton
(029 17) 274
Bulmer (H)

TINTERN

Cherry Tree (P)
Devauden Road (off A466)
Tel: Tintern (029 18) 292
Bulmer (W)
In Wye valley near Tintern
Abbey; railway enthusiasts
will welcome the preserved
station, now a picnic area
with display of the former
line. Old fashioned pub with
40 year old 4 pin bar billiard
table.

TRELLECK

Lion Inn (P)
on B4293
Tel: Monmouth
(0600) 860322
Weston (PC)
Traditional country inn.
Meals and snacks lunchtime
and evening; garden;
accommodation.

WHITEBROOK

Crown (P)
Tel: Trelleck (0600) 860254
Weston (PC)
17th century hotel. Meals and
snacks lunchtime and
evening; garden;
accommodation.

GWYNEDD

LLANDUDNO

Kings Arms (P)
Mostyn Street
Tel: Llandudno (0492) 75882
Coates (H)
Central for shops and beach.
Meals lunchtime; evenings in
summer; garden; children's
room.

MORFA NEFYN

Tycoch (P)
Bulmer (PC)

Powys

ARDDLEEN

Horseshoe (P)
Tel: Guilsfield (093 875) 318

Weston (H)
Old fashioned pub in small
village on Shropshire Union
Canal north of Welshpool.

Meals and snacks lunchtime
and evening; garden;
children's room;
accommodation.

BLEDDFA

Hundred House (P)
on A488
Tel: Llangunllo (054 781) 225
Bulmer (H)
Traditional country pub on
edge of Radnor Forest. Meals
and snacks lunchtime and
evening; garden;
accommodation.

BRECON

Brecon Farmers (OL)
Symonds (PC)

BUTTINGTON

Green Dragon (P)
near Welshpool
Tel: Welshpool (0938) 3076
Weston (PC)

BUILTH WELLS

Stores (OL)
Symonds (PC)

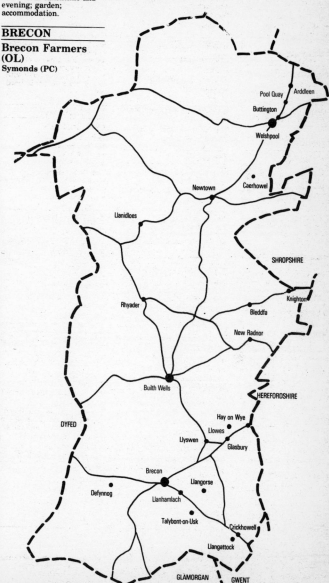

133

CRICKHOWELL

Gliffaes Hotel (P)
Tel: Bwlch (0874) 730371
Weston (PC)

Nantyffin Cider Mill Inn (P)
on A40 west of town
Tel: Crickhowell
(0873) 810775
Bulmer (H)
Meals.

GLASBURY

Harp (P)
Hay Road (off A438)
Tel: Glasbury (049 74) 373
Dunkerton (B)
Bulmer (PC)
Weston (PC)
Overlooking River Wye.
Snacks 12-2 and 7-10; garden;
games room; accommodation.

Llynau Bach Lodge Hotel (P)
Tel: Glasbury (049 74) 473
Dunkerton (B)

Maesllwch Arms Hotel (P)
Tel: Glasbury (049 74) 226
Dunkerton (B) (PC)
Snacks; meals evening;
garden; accommodation.

Three Cocks (P)
Tel: Glasbury (049 74) 215
Dunkerton (B)

HAY ON WYE

Blue Boar (P)
Castle Street
Tel: Hay-on-Wye
(0497) 820884
Bulmer (H)
Town centre pub. Meals
lunchtime.

Bull Ring Off Licence (OL)
Tel: Hay-on-Wye
(0497) 820 467
Weston (PL) (PP)

Granary (P)
Broad Street
Tel: Hay-on-Wye
(0497) 820 790
Dunkerton (B)

Hay Wholefoods & Delicatessen (OL)
Lion Street
Tel: Hay-on-Wye
(0497) 820708
Dunkerton (B)
Dunkerton Perry (B)
Full range of wholefoods and
delicatessen items, many
locally made; yummy foods;
real dairy ice cream; exotic
sandwiches; organically
produced wine.

Lions Corner House Restaurant (P)
39 Lion Street
Tel: Hay-on-Wye
(0497) 820175
Dunkerton (B) (PC)

Old Black Lion Restaurant (P)
Lion Street
Tel: Hay-on-Wye
(0497) 820841
Dunkerton (B)

Pemberton Hotel (P)
Dunkerton (B)

Three Tuns (P)
Weston (PC)

LLANHAMLACH

Old Ford (P)
on A40
Tel: Llanfrynach
(087 468) 220
Bulmer (E)
Fine views over Usk Valley.
Meals lunchtime and
evening; garden;
accommodation; camping
nearby.

LLANIDLOES

Queens Head Hotel (P)
Longbridge Street
Tel: Llanidloes (055 12) 2383
Weston (PC)
Meals and bar snacks
lunchtime and evenings till
9pm; separate dining area;
outdoor drinking area;
accommodation.

LLOWES

Radnor Arms
Tel: Glasbury (049 74) 460
Dunkerton (B)
Symonds (PC)
In small Wye Valley village
near Hay; giant cross in
churchyard. Meals lunchtime
and evening; restaurant.

NEW RADNOR

Radnor Arms (P)
on A44
Tel: New Radnor
(054 421) 232
Weston (H)
Village pub near 11th
century castle. Meals and
snacks lunchtime and
evening; children's room;
accommodation.

NEWTOWN

Elephant & Castle (P)
Broad Street
Tel: Newtown (0443) 26279
Weston (PC)
Meals and snacks lunchtime
and evening; accommodation.

Powells Off Licence (OL)
Weston (PC)

POOL QUAY

Powys Arms (P)
Weston (PC)

RHAYADER

Elan Valley Hotel (P)
Tel: Rhyader (0597) 810448
Weston (PC)

Llawzam Off Licence (OL)
Weston (PL) (PP)

TALYBONT ON USK

Travellers Rest (P)
Tel: Talybont on Usk
(087 487) 233
Weston (PC)
On bank of Brecon Canal.

White Hart (P)
on B4558
Bulmer (H)
Meals and snacks all sessions;
restaurant; children
welcome.

WELSHPOOL

Mermaid (P)
28 High Street
Tel: Welshpool (0938) 2027
Weston (PC)

Pinewood Inn (P)
Broad Street
Tel: Welshpool (0938) 3067
Weston (PC)

Rylands Farm Supplies (OL)
Symonds (PC)

Vaults (P)
The Vaults Hotel,
Broad Street
Tel: Welshpool (0938) 3032
Bulmer (PC)
Busy young peoples pub.
Snacks 12-3 and 6-11; meals
12-3 and 6-12; restaurant;
outdoor drinking area; disco.

The Cider
Directory

ADDLESTONES DRAUGHT CIDER

Lyn Hughes, Marketing Manager
Showerings Ltd., Kilver Street,
Shepton Mallet, Somerset
BA4 5ND
Telephone: Shepton Mallet (0749)
3333

Showerings (Coates-Gaymer)
have reaffirmed their continuing
commitment to traditional cider
with the introduction of a cask-
conditioned brand, dispensed by
handpump. Together with their
mass market brands, Olde English
and Copperhead, they feel that
they can now satisfy the needs of
all their customers for draught
ciders. Their new brand,
Addlestones, is aimed at the "seri-
ous cider drinker". It has been
introduced in a selected number of
pubs, chosen for their cellar conditions, for this is a "live" cider, and
demands the same care as a cask-
conditioned real ale.

Addlestones takes about 200
days to make. Using cider apples
and traditional West country
methods, a little modern technology has been introduced in the
form of two way valves that allow
the cider to breathe in the cask as
it is being hand drawn through the
pump on the bar, and it is these
valves that let the cider ferment
naturally in the pub. There is no
carbonation or pasteurisation. The
cider has a full flavoured live taste,
and is naturally cloudy. "You can't
make a real cider bright", explains
Showerings cider maker Phil
Owens. "Our cask conditioned
'liquor' is not filtered, so it retains
the natural cloud from the apple
juice as it originates from the presses".

Showerings are confident that
Addlestones will become the new
bench mark for quality cider, and
have been greatly encouraged by
its performance in blind tastings.
Following good response to the
draught version, Addlestones has
been launched into the off-licence
trade, under the title Addlestones
Vintage Cider, in 1 litre glass
bottles, in a lightly sparkling form.

APPLE BLOSSOM CIDER

John Watt
The Cornish Cider Company, Tre-
vean Farm, Coombe Kea, near
Truro, Cornwall
Telephone: Truro (0872) 77177

This is a totally traditional cider,
fermented with the apple's own
yeast, and with no added sugar, or
other extraneous practices. It is
mainly a blend of Kingston Black
cider apples and Bramleys, which
produces a good balanced drink.
There is a full range of sweet,
medium sweet, medium, dry, and
scrumpy. You will find Apple Blossom widely in Cornwall, not just in
the spring, but right through the
year, and during the summer it
appears in many caravan site bars
and off-licence shops in addition to
its other outlets, which include a
number of the local National Trust
properties, plus a good selection of
off-licences selling it in bottles. It
is even to be found in a chemist's,
which says much for its medicinal
as well as its refreshing qualities.

ASHILL CIDER

C. House
Ashill Farm, Ashill, near Ilminster, Somerset
Telephone: Hatch Beauchamp
(0823) 480513

You should be able easily to find
this cider. The farm is situated
right on the main A358 Taunton to
Chard road, in the village of
Ashill. Once you arrive you can, if
you so wish, call a halt for the day,
because there are also facilities for
camping. Ashill claims on the
label to be "a cider with a real
kick", and with that in mind it
might be wise not to go too much
further after sampling it. If you do
intend camping pitch the tent

before you start on the cider, life will then be simpler.

This is a true Somerset cider, made from local cider apples by natural methods, and it certainly is strong and very pleasant, in either sweet or dry. It is sold only from the farm, and by the end of the season supplies may run out, so first come – thirst served. You may try some before you buy. It is available in the farm's own ½, 1, and 5 gallon containers, or you may bring your own. The farm is open from 10am to 6pm on Monday to Saturday, 12 noon to 1.30pm only on Sunday.

ASPALL CYDER

J. M. Chevallier Guild
Cyder House, Aspall Hall, Debenham, Stowmarket, Suffolk IP14 6PD
Telephone: Debenham (0728) 860510

Ever since the Chevalliers settled in Suffolk they have been interested in orchards and cyder. They have been growing apples for 250 years, and the first cyder was made at Aspall in 1728. Aspall Hall is an elegant moated country mansion dating back over five centuries, and only owned by two families in that time; it possesses a fine Queen Anne brick facade. Among its claims to fame, it was the birthplace of Ann Chevallier, the mother of Kitchener of Khartoum.

Cyder making at Aspall has only reached commercial levels in recent years and now about 100,000 gallons are produced annually. It is distinctive in several ways. Firstly the spelling: you will note that it is "cyder" and not "cider" – this is a Suffolk custom of long standing. Secondly, although you would expect that, being in East Anglia, the cider would comprise only culinary and eating apples, Aspall Cyder actually contains the same varieties of highly

tannined Bittersweets that are used in the West Country, with a proportion of culinary fruit added. Thirdly, it is an "organic" cyder. The apples, which are grown in some 65 acres of orchards on the estate, are entirely free of any artificial fertilisers or chemicals, and the end product is free of any preservatives.

The cyder is still made in the traditional way, the natural yeasts producing the fermentation, and is stored in oak vats to mature under a thatched roof of Norfolk reeds. The resulting cyder has a pronounced apple aroma, is clear light orange in colour, with the body of a light wine, and a good apple taste and aftertaste. It may be bought at the Hall, in ¼ litre and 1 litre bottles, and is available in still medium sweet, still dry, and still extra dry.

Cyder only accounts for about 10 per cent of the firm's business. Other products, all of which sport the Soil Association's official Symbol of Organic Quality, include Apple Juice, in ¼ and 1 litre bottles, Cyder Vinegar, and White and Red Wine Vinegars, together with other items such as honey and chutney. Aspall Cyder may be found in several local pubs and various off-licences in East Anglia, also in some London restaurants and bars. Opening hours at Aspall Hall are from 9am to 12.30pm, and 1.30pm to 3.30pm, on weekdays only.

BARNARD CIDER

Mr. & Mrs. Barnard
"Grassmere", Abinger Hammer, Dorking, Surrey
Telephone: Dorking (0306) 730941

In the good old days Surrey used to be a "hot" county for cider. You would find it almost everywhere. How times have changed! But happily the Barnards are still keeping the tradition alive. They are fortunate in their raw materials. They have friends who keep

137

horses in their orchards, and as horses and apples don't mix they are glad to have the orchards cleared. The horses do not know what they are missing, for the splendid draught cider which results makes anything else you will find in the London area very tame indeed!

The cider is not made in vast quantities, and is mainly for the Barnard's friends and those who appreciate a good thing when they taste one. But it is on sale to the public, and if you make your way along the A25 to Abinger Hammer you can enjoy it too. You may bring a container, or the Barnards can supply you with one. You will find "Grassmere" next to the Post Office, on the A25.

BATTLE VINTAGE CYDER

Alan Garnett
Garnett Brothers, Oaklands Farm, Moat Lane, Sedlescombe, East Sussex TN33 0RY
Telephone: Hastings (0424) 426587

In the Middle Ages the monks at Battle Abbey made and sold their own cider – a natural consequence of obeying the injunction "thirst after righteousness". In these latter days the Garnett Brothers have faithfully followed in the footsteps of those early brothers. They started operations about 1984 and, after a period of careful research into making and marketing are now producing Battle Vintage Cyder, a worthy successor. The cider is strong and still, and packs a punch of $7\frac{1}{2}$ per cent alcohol content – a force to be reckoned with. Culinary apples are used, giving a crisp distinctive taste which will make you wonder why people ever waste them in apple pies. Oaklands Farm is open daily, and the Garnetts will be happy to let you sample their cider before you buy. The cider is sold in 1 litre bottles. Wine is also available.

BEENLEIGH MANOR TRADITIONAL FARMHOUSE CIDER

Marketing and Sales Manager: David Brown
Beenleigh Manor Farm Foods, Beenleigh Manor, Harbertonford, Totnes, Devon
Telephone: Harbertonford (080 423) 738

Cider has been made at the medieval manor of Beenleigh for centuries. This continuing tradition produces today's cider, known locally as "original sin". Much time is spent developing cider making as a fine art: only apples from local cider orchards are used, with the fruit from each orchard being pressed and fermented separately. Natural fermentation takes place in oak casks, and no colouring, sweeteners or astringents are used. It is a natural cider with nothing added, a point reinforced by the naked couple depicted on the label. A 70 ton cider press dating from the 1930s is still in use, made by H. Bearer & Sons, Engineers, of Newton Abbot, and driven by a 1913 Crossley single cylinder 30 HP gas engine via a line shaft.

The cider is sold by the orchard, apple type or blend, all of which will be slightly different, and you will be encouraged to wander along the casks sampling each until you find one to your taste, if you get that far. Beware of one variety called "Old Pig Squeal". This is alleged to separate the men from the boys, and the tankards from their handles.

If you wish to buy cider at Beenleigh please phone beforehand, as it is a working farm. You should be lucky between 10am and 5pm on most weekdays. You make take your own container though $\frac{1}{2}$ and 1 gallon containers are also provided. In addition to the cider you may also buy perry. While in the area do not miss the nearby

138

Crowdy Mill, where you may purchase proper unadulterated stoneground flour, but again please phone. The number is Harbertonford 340 for "flour fresh from the stones".

BIDDENDEN CIDER

R. A. Barnes
Biddenden Vineyards Ltd., "Little Whatmans", Biddenden, near Ashford, Kent TN27 8DH
Telephone: Biddenden (0580) 291726

The lovely old Wealden village of Biddenden has long been famous for its Biddenden Maids, and its High Street flanked by half timbered houses. Recently it has been able to record yet another claim to fame, with the advent of Biddenden Cider. The Barnes family began planting a vineyard some 1½ miles from the village in 1969, and quickly established their reputation as wine makers. It then seemed natural, in such a traditional apple growing area as Kent, to produce a cider. As is the local custom, the cider is based on culinary rather than cider apples, and the strong still drink which results is highly distinctive and refreshingly tangy. It also possesses considerable strength, and in fact some pubs will only sell it by the half pint, at least until they get to know you. It might easily pass for a light table wine, and it is perhaps best to treat it with that sort of respect rather than downing pint after pint in quick succession, though several glasses at the end of a long hard day will do wonders for you.

Visitors are welcome to walk round the vineyard, and to sample the range of products at the shop. Biddenden Cider is sold in 1 litre bottles, medium or dry, and you should also try "Monk's Delight", a tasty cider blended with honey and spices, equally pleasant mulled or chilled. Guided tours are offered during the summer months for parties, though these must be booked in advance: the visit includes a talk on wine making, a light meal, and suitable liquid refreshment. The tours take place at lunchtime and early evening.

Biddenden Cider will be found in many free houses and off-licences throughout Kent and East Sussex, and will add greatly to your enjoyment of the other attractions of the Garden of England, such as historic castles, stately homes, and preserved steam railways.

The shop is open from 11am to 5pm, Monday to Saturday, and 12 noon to 5pm on Sunday, from May to October; from 11am to 2pm Monday to Saturday only, from November to April.

BLACK BULL CIDER

T.P. Norbury
Norbury's Cider Company, Crowcroft, Leigh Sinton, nr. Malvern, Worcestershire WR13 5ED
Telephone: Leigh Sinton (0886) 32206: Brewery 33391

Black Bull is a fairly recent cider. The Norbury family are fruit growers, and it was the difficult state of the trade consequent to Britain joining the Common Market which prompted them to start diversifying. They began experimenting with cider in 1979, using the old farm scatter and hand press, and made over a thousand gallons by these traditional and laborious methods. The result was what might have been expected, a good old unpredictable "scrumpy". By a happy coincidence, just at

that moment a well-known local cider maker, Mr. Lanchbury, retired. The Norburys bought his equipment and soon began in earnest. Since then they have never looked back. They now make over 50,000 gallons annually.

The title "Black Bull" comes from the family name, Norbury deriving from the French words noir (black) and boeuf (bull). The family crest has a black bull as the heraldic device.

Tom Norbury's original experiences making cider by completely "traditional" methods have convinced him of the need for firm control during the whole process, in order to produce a consistent and attractive drink. Thus the natural yeasts are killed off and replaced by a champagne yeast, and filtering is used to give a clear pint. The sweet variety has added sweetener. However the apples are traditional cider fruit, among them Yarlington Mill, Sweet Coppin, Dabinett, Kingston Black, and Medaille d'Or, grown on the farm. The result is highly satisfactory. The cider is extremely palatable, with good aroma, a clear light orange colour, a full bodied and almost wine-like consistency, and a subtle taste of apple with a hint of perhaps sherry: distinctive and enjoyable. Despite the name you would not call it "beefy"!

The range includes Draught Cider, medium sweet and medium dry; Draught Perry, medium dry; Medium Sweet Sparkling Cider; Medium Sweet Sparkling Perry, and Norbury's own Cherry Wine and Apple Wine. The draught cider comes in ½, 1 and 5 gallon containers and a selection of bottles and glass jars. It is available throughout the year from Crowcroft Packing House, and during the summer months from Norbury's Pick Your Own farm shop. The farm is open during normal licencing hours.

BROAD OAK CIDER

Brian Brunt
Grayfield Road, High Littleton, Avon
Telephone: Bristol (0272) 333154

Broad Oak is a new company which has only emerged on the cider scene in the last few years. They have very quickly become firmly established, and already reckon to make around one million gallons a year. The whole enterprise may be found with some difficulty in a small factory estate near the village, though once inside the vast warehouse all is reassuringly "traditional". Admittedly much of the production is aimed at the pubs and clubs, which demand a commercial cider, and for such customers they have to pasteurise and sweeten. A very popular Superior Cider, in carbonated form, is also on offer, medium or dry, in 1 litre glass bottles.

But the good news is that at Broad Oak traditional draught is also alive and well: it has a very firm local following among those who want their cider as nature intended. This is unpasteurised, and you will find it dry and tangy, cloudy and strong. It appears in a number of pubs and off-licences in the Bristol area, but also goes further afield, for Broad Oak Farmhouse Dry is one of the selection of "Saffron Ciders", which cover the eastern counties. There are in addition a couple of northern agents. Broad Oak Perry, with a similar impeccable pedigree, is also made, though amounts are much less.

BRIMBLECOMBE'S DEVON FARMHOUSE CIDER

Cliff Brimblecombe
Farrant's Farm, Dunsford, Devon
Telephone: Longdown
(039 281) 456

Brimblecombe's Cider is as traditional as you might wish. You go through a farmyard and up a flight of timber steps into a cool dark barn made of Devon cob; once you grow accustomed to the dark you will make out rows of old oak barrels round the walls. Cob webs dangle from the vast oak beams. Outside cats and hens wander happily, but here the business is strictly cider. It has been like this at Farrant's Farm for countless years. Cliff's first memory of cider making was of holding the candle for the cider makers in the barn during the War, but it was nearly 400 years earlier that the barn saw its first barrel. It had up to then been the farmhouse, but at that time a "modern" house was put up, and the barn began its changed function, and became the cider store. You may still admire the old 400 year old press as you sample the contents of the barrels.

The cider is cloudy, orange in colour, and has considerable strength, with a good apple flavour. The sweet is very sweet, and most people opt for the medium, though there is also a dry. Most of the apples used are grown on the farm, and Cliff has planted 120 new trees to keep supplies going. Most are bittersweets, Hang Me Down, Slap me Girls, Sweet Alford, Tom Putt, and some newer varieties. In these days of nylon "cloths" you will be glad to know that here, at least, the cider cheese is built up with straw, as it always has been.

The Brimblecombes advise that you keep the cider as they have, cool and dark. They are of course fortunate, for the temperature in the barn remains constant all the time, but should you not find the space to build a Devon cob barn you will have to make do with a refrigerator. They can provide 1 gallon plastic containers for you, but if the cider is to travel far they ask that if possible you bring some glass demi-johns.

Traditional honey is also on sale: a meal of bread, butter, honey and cider is strongly recommended. Keeping bees in the orchard is in any case a sensible combination, as they are needed to fertilise the trees. The honey is only available, by courtesy of the bees, from August onwards, but you may also buy mulling spices and free range eggs.

Despite the small sign, which is easily missed as you go along the Dunsford to Exeter road, there is a constant stream of callers, all delighted to find an impressive difference from the cider they are used to in the shops. People come from far and wide; on my visit I met customers from Yorkshire, Hastings and northern Spain.

BROMELL'S DEVON FARM CIDER

Eric Bromell
Lower Uppercott, Tedburn St. Mary, near Exeter, Devon
Telephone: Tedburn St. Mary (064 76) 294

Lower Uppercott is first and foremost a working farm. You may find Mr. Bromell is out in the fields when you call, but this will give you an opportunity to admire the scenery and the rural charm while you wait. The farm is on the edge of Dartmoor. If arriving from Exeter, you will have been climbing most of the way, and should be just ready to try a few samples. You may welcome the chance of taking a few pints on board before setting off for the Moors. Eric Bromell manages to combine farming with cider making without apparent effort, though he produces a considerable volume, some 30,000 gallons a year. All the apples come from within ten miles of the farm, and apart from the addition of sweetener to the sweet cider the methods and ingredients used are entirely traditional. The result is very pleasant and powerful, cloudy yellow in colour, strong and full-bodied in taste, with a subtle flavour which gives perhaps a

141

slight hint of peach.

If you propose taking some of the cider away in your car, rather than on foot, ask Mr. Bromell if he can provide some glass jars. He is not a fan of the usual plastic container, unless, that is, you are taking the cider straight back home: he regards it like any other dairy product, and fears for its safety after holiday makers load it into the car boot and cart it round the country for a fortnight before returning to Neasden, Scunthorpe or wherever. If you bring your own containers, which you are also invited to do, he will always recommend that you stick to glass.

The draught cider is sweet, medium sweet, medium, and dry, in sizes from ½ to 50 gallons; there are also 5 gallon polypins, another good way to transport cider, and 1 pint stoneware jars. You will be encouraged to taste the various options before making up your mind: Mr. Bromell finds that everybody's taste differs, and each party of visitors generally ends up taking a selection of types. The criterion for deciding is your taste in sherry, which will be a good guide. In addition to the cider farm vegetables and milk are on sale. If you are taking a walk in the area you may conveniently plan it around the various pub outlets, which are conveniently placed in the vicinity.

BRYMPTON d'EVERCY CIDER

Charles Clive-Ponsonby-Fane
Brympton d'Evercy, near Yeovil, Somerset BA22 8TD
Telephone: Yeovil (093 586) 2528

"Nearly every country house has some quality about it, whether of architecture, sentiment, historical associations or scenery. Brympton has them all." So wrote the late Christopher Hussey. Brympton has been having a soothing effect on people for hundreds of years, with its beautiful, peaceful gardens, its elegant rooms, steeped in history and heritage, and its beguiling atmosphere of unhurried pleasure. It is the family home of Charles and Judy Clive-Ponsonby-Fane, and has been owned by only three families during its long 750 year history. Each generation has added to the buildings, which now make up a veritable architectural history lesson.

The state rooms and extensive gardens are open to the public, and a range of photographic and art exhibitions are held there during the year. A visit makes an excellent day out in delightful surroundings. The old 14th century priest house contains a collection of domestic appliances and an exhibition of cider making through the ages. There are cream teas, and produce from the estate is on sale at the gift and plant shop.

At Brympton cider is not just a thing of the past. Cider making is still alive and well, and the results are on sale in 2½ litre bottles. It is a traditional cider, made from Kingston Blacks and other bitter sweet apples, and enables you to take away with you some of the quintessence of this most English of places. But there is now more than cider. Charles Clive-Ponsonby-Fane, together with his partner Julian Temperley, is producing the west country's version of Calvados, the French apple brandy, from local cider. He has set up a still, which he acquired from Normandy, in part of the museum. Cider is pumped into a header tank, and is then gravity fed through the still. It makes nearly 40 gallons a day, but though you may see it in action you will not yet be able to sample it: it has to mature for several years. In the time scale of Brympton that is only a short time to wait. Brympton is open over Easter, and then from May 1 to the end of September, every day except Thursday and Friday, from 2pm to 6pm.

BULMER'S TRADITIONAL DRAUGHT CIDERS

H. P. Bulmer Limited, UK Drinks Division, The Cider Mills, Plough Lane, Hereford HR4 0LE
Telephone: Hereford (0432) 270622

It is a far cry from a few barrels of home-made cider to a multi-million pound industry spanning the globe, but that is the story of Bulmer's Cider, once a small family concern, and now the world's largest cider makers. The story began in 1887 the year of Queen Victoria's Golden Jubilee, when Percy (HP) Bulmer, younger son of the Rector of Credenhill, near Hereford, first pressed apples from his father's orchard. The Rev. Charles Bulmer had long been an enthusiastic horticulturalist and amateur cider maker, but it was his wife who gave the sound advice that persuaded their 20-year-old son to devote his energies to the drinks market. "Food and drink never go out of fashion," she advised.

In 1888 Percy rented a warehouse in Maylord Street, Hereford, bought apples from local farmers, and made 4,000 gallons of cider. It was well received, and spurred on by his success Percy moved to larger premises in Ryelands Street, where he was joined by his older brother Fred, who became responsible for sales. From then on it has been a story of expansion. In 1911 the company was granted the Royal Warrant, which it has held proudly ever since. In 1936 extra land was bought at nearby Moorfields, and it is there that the major development of the company has taken place, including the opening, in 1978, of a new headquarters building. The firm now stands for more than just cider, and its Overseas Drinks Division controls Bulmer Australia and Red Cheek, a leading American producer of apple juice, while the Pectin Division is one of the largest producers

Apples arriving at Hereford

of pectin in the world, and the sole UK manufacturer. In Great Britain Bulmer has the agency for Perrier and Red Stripe Lager, and through its subsidiary Dent & Reuss it distributes a wide range of quality wines and spirits.

But the cornerstone of the business remains the UK cider market. Bulmers makes about half of the total annual national sales, well over 30 million gallons, and its brand leader, Strongbow, alone accounts for a quarter of all cider sold in the UK. Everything at Bulmer is on a vast scale. Dominating the city, like some giant gas holder, is an enormous holding tank called "Strongbow", which with a capacity of over $1\frac{1}{2}$ million gallons is the largest container of drink in the world. Every year up to 50,000 tons of apples are handled at the mills, and the juice is fermented in a huge, cathedral like underground room housing 120 oak vats, some holding 60,000 gallons. Each of these is named, some after politicians such as Margaret Thatcher, others commemorating worthy members of the firm: but there is a practical purpose to this seemingly sentimental touch, for it is only too easy to get lost in this massive forest, and you need the names to keep your bearings.

Much of the promotion of Bulmer's ciders has been in the field of the keg and bottled varieties. Woodpecker, the best known, was introduced as early as 1896, and it is hard to believe now that Strongbow, its companion, only came into existence comparatively recently, in 1960. But the firm has, from the very earliest days, always made a Traditional Draught Cider, which though less promoted than the other brands, has become increasingly popular, and can now be found all over the country, in polycask and on hand-pump. It is a cask-conditioned cider, which means that a pinch of yeast is added at the casking stage, which allows a secondary fermentation to take place within the cask. This gives a slight sparkle to the drink, and also induces subtle taste changes which enhance its natural flavour. It is slightly cloudy when served, and should be drunk at room temperature. Traditional Draught comes in a range of sweet, medium or dry.

Bulmer also produce a West Country Traditional Draught. This again is a hazy cider, but in this case there is no secondary fermentation or conditioning, thus producing a completely still cider. West Country is available in sweet, medium and extra dry. Both these traditional ciders are made from bitter sweet cider apples, though a small proportion of culinary fruit has always been blended in. Both brands have a good apple flavour, and give a smooth easy drink. Not all traditional ciders are draught, as indeed are all beers. Bulmers makes what might be described as the cider drinker's equivalent of Worthington White Shield, Bulmer's Number 7. It is the oldest of the Bulmer range, dating back to 1890, and has long been recognised as a connoisseur's cider. It is a traditional, still, extra dry cider made exclusively from bitter sweet apples. Being extra dry all the sugars have been fermented out to alcohol, and it can safely be recommended for diabetics. It is also recommended for wine drinkers, as an apperitif or an accompaniment to a meal. The half pint bottle still carries the original label, depicting the Goddess of the apple trees, Pomona, with in the background the early Bulmer's factory in Ryelands Street. Number 7 can often be found in pubs which do not stock traditional draught, and is well worth seeking out.

Bulmer has a fine sense of tradition, and it is largely thanks to the company that traditional cider survived the lean years of the 1950s and 60s. Until recently it maintained a number of old style cider houses throughout the country. Although it has now relinquished them it still keeps a fatherly eye on the new owners, whom it has helped to become established.

BURROW HILL SOMERSET CIDER

Julian Temperley
Pass Vale Farm, Burrow Hill, Kingsbury Episcopi, Martock, Somerset
Telephone: South Petherton (0460) 40782

Julian Temperley makes no bones about it: he is *not* making a cider for the masses. He sticks firmly to the traditions of farm cider making the Somerset way. Though he is sad to see how the large commercial firms have swamped the market, to the extent that most people now believe that "cider" is all fizz and pop, he caters for those who still recognise and appreciate the best. "If we make a cider 5 per cent of the population go nutty about that's good for us," he says. "We cannot, and will not, supply a huge demand. We could not meet a hot summer in Glasgow, you'd have to change your ethics to do that."

The philosophy at Pass Vale Farm is that making cider should be just blending apples, not mixing chemicals: cider should be made "in the orchard", by getting the fruit right. Here there are 5,000 trees in 40 acres of orchard, including three acres of recently planted Kingston Blacks. The cider is made from Dabinetts, blended with sharper varieties. Among the apples which feature in Burrow Hill are such names as Sweet Alford, Tremletts Bitter, Porters Perfection, Yarlington Mill, Brown Snout, Chisel Jersey, Somerset Red Streak, and of course Kingston Black. Julian's adherance to tradition – he never uses artificial flavouring or colouring – is constantly vindicated in competitions at national level: in 1986 for instance his cider came top of the tasting in *Wine & Spirit Magazine,* beating 60 English and 10 French ciders. The judges described it as "a bone dry cider for the cider connoisseur, or indeed the wine connoisseur. Characterful, with good bitter-sweet flavour, a touch of tannin, quite high acidity, delicious fruit on both nose and palate, and a long apply finish".

If you visit the farm you may judge for yourself. You will be welcome to sample the cider, and to inspect the cider house. Here the cider has been made for the last 100 years, fermented in oak vats, and sold from wooden barrels. You will find no sign of chemicals: the only intruder is likely to be the bat who lives in the rafters. Burrow Hill is something of a local landmark, rising suddenly 200 feet above the Somerset levels: take time as you enjoy your sample to gaze at the outstanding view.

The farm is open all day Saturday, and there is normally someone available to sell you cider until 6pm during the rest of the week, though it is wise to phone first, for this is a working farm: on Sunday the farm is closed. Most of the cider

sold is dry, by far the best to bring out the full subtle flavour, but sweeter brands are also available. You may bring your own container, or buy the cider in 1 gallon or 5 gallon containers on sale there. Also sold are mulling spices.

CHURCHWARD'S CIDER

Vic Churchward
Yalberton Farm, Paignton, Devon
Telephone: Paignton
(0803) 558157

On a sunny day it's tempting to laze the time away on the beaches of Torbay, but wet or fine it is always worth making the effort to climb into the hills behind Paignton to Yalberton Farm. Once there Vic will be pleased to revive you with a sample of his latest product. As you drink bear in mind that you are enjoying a prize winning brand. Churchwards won three 1st prizes in the 1986 Devon County Show. His cider is made from mixed cider apples, fermented in their own yeasts with no unnatural processes, and comes in dry, Devon Mix, medium and sweet. You may bring your own container for a fill up, or buy from Vic's considerable range: 1 litre to 5 gallon polycask; 3 pint and 1 gallon glass; 1 and 2 pint, $\frac{1}{2}$ gallon and 5 litre stone flagons. The farm is open during normal hours, and should you wish to combine your visit with a spot of sight seeing Paignton Zoo is only just down the road. Churchward Cider may be found in polycask or handpump in a number of local outlets.

COATES FARMHOUSE CIDER

Lyn Hughes, Marketing Manager Showerings Ltd., Kilver Street, Shepton Mallet, Somerset BA4 5ND
Telephone: Shepton Mallet (0749) 3333

R. N. Coates Cider Company was founded at Nailsea in 1925, and was bought by Showerings in

1956. In 1968 it was joined by the old established William Gaymers, of Attleborough, Norfolk, which had been in existence since 1770, together with Whiteways, of Whimple in Devon, which was also acquired. Whiteways continues in Devon, though now concentrating on wines, the Attleborough factory produces Olde English bottled and keg cider, and the new factory at Shepton Mallet makes Babycham, and traditional draught cider.

The firm is fully committed to continuing its traditional range, and it has in fact expanded it with the introduction of the cask-conditioned Addlestones. Its Coates Farmhouse dry and medium are both widely distributed, from Tyne-Tees to the South West, with South Wales, the South West, East Anglia, and Birmingham being the most important areas in terms of volume. The cider has a fair aroma, is cloudy orange in colour, with a strong consistency, fair apple flavour, and good aftertaste, and is worth searching for: a pleasant cider for drinking by the pint. Showering's commitment to tradition extends further than cider: within the grounds of the Shepton Mallet plant is the huge railway viaduct which until 1966 carried the Somerset & Dorset Railway on its journey from Bath to Bournemouth. The firm has acquired it, and planted out around it a splendid garden.

COOMBES SOMERSET GOLDEN BLEND CIDER

Chris Coombes
Japonica Farm, Mark, near Highbridge, Somerset
Telephone: Mark Moor
(027 864) 265

Chris is the third generation of the family firm, which began in 1919, and has been pressing on ever since. There are five acres of orchards on the farm, and the rest of the fruit comes from nearby. The cider is made totally traditionally, with no artificial additions or processes: you may check this in the autumn, when you may view the whole process. At other times you may inspect all the equipment. Varieties of cider apples used include Morgan Sweet, Brown Snout, Breakwell's Seedling, Somerset Red Streak, Taylor's, Yarlington, Chisel Jersey, Dabinett and Kingston Black. The labels promise that "Coombes Cider will make your smile grow wider and wider", and I vaguely remember that I was grinning like a Cheshire cat when I finally left!

The range caters for all tastes: sweet; medium sweet; medium; dry and vintage. You may bring your own container, or 1 gallon plastic containers, various sizes in bottles, and ½ gallon stone flagons may be purchased. Sampling prior to buying is welcomed. Sparkling perry is also on sale, and for those who prefer the non alcoholic alternative there is pure apple juice. There is a caravan site adjoining, and being situated on the Wells to Highbridge road seems an ideal holiday location: if it rains for the whole fortnight get Chris to rig up a pipeline direct from the vats!

CORNISH SCRUMPY COMPANY

David Healey
Callestock Cider Farm, Penhallow, near Truro, Cornwall
Telephone: Truro (0872) 573356

This is a family company, which until recently operated from Domellick Farm, near St. Austell, but such has been its success that it outgrew its premises there, and is now installed at a larger farm at Penhallow. Callestock Cider Farm has a large range of traditional barns around an attractive courtyard, and the land includes a standard tree cider orchard. David Healey is also planting a further 30 acres, with varieties such as Yarlington Mill, a mild bitter sweet, Dabinett, a full bitter sweet, Harry Masters Jersey, Sweet Coppin, Sweet Alford, and Northwood, all South Devon sweets. The trees have been selected for high quality juices, and resistance to scab and canker, potential problems in these parts. He is also including some Ashton Brown Jersey and Dunkerton Late, valuable for their ability to harvest late. The aim is to become completely self-sufficient for fruit in due course.

The firm's popularity has largely been due to its cheerful publicity, which promises that with Cornish Scrumpy you will be "legless but smiling". People always assume that scrumpy is stronger than ordinary cider, and David helps satisfy this assumption, by testing the specific gravity before fermentation, and if necessary adding sugar to raise the alcohol content to just under the legal limit of 8·5 per cent. It is a policy which has certainly found the holiday makers smiling, and has seen Cornish Scrumpy become the largest cider maker in the Duchy. Apart from the sugar, and replacing the natural yeasts with a champagne yeast, the cider is pressed and fermented in the traditional farm style. The apples are bitter sweets, with a few Bramleys or equivalent to raise the acidity when necessary.

A visit to the farm will prove most rewarding – but be sure you come away with your legs. You may inspect the various barns in which the cider making takes place: the Press House, where a large wooden hopper holding up to 4 tons of apples loaded through the roof links to a modern hydraulic press; the Fermenting Barn, containing a number of 23,000 litre fermenting vats; the Racking Barn, where the cider is drawn off, left to clear and mature; and the Bottling Barn, where the blending and bottling is carried out. Don't miss the Round Barn, which contains a large horse drawn granite mill with its original granite press bed (unique to Cornwall and the Channel Islands), and the Traditional Cider House containing a collection of hand presses and mills through the ages.

There is a shop, where the range of cider, scrumpy, and wine can be sampled before buying. The Scrumpy is in dry, medium dry and medium sweet, and is over 8 per cent alcohol. There is also Cornish Gold, a sparkling cider, medium dry, and about 4½ per cent alcohol, in 1½ litre PET bottles. In addition, and only available at the shop, are perry and elderberry wine. There is a wide range of containers, including 1 gallon polyjars, 2·4 and 5 litre carry kegs, 5 gallon polycasks, and various sizes of stone jar.

The shop is open every day except Sunday, from 9am to 6pm. Should you run out, as no doubt you will, you will be sure to come across Cornish Scrumpy quite a lot during your time in the far west.

COTSWOLD FARMHOUSE CIDER

R. W. Smith
Smiths Garden Centre, Station Road, Chipping Campden, Gloucestershire GL55 6JD
Telephone: Evesham
(0386) 840367

A visit to Chipping Campden is well worth while. First there is the picturesque Cotswold town to enjoy, with its splendid Wool Church, the 17th century Market Hall, and many fine old houses, some dating back to the 14th century. Cotswold Farmhouse Cider is sold at Smiths Garden Centre, just ½ mile from the centre of Chipping Campden on the Shipston-on-Stour road. The cider is made from a local mixture of dessert, culinary, and cider apples, and is available in ½, 1, and 5 gallon containers from refrigerated barrels. You may taste before you buy and choose from Sweet, Medium, or Dry. It is a smooth refreshing cider. While you are there, spend some time looking round the Garden Centre, where many improvements have taken place. There is always a good selection of plants, shrubs and trees to choose from, as well as a good range of most other garden requirements.

COUNTRY FAYRE CIDER

Miss Jacobs
West Stoughton, Wedmore,
Somerset
Telephone: Wedmore
(0934) 712801

Miss Jacob's products may be found chiefly in such tourist spots as Cheddar, under the title of "Zummerzet Kneecracker". It is a popular and good cider, and passes the critical palates of the experts. I cannot speak for your knees, but it will certainly put a spot of sunshine into your life. There is a draught version, in dry or medium, also 1 litre bottles and a wide range of stone jars, from 5 oz. to 1 gallon, plus plastic containers.

COUNTRYMAN CIDER

Nigel W. Lawrence
Felldownhead, Milton Abbot,
Tavistock, Devon PL19 0QR
Telephone: Milton Abbot
(082 287) 226

"Lancaster's Countryman Cider" was for many years well known in south Devon. Over five generations its popularity had grown, and by the early 1970s the then owner, Horace Lancaster, decided to give up farming and concentrate on making cider full time. He retired in 1978, and Nigel Lawrence took over, changing the name to just Countryman Cider. But even to this day however you may still hear people talk about "Lancaster's Cider". The business has continued to prosper. In 1985 the St. Austell Brewery acquired a 49 per cent stake in the firm, which opened access to a large new market. Countryman is now exensively available in the brewery's tied houses and off-licences, and through their free trade outlets. A special brand, "Cornish Wreckers Scrumpy", is produced for this trade.

Though the firm may have grown, the quality has remained the same. Being perched some 600 feet up in the hills you will find no orchards at Felldownhead; but the best local apples are bought in. No concentrates or extraneous ingredients are used. The apple juice is fermented using the natural yeasts, and apart from filtering to remove any bits of apple and yeast the method of manufacture is completely traditional. Most of the sales remain as still natural farm cider; clear orange colour, full bodied, and of a wine-like consistency, with a subtle flavour which might remind you of sherry.

Countryman "Scrumpy" is available in dry, medium or sweet in draught form for takeaway at the farm, and also in PET bottles, stone jars, plastic containers and bag-in-box. In addition a sparkling version is sold, called "Devon Gold". There is a cider museum to view, and the farm is open to visitors from 9am to 5pm on Monday to Friday, throughout the year. The cider may be found in a large number of local off-licences and pubs, though some of the latter only stock it during the summer months.

COWHILL CIDER

John Tymko
Cowhill Farm, near Oldbury on Severn, Avon

Oldbury is right out on the flat expanse of the Severn estuary, but as you approach you will see a church on top of a hill in the otherwise regular landscape. This is Cowhill, and just over the far side lies the small Cowhill Farm and its orchards.

Until a few years ago the cider here was made by a well-known local character, Tommy Jones, but now his son-in-law has taken over the task. Here you are light years away from the high tech and chemistry of the commercial cider makers. Milling and pressing takes place in the open air, under a makeshift erection of corrugated iron and wood. The cider press is such as you more usually see nowadays on cider makers trademarks, but this old wooden machine is still in use.

From the very start John believes in letting nature dictate her own terms. For him this is part of the fun, not knowing until you taste it what the result will be like. This philosophy would not appeal to the large firms, whose customers demand a consistent product, but John is quite content to let them go their way while he goes his. He makes a cider for the enthusiast, who welcomes different taste experiences. The old oak cider barrels are set up in the orchard, under the trees from which the juice derived. Some of the taps are dripping, and the odd horse pauses to catch some of the liquid as it falls. There are some well established trees, but among them have been added some new standards, such as Yarlington Mill, Dabinett, Kingston Black, and Malvern Sweet. It is here, in the orchard, that John does his blending, before any crushing or pressing. After that, it's up to the cider. This then is cider as it used to be, and now so seldom is. No additions, no subtractions, and above all no interference. When John finally samples a new barrel in the orchard he is often surprised, for nature is nothing if not unpredictable. If, like John, you have a thirst for the genuine article, head for the church on the hill, and share in his pleasant surprise.

CROSSMAN'S PRIME FARMHOUSE CIDER

Ben Crossman
Mayfield Farm, Hewish, near
Weston-Super-Mare, Avon
BS24 6RQ
Telephone: Weston-Super-Mare
(0934) 833174

Ben's farm is conveniently situated in holiday country, on the main road from Bristol, and should on no account be passed. His cider is made from a number of varieties of cider apple, including Bulmer's Norman, Yarlington Mill, Dabinett, Michelin, Chisel Jersey, and the legendary Kingston Black. The dry version is entirely traditional, while the sweet includes added sweetener. If camping or self-catering nearby you will be glad to know that you may also obtain fresh farm eggs and general farm produce, a further good excuse for a call. The cider is available in medium, dry and sweet, either in your own container, or in $\frac{1}{2}$, 1 and 5 gallon containers from the farm. Hours of opening are 8.30am to 7.30pm on weekdays, extended to 9pm during the summer months and 12 noon to 2pm on Sundays.

TONY CULLIMORE'S GENUINE FARMHOUSE CIDER

Tony Cullimore
Berkeley Heath Farm, Berkeley,
Gloucestershire
Telephone: Dursley (0453) 810220

At Tony's shop you can buy any-thing you need, from a brace of decoy pigeons to a roll of wire fence, for this is a store for general agricultural requirements. It is good to know that local farmers still consider that part of their requirements is a regular top up of good honest cider. The cider is made from a mixture of cider apples and culinary fruit, in the traditional way, with sugar added to the sweet variety. Dry and medium are also available, and you may try them first before you choose. It is sold in 1 gallon con-tainers, or you may bring your own. You may also buy apple wine, mead, and sometimes perry. As well as the decoy pigeons there is a range of real farmhouse food for sale. The shop is very near Ber-keley Castle, an impressive 12th century building, in which Edward II was murdered in 1327. Tony is open for business from 8.30am to 1pm, and 2pm to 5.30pm, on Mon-day to Friday, 9am to 1pm on Saturday. He is also open on Saturday afternoon and Sunday at certain times, but please phone first and check.

DERRICK'S CIDER

Tony Derrick
Cheddar Valley Cheese Depot, The
Gorge, Cheddar, Somerset
Telephone: Cheddar (0934) 743079

In 1762 the Rev. Augustus Top-lady, on a trip to these parts, shel-tered in the rocks during a violent rain storm, and received divine inspiration to pen the words to the now famous hymn "Rock of Ages". Nowadays it is the crowds rather than the clouds which are likely to get to you, and if you write any-thing on the postcard home it will probably be "Help!". Cheddar has become a tourist mecca, and up and down the gorge you may see the grockells (the native term of derision for the visitors) clutching plastic containers of a yellow liquid and making Mummerset rustic noises. It is easy to be ripped off, and find yourself buying cider which hits your wallet and your legs. In the midst of the throng you need to keep your wits about you, and spend wisely. Fortunately help is near at hand, for at Tony Derrick's shop you will find a good selection of ciders, with rustic names, but reasonable prices. Country Bumpkin sweet or dry; and Tanglefoot medium sweet. The dry cider is totally traditional, while the sweet has sugar added. They come in a variety of sizes: containers from ½ litre to 1 gallon, a range of bottles, and stone flagons. Tony's cider is a clear orange col-our, with a good apple aroma, strong tangy apple taste, and pleasant aftertaste. He also sells a large choice of English wines, plus mead.

DUNKERTON'S CIDER

Ivor and Susie Dunkerton
Hays Head, Luntley, Pembridge,
Leominster, Herefordshire
HR6 9ED
Telephone: Pembridge
(05447) 653

I'm not sure whether I'm more con-cerned about Ivor and Susie's theology or their morality. They call their bottled cider "Old Adam", and their trade mark depicts a naked couple in the Gar-den of Eden, contemplating a fully laden apple tree and wondering what to do next. Actually to set the record straight the Good Book never says that it all began with an apple, but in the case of Dunker-ton's it did – and not so long ago. We won't ask who the natural ones are supposed to be, but it does make the point about original purity, which is what Ivor and Susie's cider is all about.

From the start the Dunkertons have concentrated on quality. They specialise in producing strong, full-bodied ciders made only from genuine cider fruit. Apples such as Foxwhelp, Binet Rouge, Yarlington Mill, Cider Ladies Finger, and the unique Kingston Black, are pressed and fermented separately. The ciders are blended according to their individual flavours and qualities — tannin, sharpness and sugar content — producing final blends which are still and aromatic, with a very respectable alcohol content of around 6 per cent plus. No water or colouring is added. Great care is taken to ensure that all the fruit supplied is unsprayed by chemicals.

Apples come from neighbouring farms, and the orchards contain varieties unique to the area. Sometimes a cider is made from one variety only, rather than a blend, such as Goddard, and of course Kingston Black. There is also a perry, made from the increasingly rare Herefordshire perry trees, including Moorcroft, Blakeney Red, Barland, Butt, and Red Horse. Even before you sample their wares you will catch some of the Dunkerton's enthusiasm for their cider and perry, which they handle with the same care as a wine, and indeed it does have something of the character of a light wine about it. There are four degrees of sweetness: Traditional Dry, crisp, fruity and full bodied; Medium Dry, mellow and fragrant; Medium Sweet, refreshing and tasty; and Sweet, rich flavoured. For those who prefer their cider to have a slight "lift", though without being fizzy, there is the medium dry "Old Adam", bottles of which are widely available in local outlets. The cider is sold in 1 litre bottles, 1 gallon jars, and 5 gallon polycasks. The farm is open from 10am to 7pm, Monday to Saturday, and 12 noon to 2pm on Sunday, during the summer; from 4pm to 7pm only on Monday to Friday, and 10am to 7pm on Saturday during the winter.

ENGLISH FARM CIDER CENTRE

John Pile
Middle Farm, Firle, Lewes, East Sussex
Telephone: Ripe (032 183) 411 or 303

For those of us not fortunate to live in the west the English Farm Cider Centre is a godsend. John Pile and his team collect a vast selection of ciders from not only the west country, but also East Anglia and the heart of England, by the van load, on regular runs, and bring them back to what must be one of the most comprehensive cider displays in the land. Middle Farm is a distribution centre, with ample storage in an insulated air conditioned environment. Not that the cider stays there long, for it soon goes out into pubs and off-licences in the south east, and a large proportion gets snapped up by an ever growing number of visitors. Callers are treated to what amounts to a live cider exhibition, which gives them a unique introduction into the delightful variety of traditional draught cider, and indeed perry too.

John looks for farms using only purpose-grown cider apples, and only selects those cider makers who can guarantee to supply a product of consistently high quality using traditional methods. You may pick, or rather drink, your way through this comprehensive array, and you will be encouraged to do so, for John considers sampling by his visitors to be important, because of the wide variation and flavour and bouquet to be found: this is due to the many different apples used, the type of soil, the season experienced in any particular region, the cider making tradition of the individual firm, the fermentation, and the degree of sweetness.

Usually available are: Churchward, Gray, Hancock, and Inch from Devon; Bulmer, Black Bull, Knights, Crumpton Oaks, Dunkerton, Symonds and Weston from Herefordshire; Burrow Hill, Coates, Country Fayre, Perrys, Rich, Sheppy, Taunton, and Wilkins from Somerset; Thatcher and Williams Bros. from Avon; James White and Aspall from Suffolk; and Biddenden from Kent.

You may take your own containers, and 2½ litre, 1 gallon and 5 gallon containers are also available, plus various sized bottles and stone flagons. The Farm Shop sells fruit, vegetables, eggs, butter, fresh cream, milk from the farm's own dairy herd, farm made yoghurts and ice cream, an excellent range of over 25 English cheeses, home made jams and marmalades, lemon curd, chutney, honey, biscuits, various pure fruit juices and flavoured vinegars, bottled ciders, perrys and English wines, fresh bread, home made cakes, frozen food and pies, and an assortment of house plants: there is also a butchery department.

Opening hours are 10am to 6pm Monday to Friday, 10am to 5pm Saturday and Sunday. Nearby are the South Downs and the sea, and many other attractions, should you need an excuse. But I suspect that wet or fine, Middle Farm will soon become an established part of your way of life, and the bucket and spade, and walking boots, will have to take second place.

You may have noticed some unusual ciders on offer in some of the south east pubs in the Guide — these are probably supplied from the Centre. For full up to the minute information on outlets in your area please telephone for details.

FARMER JOHN'S DEVONSHIRE FARMHOUSE CIDER

John Cligg
Parson's Farm, Newton
Poppleford, Sidmouth, Devon
Telephone: Colaton Raleigh (0395)
68152

At Farmer John's there is something for even the younger members of the family, for not only is cider made on the premises but also the most delicious Devonshire ice cream. There is in fact an ice cream parlour, and space for the children to play, while you get on with the important business. Farmer John's Cider is made in the traditional way, as produced by Devon farmers for generations. John Cligg's father, a farmer, used to make cider like that as a young man, as did his father before him. The cider press dates back to 1835, and John assures me it is still in good working order, though I noticed that he has just bought a hydraulic press, so perhaps it can now look forward to retirement.

The quality of the cider is governed by the type of apples used, and the soil they are grown in is of great importance. The rich red soil of Devon is renowned for producing good fruit, and John takes every care to ensure a quality product by only using locally grown cider apples. He uses no concentrates, and the juice is fermented by its own natural yeast, and racked and matured in the old way. It is a clean still cider, and comes in two types: Original, a bottled high quality vintage cider, which will be appreciated by the wine drinker; and Old Rascal Original Scrumpy, a robust "man's drink".

You will thoroughly enjoy your visit to Parson's Farm. You can sit and enjoy refreshment in quiet surroundings, with ample car parking space, and let the day float by on a haze of cider and ice cream. After a few pints of Old Rascal

John became quite poetic, and burst into verse:

> *Me Grandad drunk this special brew,*
> *And lived til 'e was ninety two,*
> *'E said, "me lad you do like I,*
> *And then you'll live until you die."*
> *I learnt me trade from this advice,*
> *To keep the cider clear and nice.*
> *Made from this cider apple brew,*
> *I'll pass it on from him to you.*
>
> *PS. Granny liked it too!*

GODSHILL FARMHOUSE CIDER

Peter Cramp
The Cider Barn, Godshill,
Isle of Wight
Telephone: Isle of Wight
(0983) 840 680

Godshill is an attractive village of thatched houses, dominated by a 14th century church, and is a must for all visitors to the Isle of Wight. For those whose interests extent to other things, it is also part of the required itinerary, for here is the home of the Godshill Cider Company. Godshill Farmhouse Cider is made mostly from cider apples, including Yarlington Mill, Chisel Jersey, and Dabinett. The sweet variety has some sugar added, but most is unfiltered, and none is pasteurised. You may sample the various types on offer; medium sweet, medium, and dry. $\frac{1}{4}$ and 1 gallon containers are available, also 1 and 2 litre bottles, and 2 oz., $\frac{1}{2}$ pint, and 1 pint stone flagons.

You may also buy apple wine and mead, plus a wide choice of souvenirs such as cider mugs, sweatshirts, tee shirts, and badges, to say nothing of jams, mustard, and other general produce. The Cider Barn is centrally sited in the village, and is open from April to September, 10am to 6pm daily, though cider is not permitted to be sold on Sunday.

GRAY'S FARM CIDER

Mr. & Mrs. Tom Gray
Halstow, Tedburn St. Mary,
Exeter, Devon
Telephone: Tedburn St. Mary
(06476) 236

Gray's Farm Cider is made at Halstow, a Domesday Manor on the Tedburn St. Mary to Dunsford road. It has been farmed for 300 years by the Gray family, who are the oldest established cider makers in Devon. The cellar, a listed building of stone and Devonshire cob, custom built for cider making and storage, is cool in summer and warm in winter, giving ideal conditions for fermenting and storing cider. The cider is made by a traditional and entirely natural process, without preservatives or colouring. About 20 acres of apple trees grow on the farm, others come from local farms with orchards on Culm measures, the best soil type for heavy gravity slow fermenting cider. Most of the apples, which are all cider fruit, are sweets and bittersweets, with some sharps, and possess lovely names such as Fair Maid of Devon, Hangy Down Clusters, Sweet Alford, Slap me Girl, and Johnny Andrews. Bramleys, Coxes and most dessert and culinary apples are considered unacceptable.

Many of the old orchards are now reaching the end of their effective lives, so the Grays are planting new ones, with modern bush trees, again to produce mostly sweet and bitter sweet cider apples. The Grays make about 20,000 gallons of cider each year, and it is a strong and palatable drink. The family drinks it themselves each evening, which ensures that the quality is constantly monitored. The basic range is sweet, medium and dry, but you are invited to try them out and create your own blend before buying. The farm is open to callers from 7.30am to 7.30pm on Mondays to Saturdays.

HALL'S CIDER

Stan Hall
Wisteria Farm, Fordgate, near
Bridgwater, Somerset
Telephone: Weston Zoyland
(027 869) 568

Stan is a farmer, with a taste for
cider. He likes nothing more in the
early morning than to come down
to the cider barn and pour himself
a pint from one of the many
wooden barrels lining the walls.
He has been doing it for years, and
declares that it is the best way he
knows to start the day. Even in
these days there are still plenty of
small cider makers in the country,
and this is never more true than in
Somerset, "where the Zider apples
grow". The main problem is tracking them down, for they are mostly
farmers who make enough to keep
them, their friends, and the village, happy. It was in fact a chance
conversation in the village pub
that led to me being introduced to
Stan Hall. I recommend that in
this part of the world a few discreet
enquiries may yield similar
dividends, for there are other
Stans around too, if you can find
them.

In the barn Stan will talk lov-
ingly of Bitter Jeyes, Sweet Hangdown, Woodbine, Bulmers Wonder, Sweet Lemon, Old Soldiers,
Dunkey Chuckers, Sheeps Nose,
Crimson King, Sour Hangdown,
and Stickfire. Anyone eavesdrop-
ping might think he was going
through the runners for the 2.30 at
Wincanton, but these are of course
the varieties of cider apple which
he uses. He will show you the press
where it all begins, and then let
you try some of the finished product, a strong, dry, farmhouse
cider, of which he is justly proud.
You will need little persuading to
buy some to take away: if you have
not come with a container Stan can
provide one, from 1 gallon or
upwards. On my visit I walked to
the farm along the towpath of the
canal from Bridgwater, and this is
perhaps most in the spirit of the
experience: but if you must, you
can leave the M5 at Junction 24,
though a car will rather cramp
your style for sampling in the barn

HANCOCK'S DEVON CIDER

N. W. Hancock
Clapworthy Mill, South Molton,
North Devon
Telephone: South Molton (076 95)
2678

The Hancock family has been
making their traditional Devon
Cider with skills handed down
from father to son for at least 100
years. They started with the old
style presses, but for the last 50
years have used hydraulic oper-
ated presses, working at $1\frac{1}{2}$ tons
pressure per square inch. The
apples are bought locally, bitter
sweets for quality, blended with
others to get the right aroma. The
cider is highly regarded, and over
the years has won more than 40
prizes. They are rightly proud of it,
and have invented an acronym
from their own name – Have A
Noggin Cause Ours Can Kick
Some; this says something for
their cider's strength, not to say
their own ingenuity. After a few
pints perhaps you'll start making
up your own acronyms!

A trip to Clapworthy Mill makes
an ideal day out: it is situated in
the lovely Bray Valley, some three
miles south west of South Molton
on the B3226 from Exeter. Once
there you may buy not only cider
but also honey and clotted cream,
see a colour photo exhibition on
cider making, and inspect the craft
centre. There is a good range of
cider on offer: Farm Scrumpy,
which is extra dry, dry, medium
dry or sweet, in 1 gallon jars, or
bottles of medium sweet, medium
dry or scrumpy in 2 litre size.
Opening hours are Monday to
Saturday 9-1 and 2-5.30pm; Sunday 10.30-1pm. The Mill is open on
Spring and Summer Bank Holidays.

HARTLAND'S FARMHOUSE CIDER

Derek Hartland
Flat Farm, Eldersfield,
Gloucestershire
Telephone: Staunton Court
(045 284) 213

Ray Hartland and his son Derek farm 52 acres in this quiet part of Gloucesterhire, with fine views across to the Malvern Hills in the west. They mostly concentrate on cattle and sheep, though a number of free range hens (rescued from a battery unit) also wander happily in the yard. The whole set up is as traditional as they come. The cider making is a father and son enterprise, and an old man of 80 also helps with the actual pressing. An elderly hen called Alfie presides in the cider barn and makes sure all goes well. She is the most enthusiastic customer, and keeps sampling the barrels to check the quality; her course around the place is somewhat erratic.

It is best to allow plenty of time for your visit. Life is delightfully relaxed in rural Gloucestershire, and Ray and Derek will keep you entertained for hours with country tales that will make you imagine you've stepped into the script of the Archers. All the while you will, I am sure, have a glass in your hand, and be trying the magnificent product, which will spoil you for ever for the bland offerings on the supermarket shelves. It is obviously a totally addictive drink: most of the village seems to live on it, and even the former Bishop of Worcester, who lives nearby, comes in for a drop.

The range is sweet, medium and dry, and there is also a perry, which you must try too. Come armed with your container, and make your choice. As you will gather, it is worth making the effort to get to the farm – you could walk along the bank of the Severn from Gloucester if you felt energetic. You may however also find Hartlands Cider in other places, it is on the range of Westrays Cider, who distribute in the north of the country, and may appear from time to time at beer festivals.

HASCOMBE CIDER

Otto Caslavsky
Hascombe Vineyard, Lodge Farm,
Hascombe, Godalming, Surrey
GU8 4AT
Telephone: Hascombe
(048 632) 343

It is good to be able to report a cider so near to London, especially as it is easily possible to combine a visit there with a few pints at the Ram. You might even be able to walk there after they call last orders, and be back in time for the start of proceedings in the evening. It is also accessible by bus, Alder Valley no. 246 between Godalming and Cranleigh, though there are only about five a day.

They make a medium dry cider, still, clear and filtered. There are two brands, a scrumpy, a young cider, and a vintage, over a year old, and stronger: this latter is well over 6 per cent alcohol content. It is perhaps not surprising that being a vineyard they should treat their cider with the love and care of a wine. They are concerned for its welfare, and unlike many cider makers, who invite you to come and fill up, they do not permit you to bring your own container. Otto explained the logic of this to me, which basically is that they are not prepared to take any chances with what you might have had in the container before: almost anything could taint the cider, and of course it is always the cider which gets the blame. I must say he does have a point, and one wonders just how many complaints voiced by angry holiday makers when they open their cider up are due to the previous contents rather than the cider "not travelling well". Here they ensure good travelling too, for the cider is sold in 1 litre screw top glass bottles, either singly, or if you are feeling thirsty, by the crate.

The good news is that Hascombe Vineyard is open all Saturday and Sunday, from 10am till dusk: the bad news is that they close on Monday and Tuesday, though they reopen from Wednesday to Friday, at the same times, so there is plenty of opportunity to pay a call.

HECK'S FARMHOUSE CIDER

John Hecks
9 & 11 Middle Leigh, Street, Somerset
Telephone: Street (0458) 42367

You automatically expect a farmhouse cider maker to be miles out in the wilds, probably down a muddy track which does terrible things to the car springs, or turns your ankle over. Many of them are, and such are not for the faint hearted or inadequately shod. But here, for once, is a cider maker just off the street, if you'll pardon the pun. It is a family business, which has been going strong since 1896, and combines a cider and general produce store, in the centre of the town. It must be greatly appreciated by all the inhabitants.

Hecks Farmhouse Cider is traditionally made, from a number of varieties of cider apple, among them Kingston Black, Loyal Drain, Doves, and Dabinett. A certain amount of sugar is added to the sweet brand, but that is the only extra process. It is a prize winning cider: John took the Devon County Championship with it in 1985, and was runner up in 1986 – no mean feat, for many of the names in this guide were competing, and none of them make a bad drop. Sweet, medium and dry are all offered, and may be sampled. 1 and ½ gallon carry kegs are available, or you may bring your own. General farm and garden produce is also on sale. The open-

ing hours are from 9am to 6pm Monday to Saturday.

To reach the store from the middle of Street, turn out of the High Street into Vestry Road, then keep straight into Merryman Road and Oriel Road. At the junction with Middle Leigh you will find Hecks' to the right.

HENRY'S CIDER

Harold and Dawn Pring
Tanpits Cider Farm, Tanpits Lane, Bathpool, near Taunton, Somerset
Telephone: Taunton (0823) 70663

Cider has been made here for a hundred years, started by Harold's great grandfather, who's name was Henry. In the early days of motor transport Henry's broke new ground, by taking a barrel round on a lorry and filling up the jars of the eager locals. The cider is made with local fruit, and is all matured in wood, after being broken down in a splendid old stone cider mill. Made by Dening & Son, of Chard, this is a survivor of the once familiar portable mill, which used to go from farm to farm crushing the farmer's apples in the orchard. The fruit is poured in at the top into a large hopper, and passes through a pair of granite rollers, turned by hand, to fall into a trough at the base. Modernity has however taken over from there on, in the form of a hydraulic Bucher press, which produces about 50 gallons from each cheese.

All this may be inspected in the specially built barn, where it is hoped to start a small museum. From here the cider, which comes in dry and sweet, may be sampled. The sweet variety has artificial sweetener added, the dry is entirely natural. You may bring your own container, or buy in a ½ gallon plastic container, and a range of 1 pint, 2 pint, and 1 gallon stone jars. The farm also sells its own goats milk and eggs, and at least on the occasion of my visit, kittens. The best way to approach the farm is by the canal towpath from Taunton. At Bathpool cross the canal by a timber swing bridge, and turn left along Tanpits Lane. Henry's is about 100 yards on the right. From the A38 turn into Tanpits Lane just north of the canal bridge.

HUNT'S DEVON CIDER

W. Hunt
Higher Yalberton Farm, Collaton St. Mary, near Paignton, Devon
Telephone: Paignton (0803) 557694

Holiday makers in the Torbay area don't have far to go for their supplies of cider. As you lie on the beach at Paignton you may glance inland towards the rising ground behind the town, and say to yourself "There's liquid gold in them there hills". At Higher Yalberton you will find in fact, a choice of cider makers side by side. One is Mr. Churchward, previously described, the other is Mr. Hunt.

Hunt's Devon scrumpy is as traditional as you could wish for. Each barrel may vary, for no chemicals are added to control the natural processes, and for many this is its attraction. If you are looking for a bland "pub" cider then forget it, but if you prefer a good, strong, full-flavoured cider of body and character, you have come to the right place. Should you want proof that Hunts is worth hunting for, join the queue at the door behind the customers who have come back for more. You may, like them, bring your container for a fill up, or buy one there. After the usual sample you will be finally converted.

INCH'S CIDER

Derek Inch
Inch's Cider Company, Western Barn, Hatherleigh Road, Winkleigh, North Devon

Telephone: Winkleigh (083 783) 363/560

In 1916 the young Sam Inch was taken on at one of the local farms, on condition that he would not be paid, but at the end of the year could help himself to the apples in the orchard. This did Sam no harm at all, for he got far more from selling the fruit than ever he would have done on a farm worker's wage. Sam soon turned his hand to cider making, and produced two barrels. The problem then was how and where to sell it. Here fate took a hand, for Sam invited the travelling watchmaker round one day to advise him on a grandfather clock he'd just bought. The watchmaker soon told Sam the clock was beyond repair, but as a reward for his trouble he was offered a taste of the cider. The watchmaker was impressed, and through his help Sam was able to deliver the two barrels to his first customer, the White Hart at North Tawton. They must have liked it, as they are still taking it to this day.

From that time Sam never looked back, and Inch's Cider soon became the staple diet for many Devon folk. In recent years its fame has spread far further than its native heath, and it can now be found widely throughout the country, though still in greatest quantity in Devon. Western Barn may sound, and even look, delightfully

rural as you approach, but once through the gate it has every appearance of a thriving and expanding enterprise. Modern fork lift trucks operate in the huge concrete yard, and there is an air of efficiency about the place. In the small shop however you will find that the old rustic atmosphere still survives. The air is thick with rich Devon accents from staff and local customers alike.

Inch's is still a family firm, one of the largest of the small cider makers, now making 1 million gallon per year. Much modern equipment has been installed, such as sophisticated bottling plant, and modern methods of making the cheeses are used, which take only 15 minutes, rather different from the old days. But the important things have not, and according to Derek Inch, will not, change. He strives to keep to traditional methods, and in fact still uses his father's original recipe from 1916, which he in turn got from a book printed in 1646: you can't get much more traditional than that.

The one thing you won't see at Western Barn is orchards: there is just one token tree on the farm. Most of the cider apples come from the Crediton area, and are grown on the rich red sandstone soil which is a distinctive feature of this part of Devon. This produces a ruddy complexion, not only to the drinkers, but to the actual drink, and is particularly noticeable in the sweeter varieties.

Derek is proud to talk about his "scrumpy", and claims to be the biggest "scrumpy" maker in the world. The impression many people get nowadays is that scrumpy is an inferior type of cider, but at Inch's the exact opposite is the case: the "scrumpy" brand is the top of the range. It is fermented naturally in oak vats, as is all the cider, but in this instance the fermentation and maturing is a much longer process than usual: the cider has been allowed to stand for

up to three years before sale, which increases the alcohol content to its full potential, some 8 per cent. By comparison, the basic brand is about 6 per cent, which is still a strength to be respected.

You will find the full range on sale at the Cider Shop at Western Barn. Four litre minicasks of Sweet, Medium or Dry Cider, and Harvest Waeshal Scrumpy; two litre minicasks of Medium Cider and Harvest Waeshal Scrumpy; two litre glass jars of Medium Cider and Harvest Waeshal Scrumpy; one litre bottles of Sweet, Medium or Dry Cider, and Harvest Waeshal Scrumpy; and for that very special occasion, glass jars of the special Pipkin Vintage Scrumpy. Polycasks of the full range are also available. The shop is open on weekdays and Saturday morning (closed 1-2pm).

JAMES WHITE SUFFOLK CIDER

Michael Hall
The Cider House, Bridge Farm,
Friday Street, Brandeston,
Woodbridge, Suffolk IP13 7BP
Telephone: Earl Soham
(0728 82) 537

"East is east, and west is west, and never the twain shall meet." So the saying goes, and in the world of cider it is quite true. In East Anglia the tradition is *not* for making the drink from cider apples, but rather from eating and cooking apples. James White is a good example of this Eastern philosophy. It is made from best quality English apples, produced like wine with champagne yeast, and aged in oak. The firm maintains that "real" cider should be like a fine white wine: cider always used to be drunk in this way, and it was only in the 17th century that people began "stretching" it by adding water. No such additions are made to James White, and the result is an alcohol strength of over 8 per cent, right up to the legal maximum, beyond which it would be taxed as wine.

Although James White only started in about 1980, growth has been rapid, which says much for the enthusiastic reception the cider has enjoyed from an appreciative public. In the first year 1,000 gallons were produced, but with a recent move to larger premises capacity is vastly more, between 40 and 50 thousand gallons. The cider, and also an excellent apple wine, may be found in a wide variety of outlets throughout East Anglia, and even as far as London. You will discover it to be strong, clean, crisp and very refreshing.

KING OFFA CIDER

Tony Carr
The Cider Museum, Pomona Place, off Whitecross Road, Hereford HR4 0LW
Telephone: Hereford (0432) 54207

Situated in a former cider factory, this museum brings the world of cider and the cider maker to life. It is right at the heart of "Cider City" as the CB fans call Hereford, an apt title, for H. P. Bulmer, just across the road, is the largest cider maker in the world. The museum traces the history of cider making from the earliest times to the present day: you may see for yourself the methods and equipment used in the past – among the many interesting displays is a huge French beam press from Normandy, a reconstructed farm cider house, and travelling cider makers' portable press and mills which used to go round the farms each autumn. You can watch a working cooper, making wooden barrels in the traditional manner, and walk through the cellars where cider was first made by the champagne process.

In many parts of the country until comparatively recently cider making, and of course cider drinking, were an integral part of the way of life. Anyone at all interested in our rural traditions and customs will be fascinated by the displays: much of the equipment has been collected from farms and cider works, and much of it has been in use for over 300 years. One striking exhibit is a French Calvados still, used to distill cider to make cider brandy. It is over 200 years since cider brandy has been permitted to be produced commercially in this country, and the museum has been granted special authority to make and sell the distilled liqueur.

The museum sells cider and perry under the King Offa label in its gift shop. The museum is open from April to the end of October every day, from 10am to 5.30pm, and often at other times during the winter months. Please phone for details.

KNIGHT'S CRUMPTON OAKS FARM CIDER

Keith Knight
Crumpton Oaks Fruit Farm, Storridge, Malvern, Herefordshire
Telephone: Malvern (068 45) 4594

Crumpton Oaks Farm has a spectacular backdrop of the Malvern Hills, in an area of outstanding natural beauty. The farm specialises in the growing of high quality fruit – strawberries, raspberries, gooseberries, tayberries, red and blackcurrants, and of course apples – all of which you may pick yourself, or buy from the farm shop. Knight's Crumpton Oaks Farm Cider is made on the farm in the traditional manner, using local apples, many of which are grown on the farm. Keith has been planting hundreds of new trees, a welcome contrast to the state of affairs in other parts: he now has 40 acres of orchards. He is very concerned with cider apple production, and is the founder and chairman of the Herefordshire Cider Fruit Growers Association.

Three generations of Knights play their part in the cider making, and produce over 50,000 gallons per year. The cider is clear and golden, with a strong consistency, good apple taste and aftertaste, and contains no artificial sweetener or colouring. Dry, medium or sweet are available, or the Knight family is quite happy to blend draught to your taste. You will always be offered a sample of the ciders before making up your mind. You may buy ½ and 1 gallon plastic containers at the shop. If you visit in July you may even be able to work your passage, for pickers are needed then for the soft fruit crop. Please telephone first for up to date information about picking and fruit availability.

The farm is open seven days a week, from 10am to 8pm in summer, and 11am to 5pm in winter. The cider may also be found in selected local outlets, and over a wider area may be enjoyed as "Aston Manor Cider" in supermarkets.

LANE'S CIDER

Gary Lane
Overton, West Monkton, Taunton, Somerset TA2 8LS
Telephone: West Monkton (0823) 412345

It seems we are at a kind of watershed in the cider world. Even in Somerset you may see orchards of old gnarled trees on their last legs, or should it be roots. But there is a wind of change blowing through the farms, for a new generation of cider makers is emerging, determined to reverse the depressing trend. Gary and his father are a good example of the new enthusiasm. On their hill top farm, overlooking the Vale of Taunton, you will find an orchard of new apple trees, planted systematically over the last ten years.

A walk round reveals a good variety of types, which enables supplies to hold up even in the lean years, for if one tree fails the next is likely to be yielding a good crop. The mixture is of Dabinett, Yarlington Mill, Taylor, Chisel Jersey, Cort Royal, Michelin, and even some young Kingston Blacks – who now can claim that this legendary tree is fading from the scene! It is obviously an award winning formula as Lane's Dry Cider took second prize at the 1986 Royal Bath & West Show.

While keeping the old cider making plant as a point of interest and nostalgia, the Lanes have installed more modern equipment together with increased storage capacity. Production has been increased, and quality improved. The cider can be found in many off-licences in the Bridgwater and Taunton area, also in many local free houses, and through West Country Products.

LANGDON'S WEST COUNTRY CIDER

Brian Langdon
The Cider Mill, Hewish, Weston-Super-Mare, Avon BS24 6RR
Telephone: Yatton (0934) 833433

Brian Langdon is one of the biggest cider makers in the country. That is not to say that he makes thirty million gallons a year, but purely refers to his striking physical stature. He does however make an increasing amount of very pleasant cider, using such apple varieties as Bulmers Norman, White George, Dabinett, and Yarlington Mill. If you recognise those names you will have some idea of the authenticity of the taste. Much of the output is made with no additions, using the natural yeasts, while in the sweeter brands a sweetener is added.

The cider is available in draught form in 5 and 11 gallon polycasks.

Langdon's is a prize winning blend: Brian achieved the Reserve Champion Prize at the 1985 Devon County Show, and was overall winner in a cider judging by the Friends of Hereford Museum of Cider. This fact, and the convenient position of the cider mill, which is only just off the main Bristol to Weston road, ensures that a steady stream of tourists and locals beat a path to his door.

The cider is available in sweet, medium, dry and vintage; in draught form in various containers, ranging from 11 gallon polycasks to 1 gallon and ½ gallon plastic carry kegs; still and carbonated in 2 litre PET bottles; Superior Cider and Perry carbonated in 70 cl glass bottles. There is much country produce on hand too, including free range eggs, cheese and tomatoes, all of which go rather well with the cider. You may also buy mulling spices, tea towels and pottery mugs. The latter have a thoughtful verse thereon:

What makes the cider blow its cork,
With such a merry din?
What makes the little bubbles rise
And dance like Harlequin?
It is the fatal apple boys,
The fruit of human sin.

Perhaps you ought to avoid the sparkling varieties and stick to the still.

The Cider Mill is open from 9am to 8pm on weekdays, 12 noon to 2pm and 6 to 8pm only, on Sunday

Langdon's West Country Ciders are distributed in the Midlands, South Wales, London and the South Coast, by Wade and Lodge. For further details please contact the firm, at The Warehouse, Boxbush Lane, Rolstone, Banwell, Avon; telephone Banwell (0934) 820718.

LLOYDS COUNTRY BEERS

C. K. Voyce
John Thompson Inn, Ingleby, Derbyshire

Telephone: Melbourne (033 16). 3426 or 2469

What, you may ask, is a beer firm doing in a guide to cider? In fact Mr. Voyce is also a cider enthusiast, and does his bit to help bring a spot of west country cheer to the thirsty folk of Staffordshire and Derbyshire, a gesture which is much appreciated. He deals in the popular and tasty Weston's range, including their Scrumpy and Vintage which can now be obtained in a handy 3 pint glass jar. Larger quantities of two and five gallons may also be had, together with the Weston brands in 1 litre non returnable glass bottles. Weston's Perry is also available. The full cider range is: Bounds Brand: sweet, medium sweet, medium, dry, and vintage. Country Brand: medium. Scrumpy Brand: medium and dry.

Mr. Voyce is usually open during daytime licensing hours.

LONG ASHTON SUPERIOR QUALITY CIDER

Lee Court
Long Ashton Research Station, Long Ashton, Bristol, Avon
Telephone: Long Ashton
(027 580) 2181

Long Ashton Research Station was originally established in 1903 to carry out research into cider fruit, its characteristics, and chemical composition, for the benefit of the cider industry. In 1912 it became absorbed into Bristol University's Department of Agriculture & Horticulture, and broadened its research to include other fields. In recent years there has been much rationalisation: the food and beverage section has been hived off to Reading, and the fruit tree research is now centred at East

Malling in Kent. But to date the Cider House has survived, and though since the departure of the last Cider House Officer, Jeff Williams, no one has been appointed in his place, affairs are capably run by a genial gang of three, Lee Court, David Siviter and Bill Toy, with some part-time assistance.

The future looks promising, subject to any further government cutbacks. New equipment has been installed, much more cider is being sold, and the gang find themselves busier than ever dealing with queries and problems from the many small cider makers, who have for so long relied on their expert advice on cider production and hygiene. They charge a £15 consultation fee if a maker comes in on a short visit, and if out on location, or for more lengthy cases, £10 per hour. With the inevitable retirement of many of the old makers, who knew, or thought they knew, all the tricks, this guidance is even more vital, for many of today's cider makers who have taken over the reins from their father, or started up from scratch, are inexperienced, and need all the help they can get.

For many years the only cider made at Long Ashton was purely in the interests of research, and was only for internal consumption. But lately the Cider House has been obliged to become self supporting, and the cider is now made on a commercial basis. It is still made in the old way, from about 15 varieties of cider apple, but Long Ashton practice what they preach, strict chemical control and a consistent product, and add sulphur dioxide to correct the level of acidity, while replacing the natural yeasts with a cultured yeast to give predictable results. By these means they produce a balanced taste experience, which some would claim to be the perfect cider. They do not pasteurise, this is considered to leave an unpleasant aftertaste, but they do filter, to give a clear light amber cider of strong consistency, almost wine like, and with a woody apple taste and aftertaste.

Long Ashton cider may be purchased at the Cider House. It comes in dry, medium dry and medium sweet; draught, in 1 gallon glass jars; and also a sparkling medium sweet in 70 cl glass bottles. There is a medium sweet sparkling perry, in 70 cl bottles, and apple juice subject to availability. The cider is marketed by Saffron Ciders and West Country Products, though mainly in bottled form, and may be found in selected outlets in the southeast of England. It also appears from time to time at Beer Festivals, in draught form.

The Cider House is open to callers from 8am to 1pm, and 1.30pm to 4.30pm, from Monday to Friday, also on Saturday morning.

LUKEE'S SOMERSET SCRUMPY

G. Lukins
Lillypool Farm, Cheddar, Somerset
Telephone: Cheddar (0934) 743942

Lukee's initials really ought to be "JR", for this is the wild west of England, which makes Dallas look like a poor relation. Round these parts they use ten gallon hats instead of polycasks and the man under the hat will tell you that you've arrived in "Lukee's Kingdom", an area loosely affiliated to the rest of Great Britain. Lukee's farm is on the road from Cheddar to Shipham, high in the hills, and there he has created his own ranch style cider world. The place is built for visitors, with a large car park and toilet facilities. You may soon be persuaded to partake of one of Lukee's famous ploughman's lunches, which comes complete with a glass of cider. While you are enjoying it you may wander through the well stocked shop-cum-museum, where a host of appetising farm produce, cheeses, soft drinks, and cream teas, are set out to tempt you. Coaches are welcome, and certainly if you are coming by road you will find it much easier to stop here than to try and park down in Cheddar itself.

After a few jars of the cider, and perhaps a cream tea, you may not feel much like moving on. Not to worry, for there are plenty of camping facilities here too, so there is every incentive to stay. Visas are only required for periods of over six months.

Lukee's Somerset Scrumpy puts you in a laid-back mood. It is naturally made and matured in the wood. You may choose from sweet, medium or dry, either draught in your own container, or in bottles from 1 pint upwards. Lukee will invite you to sample: "Try before you buy" is the motto. For those who don't want to become an "alcofrolic" there is also pure apple juice. Lukee maintains that a glass of apple juice a day keeps the doctor away. Lukee's Kingdom, rather like the Windmill Theatre, never closes and is open all week throughout the year.

LUSCOMBE CIDER

Jonathan Nance
Luscombe Farm, Buckfastleigh, Devon
Telephone: Buckfastleigh
(0364) 42373

One of the problems of Devon in high summer is avoiding the crowds. The Dart Valley, beautiful though it is, can become something of a nightmare at times, with cars nose to tail along the main road from Buckfastleigh to Totnes. You can of course take the steam train, but may I suggest that if it's cider you are after you seek out the road at the other side of the valley. It is really little more than a made up footpath, and it leads to Luscombe Farm, away from the mighty roar of Devon's traffic. The farm's

owner, Julian David, is a psychiatrist, and living in such a peaceful spot far from the madding crowd must surely help his own state of mind. The cider making is a team effort. Mr. David provides all the raw material and the equipment, but the skill and hard work come from his colleague, Jonathan Nance.

Jonathan is a master at his craft. He has won first prize for dry cider at the Devon County Show, and established a well-deserved reputation. The cider is clear and golden, with a distinctly woody flavour, smooth but strong: a drink of very high quality. The secret of its success is that firstly it is completely natural, with the cider apples being allowed to work out their own chemistry, but even more importantly, it is overseen and blended by an expert – and it shows. The apples include Sweet Alford, Dabinett, Chisel Jersey, Pigs Snout, and Somerset Red Streak. But I guarantee that if *you* put them together you wouldn't finish up with Luscombe Cider. It is good, traditional "scrumpy", and Julian David is confident that there is a bright future for this end of the market, despite claims by some makers that cider should go more "up market". Luscombe Cider is certainly quite happy where it is, and should you sample it, so will you be. I am tempted to wonder if Mr. David recommends it to his clients.

Luscombe Cider can be bought in $\frac{1}{2}$, 1, and 5 gallon containers, though it is helpful if you can bring your own. Please phone before you visit: the farm is open at most times, but warning would be appreciated.

MEADOWSWEET CIDER

Clive Williams
Meadowsweet Farm, Bicknoller, Near Taunton, Somerset
Telephone: Stogumber
(098 46) 409

Everything about Meadowsweet Farm is natural and unspoilt. It is tucked off the main road down a pleasant winding lane, and if you are lucky you may hear the gentle beat of a steam engine on the nearby West Somerset Railway which passes nearby. Clive Williams believes in natural things. He is an enthusiast for organic goats milk yoghurt, which he is convinced will cure you of all ills, and he also produces soft goats and cows cheeses. His philosophy extends to the manufacture of his cider, which is made only from cider apples, with nothing added or taken away. I suspect that you will come away with a good supply of the cider, the yoghurt, and the cheeses, all of which will give you a new outlook on life. The farm is open to callers at any reasonably civilised hour, and you are asked to take your own container if at all possible, as Clive only keeps 5 gallon casks.

MERRYDOWN TRADITIONAL DRAUGHT CIDER

Marketing Director, Robert A. Howie
Merrydown Wine PLC, Horam Manor, Horam, Heathfield, East Sussex TN21 0JA
Telephone: Horam Road (043 53) 2254

It all started in 1946, when two amateur wine makers, Jack Ward and Ian Howie, decided to experiment with making cider. They borrowed a 200-years-old press from a nearby farmer, set it up in the garage of Jack's house at Rotherfield, and produced 400 gallons of potent cider, 18 per cent proof. They called it "Merrydown Vintage" – Merrydown after the name of the house, and Vintage since the cider was made from apples of a single year crop. Needless to say the 400 gallons soon sold out. A similar quantity of red currant wine also went down well. Encouraged by their success, the two friends resolved to expand, and next year bought the freehold of the burnt-out ruin of the 17th century Horam Manor, 13 miles north of Eastbourne. Now seven acres of the site are occupied by the company's pressing, fermentation, storage and bottling facilities and offices. Another 14 acres nearby are used for storage and maintenance.

Merrydown Vintage became the party drink of the early 1950s, and one can still come across many people who hazily remember their first encounter with it. But in 1956 the government imposed wine duty on all cider over 15 per cent proof, so the firm diversified into apple and other country wines and cider vinegars. In 1975, with yet another drastic increase in duty, Merrydown decided to re-enter the cider market. The original medium sweet Vintage Cider was re-launched, and was so well received that within two years a Vintage Dry was also introduced. Although they are carbonated products they are worthy of consideration, containing no artificial colouring, flavouring or sweetening, good news for those seeking a pure drink. A new still medium dry cider joined the Merrydown range in 1981. Called Traditional Draught Cider, it is available from 10 litre bag in box dispensed by hand pump in carefully selected outlets. It is round and full-bodied, and at nearly 6 per cent alcohol content is designed to be quaffed rather than sipped. As with Vintage, it is made from English eating and cooking apples obtained locally, with the same standard of purity. It can be widely found in the south, with some other more distant outlets, and is well worth tracking down. A bottled version is obtainable in PET bottles, in sparkling form.

Horam Manor is on the A267 Tunbridge Wells to Eastbourne road, and a call at the off-licence shop, open during normal hours, is highly recommended. All the Merrydown brands are on sale, including meads, country wines, apple juices, and a range of speciality vinegars and marinades.

Through the years Ian Howie and Jack Ward retained an active interest in the firm they had founded, and must have been amazed to see it develop into the fourth largest cider maker in the country. Sadly in 1986 they both passed on, within a few months of each other, but their enthusiasm and commitment to quality still live on, and Merrydown continues as an independent company whose products go from strength to strength, a fitting memorial to the original initiative and enterprise of two lifelong friends.

MILL HOUSE CIDER

D. J. Whatmoor
Millhouse Nurseries, Owermoigne, Dorchester, Dorset DP2 8HZ
Telephone: Warmwell (0305) 852220

Mr. Whatmoor, together with his wife and two brothers, runs a nursery for bedding plants. Pride of place is his selection of 300 varieties of fuscias. But his real passion is for collecting cider making machinery: he has 20 presses and at least 12 crushers which he has rescued over the years. Having restored them to working order the next step was to find if they really did work. The result was Mill House Cider.

The crusher used is an 1864 Albert Day, from Mark in Somerset, which is the Victorian high tech answer to the old stone trough. It consists of a "mangle" followed by two granite wheels. Mr. Whatmoor describes his cider making as being "inefficient": by this he means that he deliberately does not try to extract the very last drop out of the apple pulp, as he firmly believes that going easy on

the pressure helps the cider to keep its body. As you would expect the whole process is totally traditional. No sugar is added, and the cider is matured in oak. The cider is over 7 per cent alcohol content, and is recommended for drinking in a wine glass. It is also ideal for mulling, and makes an excellent drink for a cold winter evening or a party.

Mill House Cider is sold on the premises by the polycask, or in lesser quantities of 1 and ½ gallon, and 1 litre, containers. You may however bring your own receptacle. Sampling is encouraged. Also on sale are mulling spices, to say nothing of the large choice of bedding plants and the 300 fuscias. Opening hours are 9am to 5pm every day, except for 1pm to 2pm, when Mr. Whatmoor takes time off to enjoy his lunch and check that his cider is still tasting good.

NAISH'S CIDER

H. & F. Naish
Piltown Farm, West Pennard, Glastonbury, Somerset BA6 8NQ
Telephone: Pilton (074 89) 260

In Somerset cider has long been a way of life. Every village could well into this century boast at least half a dozen presses, and precious few children waited till they were 18 before they took their first sip. They were all but weaned on it. Nowadays you will be lucky to find one cider maker to each village.

But those that do remain are true enthusiasts for the craft. Such are the Naish family. They have been making cider for well over 150 years, starting at the village inn, the Red Lion. They still own nine orchards, but sell much of their crop; however they do make a limited gallonage, for it is something you can't give up. In good years they sell some of the apple juice direct from the press, and some of their customers then make it into their own cider, or in some cases apple wine. If you are down that way the Naishs are well worth a visit, for they are a splendid example of a traditional small Somerset cider making firm. If you strike lucky you may find they have some cider to spare, so take a container with you just in case. 5 gallons is the minimum quantity sold.

OWLET CIDER

Colin Corfield
Owl House Fruit Farm,
Lamberhurst, Tunbridge Wells,
Kent TN3 8LY
Telephone: Lamberhurst (0892) 890553

Colin first became interested in cider making in 1979, and spent several years researching the subject in the west country. His early experiments using Kentish fruit were not entirely successful, but he has now settled on a satisfactory blend. His combination of apples will no doubt cause raised eyebrows, for Owlet Cider is probably the only Kent cider to include a proportion of bittersweet cider fruit, which he mixes with dessert apples. The latter are grown on the farm, but the cider apples have to be bought in from the west, and it is Colin's ambition to plant his own cider apple orchard so that in time he can be self-sufficient. He maintains that the bittersweets make all the difference, their tannins being essential for a balanced

cider. He uses a 35-years-old mobile press imported from France, and during the year takes this to various local fairs to demonstrate the gentle art of cider making. Owlet Cider is made traditionally, the only concessions being the introduction of a pure strain of cultured yeast, and the addition of small amounts of sugar to produce a strong cider, of 7 to 8 per cent alcohol content.

Owlet is sold in bottles of still medium dry, and dry and medium draught, which have a slight lift. Also on sale at the farm are mulling spices for cider or wine, and during the pressing season, in October and November, fresh apple juice. In addition to the farm sales Owlet can be found in a number of local off-licences, and one pub, all of which stock the bottled variety.

PARADISE CIDER

H. A. Coules
Cherry Tree Farm, Ilketshall St.
Lawrence, Suffolk (on A144
Bungay-Halesworth Road)
Telephone: Ilketshall (098 681) 353

Cider has been made in Suffolk since about 1300, and was the common drink for all at that time. Farm ciders were still being produced well into the 20th century, but by the end of the last war this had died out. Recently however the Coules family has revived the art of making farm ciders, and put Suffolk back on the map – a case of "Paradise Regained". Ciders and apple juices are produced using only original wooden grinding mills and presses dating from 1864, which handle over a ton of apples at a time. Most of this work is done on Saturdays during September to November. All the cider is matured in oak barrels for two years. No filtration or pasteurisation is practised.

The family is also proud of its range of apple juices. There are four varieties, with no sweeteners, preservatives or other additives, in two litre bottles. They also have a selection of about a dozen country wines, all made on site from fruit and flowers which they grow themselves; these come in 70 cl bottles. The Paradise Cider is in 2 litre bottles, but if you want larger quantities of this heavenly blend you may bring your own containers to be filled up. You are of course encouraged to have a taste before you buy. The range is sweet, medium sweet, dry, scrumpy, and vintage. The farm is open from 9am to 5pm daily including weekends.

PEPE & SON

G. Cannizzaro
Torquay Winery & Vineyard, Newton Road, near Scotts Bridge, Torquay, Devon

When I first came across Mr. Cannizzaro he was sunning himself on the river bank by the Maltsters Arms at Tuckenhay. In those days he conducted his business in a sort of Aladdin's cave under the pub, a glorious place crammed full of casks and bottles. It was like something from a small Italian village, and on that occasion at least the weather was suitably Continental. But when I tasted the cider it was as English as any local farm could make: naturally produced, from Devon apples. I had a lot of walking to do that afternoon, but the bottle I took away with me made the miles fly by.

Much has changed since then. The firm has moved to new and more accessible premises near Torquay. But the cider remains the same, and whether you are walking, or just spending the day on the beach, should not be missed. It comes in sweet, medium or dry, with 1 gallon containers to take away. There is also a good range of red and white table wines, dessert wines and marsala sherry, all made on the premises. Opening hours are from 11am to 6pm.

PERRY'S FARMHOUSE CIDER

Henry Perry
Perry's Cider Mills, Dowlish Wake, near Ilminster, Somerset
Telephone: Ilminster (045 05) 2681

Dowlish Wake is deep in the Somerset countryside, and approached from all directions along winding lanes. At the heart of the small village is a 16th century thatched barn, with a stream running by alongside, and it is here that the Perry family has been making cider for many generations. The barn houses a fascinating collection of country bygones, which include wooden cider presses, farming tools, wagons, and horse harness. As Mrs. Perry explained, "We had such a lot of things that it seemed a pity to throw them away. We put them all in the barn, and the display started from that". Thank heaven for people like the Perrys who don't throw anything away, for there is now a museum of great historic value for visitors to enjoy.

There is plenty more to see, for there is a shop, selling a range of stone cider jars, country style pottery, cider mugs, corn dollies, garden tubs and water butts, enough in fact to start up your own museum. There is also a pictorial display of how the cider is made, which is very much as it always has been, though the massive old timber presses which were once used, and are now in the museum, have been superseded by modern steel machines: the actual surfaces which come into contact with the juice are naturally still made of wood.

All Perry's cider is made from locally grown cider apples, and these include such varieties as Kingston Black, Brown Snout, Bulmers Norman, Dabinett, Yarlington Mill, Sweet Coppin, Tremlett Bitter, and many others which are only found in the older orchards. Because most of the apples are grown by small producers the orchards are nearly all organic. Traditional methods are still used, the cider being naturally fermented and carefully blended, good cellar practices being strictly adhered to. The cider has a strong consistency, with a hint of plum to the subtle taste, and a good mellow apple aftertaste.

Perry's Cider Mill makes an ideal afternoon out: there is free parking available, and coaches are welcome by arrangement. The shop and museum are open throughout the year, Monday to Friday 9am-1pm and 2-5.30pm; Saturday 9.30am-1pm and 2-4.30pm; Sunday 9.30-1pm only. Spring and Summer Bank Holidays are as Saturday times.

PIPPINS CIDER

D. J. Knight
Pippins Cider Company, Pippins Farm, Stonecourt Lane, Pembury, Tunbridge Wells, Kent TN2 4AB
Telephone: Pembury
(089 282) 4624

This is a truly local cider. The apples are all grown on the farm, and the cider is made in an old oast house – rather a change from the building's original purpose, but at least it is still helping to keep quenched Kentish thirsts. They are particular about making their cider down at Pippin Farm: they use only good quality undamaged fruit, and point out that putting any rotten apples in the mixture produces toxins which finally result in you waking up with a sore head. They use a blend of Coxes, Worcester Permain, and Bramley, and these traditional English varieties produce a fine cider of almost wine-like quality. Having the whole process under their control, from growing to pressing, enables

them to maintain a consistent result.

The best time to come for your Pippins Cider is in the autumn, as it soon gets snapped up. It is on sale from the Farm Shop, accessible from the Maidstone Road, where it is available in $\frac{1}{2}$ gallon containers. Opening hours are on Saturdays, from 9am to 6.30pm during the soft fruit season, and 10am to 5pm during the apple and plum season, also on Sundays from 12 noon to 2pm. In addition you may go, container in hand, to the door of the Oast House on Saturdays from 10am to 4pm for a fill up. The times of opening may vary, so please phone first. The Oast is approached via Stonecourt Lane.

You will gather that Pippin Farm is a general fruit farm, and pick your own and ready picked soft fruit and apples are sold from June to the end of October.

PLUM TREE CIDER

Stan Stone
Plum Tree Farm, Summer Lane, Westwick, Weston-Super-Mare, Avon
Telephone: Weston-Super-Mare
(0934) 510707

Weston-Super-Mare seems to go on for ever. The outskirts stretch out for several miles, and it is only after you cross the main railway line that you reach open country. There you will find Plum Tree Farm, a curious name for an establishment which produces cider. Mr. and Mrs. Stone are justly proud of their cider, which is entirely traditional, using cider apples such as Morgan Sweet, Stoke Red, Hangdown, Bulmers Norman, and Yarlington Mill. You will find in Plum Tree Cider a strong consistency, a lemon/apple taste, and a very good apply aftertaste: it is cloudy yellow, and has a fair aroma.

For holiday makers the farm is ideally situated, and also for the camping sites around. It is little effort to call in for fresh supplies at the start or end of your day's outing. But its nearness to the town is a two-edged sword, for soon Plum Tree Farm is to fall under the bulldozer. Already the housing estates of suburban Weston have reached the other side of the railway, and are now poised for a further thrust into the fields beyond. Sadly this is the last time we shall list Plum Tree Cider in this Guide, and if you want to sample it I would recommend an early visit, before the developers move in. Stan is open to visitors from 8.30am to 6.30pm on weekdays, and from 12 noon to 1pm only on Sundays.

Stan is philosophical about the future. "It will give me a chance to put my feet up," he says. I cannot imagine him doing that for too long, and my hope is that we shall meet him again soon, for you can't keep a good cider maker down. It would be nice to think that perhaps the powers-that-be could commemorate the Stones on the new estate — suggestions, on a postcard please, for a suitable street name, to the Borough Engineer and Surveyor, Council Offices, Weston-Super-Mare. For my part, I raise my glass in a personal tribute to two faithful practitioners of the cider makers art. Wassail to you both, and thanks for everything.

REDDAWAY'S FARM CIDER

John Reddaway
Lower Rixdale, Luton, Ideford,
Newton Abbot, Devon
Telephone: Teignmouth
(062 67) 5218

John Reddaway's farm makes a splendid objective for an outing, especially on a fine day, and I suggest that even if you are mobile you should consider leaving the car behind for once and taking a spot of exercise. I set out on a crisp

and sunny morning from L following the valley out of the of the town, and then slowly cli ing up and round to drop down into the small village of Luton, from where Lower Rixdale is up a farm track. It is all delightfully remote and peaceful, and you will hardly meet a soul. It should not take you more than an hour and a half, and you will enjoy some unspoilt Devon countryside. Once at the farm you will also enjoy some unspoilt Devon cider, for John wins prizes with it. A cider that can receive the O'Hagan Cup for the best cider at the Devon County Show deserves close attention. John is a farmer first — he runs 200 acres — but cider making comes a close second. His father and grandfather used to make it and then gave up, but cider making is in the blood, and John restarted in the mid-70s. The orchards on the farm were planted in his father's time, and are still going strong, though John is replacing a few of the trees. There is another orchard, but as John says it is "old and sick", so he has to cut it down. There are still plenty of apples left to make his 1,500 gallons a year though: he uses three-quarters cider fruit blended with others to give a good balance, and the result, which he pours from one of the vast old oak barrels, comes out clear and golden, with the strong tangy taste of bitter sweets.

John believes in letting nature take its course. His part in the procedure is to crush and press the apples, and allow the natural yeasts to carry out the fermentation. If the cider judges are anything to go by, and they are hard people to please, it is a recipe that works. Take a trip to Lower Rixdale and try it for yourself. You may take a container with you, and get filled up straight from "Old Tom", a venerable 200-years-old barrel, or one of his hardly less elderly friends. Alternatively John can sell you the cider in $\frac{1}{2}$, 1,

RICHARD'S CIDER

D. & G. Richards
The Corner Cottage, Smallway,
Congresbury, Avon
Telephone: Yatton (0934) 832054

This is a well-known local cider,
which has become popular with
the many holiday makers who pass
this way: the resorts of Weston-
Super-Mare and Clevedon are
nearby. Richard's shop is well
placed to attract a good clientele,
being only just off the A370 from
Bristol, and you may well have to
take your place in the queue. The
wait will be worthwhile, for this is
a strong and tasty cider, and is
very good value for money. Large
quantities are consumed by the
people of Bristol, and they know a
good thing when they see one.
Richards also enjoys a wider public
in the Midlands, Manchester, Staffordshire and Yorkshire regions,
within the list of Westray Ciders.
Containers and bottles are available at the shop, or you may bring
your own for a fill up, direct from
the cask.

RICH'S SOMERSET
FARMHOUSE CIDER

Gordon Rich
Mill Farm, Watchfield,
Highbridge, Somerset TA9 4RD
Telephone: Burnham-on-Sea
(0278) 783651

Gordon is proud of the fact that his
initials are GWR, which does not
mean that he's been going strong
for over 150 years, but if I catch his
train of thought surely implies
that he's on the right lines. In fact
Gordon's family has been making
cider for well over 70 years, and
the experience is evident in the
product. The popularity of the
cider is such that he never needs to
advertise, all the pressing is sold
without effort. People find it so
irresistable that they keep coming
back for more all the year round.

The cider is made of cider fruit
from all over the west country, and
is cloudy and orange coloured,
with a good aroma, distinctive
tangy flavour, and full body,
though not too strong, which
makes it ideal for drinking by the
pint. Gordon sells all his output on
draught, as opposed to many cider
makers who market their products
in bottles and packs. The best
value is to buy direct from the
farm, at prices which will cancel
out the cost of getting there. Bring
your own containers for a fill up.
Gordon will sell you any amount
from $\frac{1}{2}$ gallon upwards.

There is a cider for every taste:
Golden Harvest, "for the connoisseur", dry; Golden Choice, "for the
individual", medium; and Golden
Demon, "naughty but nice", sweet.
All are still, and matured in the
wood. Whenever you come there
should be plenty of supplies: pressing starts at the end of August
with the first load of Morgan
Sweets, and continues through to
March, the variety of apple changing with each month. Besides the
Farm, Rich's Cider may also be
found in enough pubs, clubs and
off-licences to keep everybody
happy.

ROSIES CIDER

Rosie Aldrich and husband David
Rose Farm, Lattiford, Wincanton,
Somerset BA0 8AF
Telephone: Wincanton (0963)
33680

Laurie Lee, of *Cider with Rosie*
fame, has given his blessing to this
venture, which is a fully traditional farmhouse cider. The apples
are drawn from many local villages, a custom going back 400
years, and this produces some
interesting variations in taste,
because apples from, for example,
Verrington Lane orchards, pro-

duce quite a different result from those of Horsington, Holton, Blackford or South Cheriton, to name but a few of the sources. Rosie won a third prize for medium cider at the Royal Bath and West Show in 1986, her first attempt.

The cider is on sale to take away from the Farm, in a variety of plastic and stone containers, and gifts on the farmhouse cider theme are also available, such as Rosies Cider tee shirts, mugs and tea towels. Rose Farm is about 1½ miles south west of Wincanton on the A357, just south of the A303. If travelling from London or the west leave the A303 at the Wincanton turn, and turn left for Templecombe. It is also possible to reach the Farm from the now re-opened Templecombe Station, on the Salisbury to Exeter line: the three mile walk will soon pass, and providing you stock up well your return journey will give you a Rosie outlook on everything and everybody. Opening hours are from 8.30am to 7.30pm on weekdays; 9am to 6pm on Sunday.

SAFFRON CIDERS

Paul Lawson
4 Church Hill, Radwinter, Saffron Walden, Essex CB10 2SX
Telephone: Radwinter (079 987) 427

Paul Lawson is a cider broker who brings a touch of west country comfort to the east. He offers a range of some 20 draught and 25 bottled varieties of traditional cider and perry to public houses, off-licences, college bars, clubs, wine bars, and CAMRA beer festivals; also direct door deliveries for parties, barbeques and business functions. The ciders are all of impeccable pedigree, from a selected number of farm cider makers who stick to the old and tried methods, using cider apples and fermenting in oak vats. The ciders will be found under the umbrella name of "Saffron Ciders" in the county section, and individual outlets may vary the choice available from time to time.

Paul now takes to the road, and you may come across his stand at one of the major agricultural shows or steam engine rallies in the Home Counties and East Anglia: there you can sample and buy a choice of ciders and perrys in half gallon containers, and view a display of cider memorabilia and photographs. Such attractions bring many visitors, and even Eddie Grundy has been seen on the stand, complete with his horned hat. Saffron Ciders are sold to the public from Radwinter, in 5 gallon polycasks, which may sound like a lot of cider, but in fact will only last you and your friends one evening. There is also a good selection of pubs and off-licences in which to enjoy the taste of the west.

Saffron Ciders comprise: Broadoak: Farmhouse Dry, and Dry Perry (draught); Superior Cider (bottled). Dunkerton: Traditional Dry, Med. Dry and Med. Sweet, and Kingston Black (draught); a full range (bottled); also draught and bottled perry. Felsted Winery Cider: a local bottled cider. Knights Crumpton Oaks: Dry/Med. (draught). Long Ashton: Superior Quality Sparkling and Still (bottled); also Sparkling Perry (bottled); Norbury's: Black Bull Med. Dry/Med. Sweet and Scrumpy (draught); Black Bull (bottled); also Black Bull Perry (draught and bottled). Sellers: Sherston Scorcher; Dry and Medium (draught); full range (bottled).Thatcher: Special Blend; medium and dry (draught); Sandford Superb, Mendip Magic (bottled). Also offered is Saffy's Scrumpy, Saffron's own bottled cider, which is filtered and slightly carbonated, not enough to make it fizzy, but just enough to give it a slight sparkle.

SELBORNE GOLD CIDER

G. Dye
Hampshire Cider Company,
4 Manor Cottages, Neatham,
Alton, Hampshire GU34 4NP
Telephone: Alton (0420) 86759

Geoff Dye operates only a small business, producing under the 1,500 gallon limit to avoid paying duty. His cider is a blend of local apples with others from Kent and Somerset, Bramleys, Coxes, Michelin, Dabinett and other varieties being used from time to time. This mix seems highly successful, and gives a strong cider with almost a wine consistency and a lemon apple taste and after-taste. It has a slight aroma, is cloudy and yellow orange in colour, and is cloudy as nature intended. In fact nothing is done to interfere with the natural processes, with no added water, filtration or other extraneous practices. Selborne Gold is available in either medium or dry, and in this case the dry really is very dry.

With the limited production the cider is quite a rarity, but is well worth tracking down. You cannot buy it direct from Neatham, but it does appear in a few pubs, though it is not always available at each location, so you are advised to make enquiries before setting out on a "Selborne crawl". It may also be found from time to time during the year at outdoor functions and beer festivals, such as Farnham and Winchester. Even hardened beer drinkers have been known to succumb to its delights on these occasions.

SELLERS CIDER

Norman Sellers
The Vineyard, Sherston,
Malmesbury, Wiltshire
Telephone: Sherston (0666) 840716

Here is a question to throw casually into your next session of Trivial Pursuits: "What is a Sherston Scorcher — a fishing fly, a wrestling hold, a racing car, or . . .?" It is in fact one of Norman Sellers' Wiltshire ciders. Norman makes his cider in the traditional manner, with no colouring or pasteurisation; though he does add occasional sweetener to the sweeter end of the range if he feels it needs it. The cider is produced entirely from cider fruit, and Norman specialises in single apple ciders, using Yarlington Mill, Brown Snout, Dabinett and Kingston Black. Other apples used in the normal range include Porters Perfection, Chisel Jersey, Browns Apple, Michelin, Harry Masters Jersey, and Normans. The different ciders are characterised by the cider apples, the natural tannins giving each a distinctive flavour. As no water is added the strength can be close to that of wine.

The range is: Sherston Scorcher: medium; Sellers Cider: medium sweet, medium, dry, and the single variety specials, in containers from 2 pints to 5 gallons. You may alternatively bring your own container. You are invited to sample the brands before deciding which to buy. Apple juice is also on sale, together with 70 cl bottles of still and sparkling ciders. A further attractive line, not unrelated, is a selection of oak barrels from 5 to 150 gallons, some made into garden furniture such as seats and water butts.

Clearly with such a "best Seller" most of the production can be sold from the farm shop without many other outlets, though the cider can be found in a few local pubs and off-licences. Followers of the Scorcher and his friends will also come across Norman's ciders in East Anglia under "Saffron Ciders".

SHEPPYS CIDER

Mr. R. J. Sheppy
Three Bridges, Bradford-on-Tone,
Taunton, Somerset TA4 1ER
Telephone: Bradford-on-Tone
(082 346) 233

Since the early 1800s, the Sheppy family has been making cider in the West Country. From 1925 they have been renowned for their quality ciders, which have gained them over 200 awards, and two Gold Medals. People come from far and wide to Sheppy's 370 acre farm, just west of Taunton, where cider making takes its place among the animals and the crops. There are 42 acres of cider orchards, producing apples with such romantic names as Kingston Black, Yarlington Mill, Dabinett, Stoke Red, Tremletts Bitter and many more. There is an excellent Farm and Cider Museum, housing antique agricultural and cider equipment, cooper's tools and those of other allied crafts. But at Sheppys tradition is blended with progress: you may see the cellar and the modern Press Room, where the apple crop is processed each autumn; and outside new bush orchards keep company with the older standard trees.

Richard Sheppy makes a cider with an individual character, superior to the mass production article, and with more variety. He is confident that there is a good future for such quality cider and once you taste it you will see why. You may sample the cider at the shop, which also sells cheese, cream, mugs and other goods. To see even more of the farm why not make up a party? Groups of over 20 can enjoy an interesting slide show explaining the art of cider making, and an orchard ride on a tractor trailer – plus of course a full selection of samples. Such parties must be booked in advance – please telephone for details of charges and availability.

Sheppys Cider comes in two brands. Farmhouse, which is robust though more refined than many, in ½, 1 and 5 gallon containers; Gold Label, a good table cider which would be an acceptable alternative to wine, in 1 litre bottles. Both brands are available in sweet, medium and dry. Opening hours are Monday to Saturday 8.30am to 7pm (6pm from October to March, 8pm from June to August); Sunday 12 noon to 2pm only, from Easter to Christmas.

Much of the annual production of around 100,000 gallons is bought direct from the retail shop, but there are a number of other outlets. Sheppys Cider is supplied to pubs and off-licences in Cornwall and north and west Devon by KK Distribution Ltd of Bude, Cornwall: Telephone Bude (0288) 55250 for details.

STANCOMBE CIDER

John & Judy Levy and
Richard Foyle
Stancombe Farm, Sherford, near
Kingsbridge, Devon
Telephone: Frogmore (0548 53)
634

This is a cider which has been enthusiastically recommended by those who have been down to South Devon on their holidays. My main impression was that they regretted not bringing a larger quantity back with them – it is an awful long way to go for a top up. As the name implies, this is a genuine farm cider, and you can therefore confidently expect a natural product. You will not be disappointed: apart from the addition of a sweetener to the sweet variety nothing is added; the apple juice ferments in its natural yeast, and there is no filtration, artificial colour, or pasteurisation. It is a still, strong and authentic drink. Local apples are used, of uncertain varieties, but this is only a stopgap measure, for they are growing their own on the farm, and before long will be entirely self-supporting.

The farm is open by arrangement, so please phone first. You may take your own container, for any quantity, or buy from their own stock of 2, 4 or 8 pint containers. There is a medium and a dry, plus some mature three year old cider. Whether this qualifies as "vintage" depends on your interpretation of that much misused word—Derek Inch would prefer to call it "scrumpy", which he maintains requires a three year maturing.

STOTTS SUPERB CIDER

C. J. Stott
Shotts Farm, Wookey, Wells, Somerset
Telephone: Wells (0749) 74731 or 73323

Firstly, don't make the mistake of asking for "Stotts Farm"; we have not made a mistake. Secondly, don't assume that the farm is near Wookey, for it is quite a step, right out on the edge of the Somerset levels, in a delightful and quiet situation. Mr. Stott makes about 5,000 gallons of cider per year. The apples used are many and varied but the cider is very pleasant and satisfying, fairly clear orange in colour, with good body, a fine lemon/apple flavour, and excellent aftertaste. Some artificial colour is added, and some sweetener for the sweet brand, but that apart it is true traditional cider as it used to be. Another thing that is as it used to be is the price, which on my first visit struck me as being remarkably good value, and on my return recently still seemed to be one of the best bargains you could hope to find. It is well worth your while to find your way here. The cider is obtainable in 1 or 5 gallon containers, or you may bring your own. Opening hours are 9am to 6pm daily except Sunday, when the farm closes at 1pm.

SUMMER'S CIDER

Rodney Summers
Slimbridge Lane, Halmore, Berkeley, Gloucestershire GL13 9HH
Telephone: Dursley (0453) 811218

Perhaps it is the name that does it, but there is something distinctly refreshing about Summers Cider. It is a fine traditional drink, made on the premises, from fruit grown free of artificial fertilisers, pesticides and fungicides. Nature is not interfered with in the making either, and the result is good and strong, very much the genuine article. You can see where the cider is made. All the equipment can be seen in action between September and December, and Rodney will gladly show you round while you take a sample with him. He says he is still trying to perfect his product, but from what I remember he hadn't got too far to go. Judge for yourself, and try also his perry. Both come straight from the wooden barrel, which I am sure contributes something to the flavour.

There are plenty of other attractions in the vicinity, such as the Slimbridge Wildfowl Trust, just down the road, and Berkeley Castle, so you can easily combine your visit with an outing. Rodney welcomes visitors, and is open on Monday to Saturday from 9am to 8pm; on Sunday from 9am to 1pm only. He can provide bottles or containers, or you may bring your own. I can forecast that, whenever you go, and whatever the weather, you'll find the Summer's fine in Gloucestershire.

SYMOND'S CIDER

Jeff Williams
Symonds Cider & English Wine Company, Cider Mills & Winery, Stoke Lacy, Bromyard, Herefordshire HR7 4HG
Telephone: Munderfield (088 53) 211

The Symonds family have been

making cider in Herefordshire since 1727, and in recent years the tradition has been kept alive by Bill Symonds, who masterminded the whole operation in the small village of Stoke Lacy. But in July 1984 the Warrington brewers Greenall Whitley bought the company, and immediately set to work to make the most of their investment. Even the casual visitor, who knew the place in its family run days, cannot fail to notice the difference. The adjoining pub, the Plough, has been incorporated into the new complex as a Greenall house, and a brand new shop and show room has been opened on the main road, providing a well-laid out display for visitors of the full Symonds cider range, plus hats, tea towels, tee shirts, and countless souvenirs. Much of the old atmosphere has gone, and there is a new spirit of efficiency and expansion.

Growth has been the keyword since the takeover. Besides the actual purchase of the firm, the most astute move that Greenall Whitley made was to obtain the services of Jeff Williams, who for 30 years had been engaged in cider research at Long Ashton Research Station. His first task was to plan and mastermind a completely new plant. Jeff took to this like a duck to water, and within 18 months the firm had diversified into apple juice, and fruit wines: cider is only a three month intensive operation, and massive investment demands a full 12 month return from staff and equipment.

The entire marketing strategy was turned on its head. Instead of just a few local outlets there were overnight 2,000 pubs in the northwest to be supplied. When Jeff and the builders had finished Stoke Lacy possessed the most modern cider making plant in Europe, capable of producing two million gallons of cider a year. A new Bucher Guyer press has been installed, which can handle up to 20 tons of fruit per hour. There is storage on site for a year's production, and modern road tankers to take the cider to the Greenall empire. The cost of all this runs into at least 2.5 million. Although the firm is now producing up to 20 times the volume of cider it was before the takeover, they still manage to obtain all their cider fruit from Herefordshire; indeed the increased demand had, it is claimed, helped strengthen the market for the local apple growers. But should you imagine, as do the politicians, that increased production equals more jobs, this twenty-fold increase meant only two extra people on the payroll – a 20 per cent increase. Automation and greater efficiency are not a panacea for unemployment.

Before the takeover most of the cider was traditional, with a large number of brands, chief among them being Scrumpy Jack. Jeff quickly evaluated the range, and set about perfecting the product, bringing to it the same degree of hygiene and control that he had so long preached, and practised, at Long Ashton. There has been a firm commitment to retaining, and expanding, the traditional image. The portfolio of brands has thus remained, with the notable addition of "Drystone", a drier version of Scrumpy Jack. But, predictably, most of these perfected ciders are pasteurised, chilled and carbonated, before being piped into the tankers for their journey north. Go into a Greenall Whitley pub in say Runcorn, and there you will find Scrumpy Jack and Drystone waiting your pleasure in their keg dispensers.

Up to 95 per cent of total production is for this market, and it seems a pity that the good people of the north-west could not have been treated to at least one traditional cider as well as the keg brands. More recently Greenall Whitley has taken over Midland brewers Davenports, a number of whose

175

pubs used to stock Weston's cask ciders, and in some at least of these Weston has been ousted by Symonds' keg, thus reducing the drinker's chance of a traditional pint.

In strictly Symonds terms however, the total amount of traditional cider made is probably much as before, bearing in mind the massive increase in volume. The range is: Delicious Sweet; Harvest Vat; Strong Vat; Luncheon Dry; Scrumpy Jack; and Drystone; plus Old Mill Perry. They span the spectrum of sweet through to medium and dry. All are available in 10 litre and 5 gallon containers, and Scrumpy Jack, Harvest Vat and Old Mill in $\frac{1}{2}$ gallons and 5 litre containers also. All the above may be bought from the shop at Stoke Lacy, which is open throughout the week from 9am to 7pm weekdays, 5pm weekends. Parties are welcomed, and are given a tour lasting about $1\frac{1}{2}$ hours, which includes introductory samples of the ciders and perry, a talk on the history of Symonds and cider making, a guided tour of the mills, and a further tasting, with a chance to buy from the extensive cash and carry at bargain prices. Light meals are also provided. Details and prices on application. It is to be hoped that the age old traditions of Symonds can continue, side by side with modern commercialism – time alone will tell.

TAUNTON TRADITIONAL CIDER

The Taunton Cider Company, Norton Fitzwarren, Taunton, Somerset TA2 6RD
Telephone: Taunton (0823) 83141

CB buffs call it "Cider Town", and indeed the name of Taunton is synonymous with cider. At the station, rail travellers are reminded that here "the cidermaker's art is still recognised", and two miles further west, to the right of the line, at Norton Fitzwarren, may be seen the acres of buildings that make up the headquarters of the country's second largest cider maker, the Taunton Cider Company. Rail fans will be delighted to note that the firm has put in its own sidings to distribute its cider nationwide.

In cider making terms Taunton Cider is a comparative newcomer, being established in 1921. In fact much of its growth has taken place only in recent years, and can be attributed largely to its highly successful keg brands Dry Blackthorn and Autumn Gold. Today the company can claim more than a quarter of the total market, with production at around 20 million gallons per year. The firm's philosophy of variety around a strong central product – Dry Blackthorn – has enabled it to out-perform its competitors, and increased demand has led to investment in new equipment, a sign of confidence in continuing growth.

In the midst of all this there is, however, still time for tradition. In the reception area at Norton Fitzwarren an exhibition traces the history of cider, including a display of cider making in a typical Somerset farm setting. Taunton Cider has accumulated a collection of relics that now form part of the exhibit, which though mainly intended for trade visitors may also be enjoyed by casual callers. The company retains a full-time cooper, who can be seen in action in his workshop as a sort of "live exhibit".

Happily one of the strands in the policy of variety has been a continued commitment to its own brand of traditional cider. Matured in oak casks, Taunton Traditional Draught Cider is a golden coloured hazy drink of medium strength with a satisfying apple tang, ideal for taking by the pint. As the list indicates, it is widely available, and is increasingly served by handpump.

TEIGNHEAD FARM CIDER

T. M. J. & C. P. French
Higher Farm, Stoke-in-
Teignhead, Newton Abbot, Devon
Telephone: Shaldon (0626) 873394

Here is an entirely traditional
farm cider, of which there would
have been many in the days before,
and even just after, the last war. At
that time most farms made their
own cider, though generally for
consumption by the farm workers.
At Higher Farm the apples are
still fermented in their own yeast,
the degree of sweetness is controlled by racking off, and no foreign
processes such as filtration, artificial colour, or pasteurisation. The
cider comes straight from the barrel by courtesy of the Goddess
Pomona.

The other attraction of Teignhead Cider is its accessibility. The
farm is situated in a popular holiday region, overlooking Torbay,
and a trip or two up from the beach
during your fortnight will help you
retain your sanity, if not your sob-
riety, after the howling of the children and the ice cream sellers.
There is plenty of opportunity to
buy stocks: the farm is open for
callers on Monday to Saturday
from 9am to 8pm, mornings only
on Sunday. You may bring your
own container, or the Frenches
will gladly provide $\frac{1}{2}$ or 1 gallon
containers of their own. You may
have a sample before making up
your mind, though I am sure that
will only be a formality.

THATCHER'S CIDER

John Thatcher
Myrtle Farm, Station Road,
Sandford, Avon BS19 5RA
Telephone: Banwell (0934) 822862

Thatcher's Cider is now probably
the largest and one of the oldest
independent cider producers in the
area. The business began in 1908,
founded by John Thatcher's grandfather, but most of its expansion

VERY GOOD CYDER.   STROKING THE CYDER

has taken place in the last 15
years. In 1982 the firm acquired
the neighbouring Cheddar Valley
Cider Company, but although
incorporated in Thatcher's it still
exists in its own right, a few yards
down the road, where Cheddar
Valley Farmhouse brand can be
bought. Its original owner, Peter
Champeney, is still alive and well,
and living in Exmouth. He retains
a friendly interest, and pops in
from time to time to see how things
are going.

By all accounts things are going
very well. There is an air of prosperity about Myrtle Farm, which
is surrounded by orchards of fine
new bush trees. About a quarter of
the total supplies are grown on the
farm, others coming in from as far
afield as Herefordshire. All the
juice is blended to give a uniform
product. Sugar is added to the fermenting vats to bring the alcohol
content up, and to start off the fermentation process. All the cider is
then allowed to ferment out to a
dry, and is then blended into dry,
medium and sweet. The cider is
light orange in colour, with a good
aroma, and is strong and tangy,
with a lemon/plum flavour and
aftertaste. There are several
brands from which to choose. The
most popular is Draught Cider, or
Scrumpy: this is a strong still
cloudy cider, sweet, medium or,
dry; it can also be blended to your
individual taste. Sandford Superb:
a finely blended cider which has
been filtered and pasteurised to
kill off any live yeast, again available in sweet, medium or dry.

177

Mendip Magic: a clear, carbonated cider, in sweet, medium or dry, completes the range.

Much of the cider is sold direct from the farm, in various sized containers from 1 litre bottles to 5 gallon polycasks, and you can bring your own container to be filled up. As you might expect, Thatchers can be found in a number of local outlets, but it may also be seen from Southampton to Bradford and Swansea to Sussex.

THEOBALDS CIDER

A. Riccini & Sons, Heronsgate Farm, Stourmouth, Canterbury, Kent
Telephone: Canterbury
(0227) 722275

Antero Riccini may not at first sight appear to be an obvious name for a traditional Kent cider grower, but in fact he and his family have readily taken to the delights of the Garden of England. Antero is a fruit grower, with over 40 acres of apples and pears, and a few years ago he began to make and sell apple juice from the farm shop. It seemed natural to progress to cider, an alternative to the massed produced gassy drinks which most people knew. Its reputation spread by word of mouth, and Theobalds Cider was established.

Antero's wife Yvonne, and his children David, William and Francesca, are all involved in the firm, and enthusiastically share in his philosophy. "Kentish Cider has a distinctive flavour of Kentish orchards, and should be strong and dry," he declares. The Theobalds Cider, named after the 400 year old barn which now houses the cider press and farm shop, certainly bears this out. It is made from Coxes, Bramleys, Discovery and Spartan, and is one of the most highly fruity ciders on the market. Control is assured by replacing the original yeast, and the cider is filtered for appearance. The flavour

is considerably enhanced by maturing in oak whisky casks. Theobalds may be bought at the Barn in polycasks, plastic containers, or bottles, in a range of sweet, medium, dry and extra dry. Also try the apple juice and perry. Heronsgate Farm is open from 10am to 6pm, except in the depths of the winter, when it is best to phone first.

VICKERY'S CIDER

Jack Vickery
Hisbeers Farm, Hare Lane, Buckland St. Mary, Somerset
Telephone: Buckland St. Mary
(046 034) 378

You get a marvellous view from Hisbeer's Farm, which is hardly surprising, for you will have been climbing all the way from Broadway, which is the best approach, whether by foot, bus, or car (you can get a bus from Taunton out to Broadway village). You will have opportunity to drink in more than the view, for the cider barn beckons, and while you are waiting you may join the company in some samples. There is usually someone interesting to talk to, everybody who is anybody tends to drop in while they are passing, and the day passes in leisurely fashion. News and gossip are exchanged, and even if you are a stranger you will soon feel you know the place and all that is going on.

Eventually someone will come in from the fields and serve you, and sell you as much as you can carry of the excellent traditional Somerset cider. But there is no hurry to leave, for life in these parts proceeds from pint to pint, so take your time. When you do tear yourself away you have the consolation that it is downhill all the way to Broadway.

WESTON'S CIDER

Brian Lewis and Michael Roff
H. Weston & Sons Ltd., Bounds,

Much Marcle, near Ledbury, Herefordshire
Telephone: Much Marcle (053 184) 233

It was in 1878 that Henry Weston came to farm at the Bounds, a splendid stone built house dating back to 1611. At that time most farms had their own apple trees and cider presses, and cider was customarily given to the farm labourers as part of their wages. Bounds was no exception, and as a matter of course Henry continued the tradition of making his own fruit from the farm orchards into cider and perry. The summer of 1879 was a poor one for local farmers, and Henry as a tenant without much capital realised that he needed another source of income if he was to survive. So in the following year he decided to develop his existing cider production into a commercial enterprise. He was probably influenced in this by his near neighbour, the Member of Parliament for Herefordshire, Mr. C. W. Radcliffe Cooke. He had for some time been advocating the development of west country cider making, so that cider could become a national drink.

Henry was one of those fortunate people who find themselves in the right place at the right time. He guessed, correctly, that the local farmers would welcome bringing their apples to him to be pressed rather than having the trouble of doing the work themselves. More importantly, he recognised the value for him of the new railway line then being built at Dymock: this new transport system, almost on his doorstep, would enable him to send his cider all over the country. Henry rapidly gained customers, though not by advertising, but rather by recommendation, a method which called for products of the highest quality and close attention to clients' requirements. This policy has been continued by the company ever since. For the first few years the only means of manufacture was the old stone mill which had been in use on the farm for many years, and an equally well used and elderly screw press; but before too long a roller mill, mechanical chain presses, and a steam engine to drive them, were introduced. To this day however you may still see the original mill and press proudly displayed at Bounds.

Within 15 years Weston's Cider was on sale in the House of Commons, doubtless being eagerly promoted, and consumed, by the irrepressible Radcliffe Cooke, and could be said to have arrived. By then it had earnt itself the title "The Wine of the West". To give town dwellers an idea of what real draught farmhouse cider should be like, Weston's opened several London cider houses, in such unlikely places as Harrow Road and Edgware Road, and a vast emporium known as Nightingales Cider House, in Wandsworth Road. Here one could enjoy the equivalent of a village inn, and not surprisingly these establishments did a tremendous trade.

Sadly all three cider houses have now disappeared, not due to any decline in popularity, but because of redevelopment. But the firm has gone from strength to strength, and is now probably the sixth largest cider maker in the country. Despite its growth it still remains an independent family firm. The Westons live in the house. Norman Weston is chairman, Tim Weston, a director, works on the production side, and another director, Henry Weston, manages the 450 acre farm, while Helen, the eldest daughter, is company secretary.

The firm's aim is not to grow larger, but to become increasingly efficient. This is done by a wonderful blend of tradition and modern methods. Much of the machinery goes back to 1923, when it was the envy of the cider making world, and some of the giant oak vats are up to 200 years old, having been bought second hand by Henry when he began in 1880. Yet within this living museum is much modernisation: a new automatic roller press operates alongside the old style presses, both playing a vital part in extracting the last drop from the pulp. Nothing is ever thrown away if there is still a job for it to do. A 1921 Aveling Porter road roller earns its keep around the drives, and a 1914 Foster stationary engine saws timber. It is hoped eventually to assemble all the relics into a proper display.

There are 50 acres of orchards on the farm, but these only account for a small proportion of the fruit needed. The rest comes in from over 200 local growers. Westons use only bittersweet cider apples, and take over 160 different varieties. There are on the farm some perry pear trees, and some in the village dating back to the days of Queen Anne, which still produce good fruit. Weston's claim to make more perry than any other firm other than Babycham; and it is a much sought after drink. On the hillside at Bounds is a large concrete deck, with water channels formed in it. In the autumn the apples arrive on this deck and run down the channels, which are fed by natural springs. This provides a cheap way of washing and transporting the fruit, and provides facilities for sorting, selecting and holding apples until they are required, rather than having to put them straight into a hopper on arrival. This fine control, and preparation, are part of the secret of Weston's cider. But though blending, and washing, are important, they attribute their success even more to the oak vats in which the cider matures. They are firmly committed to oak at Much Marcle, and as recently as 1982 went to considerable expense to build a new oak vat: they maintain that any other material affects the taste. Certainly the whole range of

Weston's ciders has a distinctive and unique flavour, and it is sobering to think, as you relish your pint, that part of the taste may have been contributed by vats that were middle-aged by the Battle of Waterloo.

Westons make four draught ciders. Special Vintage: made from the select group of special vintage cider apples, and matured for at least a year in the vats. It is a smooth rich and quite sweet cider; available in 3 pint and 1 gallon glass jars, plus 2, 5 and 11 gallon casks. Bounds Brand: a clear cider, in 1 gallon glass jars, and 2, 5, and 11 gallon casks. Country Cider: a dark sturdy medium cider, in 2, 5, and 11 gallon casks. Traditional Draught Scrumpy: allowed to settle out naturally after fermentation, and so retaining its cloudy appearance; in 3 pint and 1 gallon glass jars, 2, 5, and 11 gallon casks.

There are in addition a wide choice of bottled ciders, and also the famous Westons Perry, all with the same satisfying "family" flavour to them. Of these you should try in particular their Extra Dry, and the 1983 Vintage Centenary. Their bottles of Traditional Country Cider are very low in carbonation, deliberately to resemble a draught cider, but for outlets without a suitable cellar for the draught. Based on the Bounds Brand, it can happily be drunk by the pint. While retaining their independence, Westons have produced a special brand, Stowford Press, in keg and bottled form, for Camerons Brewery of Hartlepool, and every few days one of the biggest road tankers in the country may be seen transporting 4,000 gallons to the North East. Stowford Press can also be found in the Herefordshire region, and is somewhat misleading, in that it proclaims itself to be "Traditional Draught Cider", though it is in fact a carbonated product.

Westons full range is on sale at Much Marcle, and it is well worth the trip out there to see this "working museum" for yourself. Their shop is open during normal shop hours during the week. The ciders are widely available in pubs throughout the country, and in a number of off-licence chains, notably the Oddbin group.

WESTRAYS CIDERS

Peter Davies
2 Pandora Grove, Birches Head, Stoke-on-Trent, Staffordshire ST1 6RJ
Telephone: Stoke-on-Trent (0782) 260976

Peter Davies only started his distribution firm in 1984, but already he is selling about 16,000 gallons of cider per year, together with a number of traditional beers. His area covers anywhere, but most of his business is centred round the Stoke and south Cheshire region, though he has also found a firm following for cider in Yorkshire. The list of ciders he handles, which may vary from time to time in the individual outlets, will make interesting reading to those far from cider country. The chief are: from Avon, Richards, and Thatcher; from Devon, Inch; from Gloucestershire, Hartland; and from Herefordshire, Dunkerton, Symonds, and Weston.

WILLIAMS BROS.

Backwell Common, Backwell, Bristol, Avon BS19 1DD
Telephone: Flax Bourton (027 583) 2740

The Kingston Black cider apple has a special place in cider lore. People speak of it in hushed and revered tones, and when it is mentioned one is all but expected to genuflect. There is good reason for this mystique: it is one of the very few varieties which has the ability to produce a properly balanced cider without blending with other fruit. This must long ago have raised its status above that of the run of the mill apples. In recent years, due largely to its low resistance to disease, it has all but disappeared, and there can be little more than 60 acres of trees left. Accordingly a cider made from Kingston Black is something of a rarity, and is much sought after.

It is for their Kingston Black cider that Williams Bros. are best known. They produce a Sparkling Kingston Black, which is sold in bottles, and has been called by some the finest bottled cider in the world. After that build up you must try it for yourself. It is sold in 1 litre bottles. Draught farmhouse medium and dry, and draught triple vintage medium and dry, are also available, in your own or their containers. Williams Bros. ciders are among those stocked by both Saffron Ciders and the English Farm Cider Centre, so they are widely accessible in the southeast.

WILKIN'S FARMHOUSE CIDER

Roger Wilkins
Lands End Farm, Mudgley, Wedmore, Somerset
Telephone: Wedmore (0934) 712385

You can walk for miles through Somerset without seeing a soul. That is probably because most of them are up at Rogers's. Though the farm is at the end of a road to nowhere you will be amazed to see how many people make their way there. With Roger Wilkin's barn who needs a village community centre? Many of the callers are regular customers, and have dropped by for a refill. Roger and his wife rush around trying to keep pace with the demand, and the barn fills with good cider and good company. Roger makes around 80,000 gallons in a good year, and as well as his many visitors he supplies a number of pubs and clubs locally. Of these the most surprising is Showerings Club at

Shepton Mallet. Showerings is famous for its Babycham, and of course Coates Cider, and it is a sobering thought that the mountain has to come to Mahommet to quench its thirst.

Roger's cider announces its presence with a good strong aroma, and this continues through into the drink. It is cloudy yellow in colour, with a smooth consistency but good body, a distinct tang with a hint of lemon, and a good aftertaste. It is, as they say, very "moreish", but I can neither confirm or deny reports that Wedmore Council is currently considering piping it to every home as a substitute for the water supply. The dry version is completely traditional, sweetener is added to the others. The apples used include Morgan Sweet, Bulmers Norman, Yarlington Mill, Somerset Streak, Dabinett, and Tremletts Bitter. Containers of 1 and 5 gallons are available, or you may come prepared. You should have plenty of time and opportunity to try out all the combinations of dry, medium and sweet while you discuss the burning issues of the day. Lands End Farm is open from 9am to 9pm except on Sunday, when it closes at 1pm.

WOLFETON CIDER

Captain Thimbleby
Wolfeton House, Dorchester, Dorset
Telephone: Dorchester (0305) 63500

Wolfeton House is situated 1½ miles from Dorchester on the A37 Yeovil road. The home of Captain and Mrs. Thimbleby, it is an outstanding medieval and Elizabethan manor house with magnificent wood and stone work, fireplaces and ceilings; Great Hall and stairs; parlour, dining room, chapel, and cider house. This last gives the clue to Wolfeton's inclusion in this Guide, for Captain Thimbleby may be found within the cider house, making and selling his own traditional draught cider. This he makes from cider apples only, including Golden Ball, Sheeps Nose, Bulmers Norman, and Kingston Black. It is entirely natural in ingredients and manufacture.

All visitors may see the Cider House, and enjoy a free sample. It is sold in 5 gallon containers or 72 cl bottles, and is a vintage cider. Ploughman's lunches, teas and evening meals are offered for parties, by prior arrangement. The house is open from May to September, on Tuesdays, Fridays, and Bank Holiday Mondays from 2pm to 6pm; in August daily except weekends, from 2pm to 6pm; also at other times during the year. Should you wish to call solely to purchase the cider please telephone and make an appointment.

WONNACOTT'S CIDER

B. J. Wonnacott
Lansdown Yard, Bude, Cornwall
EX23 8BH
Telephone: Bude (0288) 3105

This is a cider for the holiday maker, and many must have come across it during their trip to the beaches of north Cornwall. The firm was founded in 1900, and caters not only for cider but also for food, so a visit to Bude will provide you with all your gastronomic requirements. The cider is a blend of Bramleys, Coxes, and several varieties of cider apple, such as Norman and Yarlington Mill. It is a cider with good aroma, a clear golden yellow colour, and is smooth and clean. You will find it possesses a good apple taste and aftertaste, and a slight hint of peach, to my palate at least. Try it for yourself, you will find it refreshing on the beach or with a picnic. To provide for such outings there are plastic containers in sizes from ½ to 4 litres; 1½ pint, 1 litre and 1 gallon bottles, and for the ambitious 2 and 5 gallon polycasks. There are two brands: Cornish Scrumpy, a medium, and Cornish Dry.

YEARLSTONE CYDER

Miss Gilian Pearkes
Yearlstone Vineyard, Chilton, Bickleigh, Tiverton, Devon
Telephone: Bickleigh (088 45) 450

It often seems that where a wine maker also makes cider there is an extra care and even dedication given to the task. Such is certainly true of Miss Pearkes and her brother. They began with the vines, and then "progressed" to cider. Miss Pearkes says her main interest is the actual growing of the vines and the trees: she has planted a wide selection of the older varieties of cider apple, and these are now starting to bear fruit. She spends much time in the orchard, and believes careful husbandry is essential, to cut down over yield in the so-called "on years" – sensible pruning (she takes a month going round her trees) is the answer to the problem of biennial fruiting. She also holds strong views on cider making. You will notice that it is Yearlstone *Cyder,* and she points out that this is the old English spelling, indicating that it is made from undiluted pure apple juice. *"Cider"* by contrast was made by covering the apple pulp from the first pressing with water, and then pressing out the diluted juice. It was this which was quaffed by the farm workers, and often used as part payment to them in lieu of cash.

Only 100 per cent rot free apples are used in the cider. These come from the Pearkes' orchards, and four other ancient farm orchards in the parishes of Bickleigh, Rewe, and Thorverton in the Exe Valley. All the orchards are stock grazed,

and none of the trees are sprayed with fungicides or pesticides. The cyder is made by allowing the milled apples to stand for an hour to extract the flavour and colour from the pulp, and then pressed just once. The juice is then fermented and matured in freshly emptied English oak ex-spirit barrels, and when still and mature is bottled in Chablis bottles, sealed with a wine cork and lead capsule. The cork allows the cider to breathe in the bottle, like a wine, and to keep for years. The single slow, gentle pressing ensures that they do not even begin to wring pithy, harsh or bitter flavours from the fruit.

There are two brands: Yearlstone Gold, a still dry vintage cyder crisp and fragrant, ideal as an accompaniment to ham, gammon, white meat and summer salads; and Yearlstone Cyder Royale, a medium sweet vintage cyder made from selected premium apples from a single Exe Valley orchard of great antiquity. This is a deep golden cyder, excellent with cheese, Italian foods, and most meat and fish. There is a limited supply of Yearlstone Perry, from five trees on the farm and that of their near neighbour, but only enough in a good year to make two barrels of the soft, pale and delicate flavoured drink. Should you find this you will be most fortunate.

These cyders will appeal to the wine drinker as well as the cider enthusiast, on their own or with a meal. It is suggested that you also try them to enhance your cooking: casseroled steak, marinaded, and then cooked in Yearlstone Gold. This is not a cheap cyder. But you are paying, firstly for the privilege of enjoying the harvest of some ancient varieties of tree (a sort of liquid history lesson), and secondly for the care in the manufacture, to say nothing of the nurture of the orchard. It is, I believe, money well spent. Yearlstone Vineyard, which also sells some excellent red and white wines, is open from 9am to 5pm all week. The cyder is available in 75 cl bottles, and in $\frac{1}{2}$ and 1 gallon containers. Sampling is permitted before purchase.

ZUM ZIDER

Peter Lyon
West Country Products,
Lyon House, 51 Lion Road,
Twickenham, Middlesex
Telephone: (01) 892 4114

Lyon House is an old pub in the back streets of Twickenham, which Peter Lyon now uses as a distribution centre for beers and ciders. He delivers over a wide area, and his range of ciders includes Symonds, Long Ashton, and Lanes. His main line however is Zum Zider, a suitably named west country make with a very distinctive flavour. It is fermented with natural yeast in wooden barrels, and is entirely different from the usual commercial brands you will find in the average pub or off-licence. Zum is an orange colour, but your behaviour after a few pints will soon tell your friends that you are not on orange squash. It is strong, cloudy, and still, with latent powers, which may reveal themselves should you not treat it with the care and respect that it deserves. It will also spoil you for lesser ciders for ever after.

Zum comes in Dry (Scrumpy), AC/DC (Medium), and Sweet. Besides being found in a number of pubs it is also available direct from the cask at certain off-licences, at what seems to me to be incredibly good value for money. Many of the Bottoms Up chain stock Zum cider, as do selected branches of Peter Dominic.

Bulmer — The early days. The Cider works in the 19th century

184

Outlook wet and windy

It is an accurate description of much of the current output from the cider industry. For those without shares in British Gas a few pints of keg or bottled commercial cider will more than compensate. The difference between fizzy beer and real ale is as nothing compared with that between keg and traditional cider. With keg cider the drinker can be so bombarded with bubbles that it becomes impossible to experience any taste at all. I have actually heard a representative of one of the Big Three advise that his cider should not be treated as a "session drink" – and indeed I doubt if anyone could spend an evening on chilled carbonated cider without suffering 100 per cent inflation.

Many who have never tried it maintain that traditional cider is "flat" and thus, if not beyond the pale, fit only for it. The true description is "still", as are many other fruit-based drinks and juices. But in fact much traditional cider is not completely still; being a living product, like real ale, it may be completing its fermentation in the cask, a term known as "cask conditioned". This gives a slight "lift" to the drink, but without an aggressive fizz. Some firms, such as Bulmer, retail both still and cask conditioned versions, and, as with most things in life, which you prefer is a matter of taste.

Rather cloudy

The appearance of a glass of farmhouse cider can cause consternation to those more used to quaffing a clear pint of beer. Many is the time that I've heard a customer return the drink to the bar, complaining that it "doesn't look right". What he, or she, really means is that you can't see through it. With cider, there is no reason to be upset: the cloudiness is quite natural, caused by particles of apple and yeast in suspension in the liquid. In fact it confirms that the cider has not been filtered from all its goodness, and still contains something other than water. People tend to drink with their eyes, which misses the true criterion of cider, which is that of taste, which begins with the initial aroma, continues as the flavour hits the palate, and lingers in a memorable aftertaste. So shut your eyes, and think of England – the old England of the cider apple and its infinite variety of flavours. Should you wish to avoid looking at the stuff, do as the real cider drinkers do, and get yourself a pottery mug: perhaps this is why the custom arose. But for those who prefer a see through cider, there are plenty of brands which bow to public demand, and produce a crystal clear drink – but it "bain't be natural moi dear!".

Dry

Without doubt this is the best way to enjoy the pure taste of traditional cider. Left to its own devices, all the sugar in fermenting apple juice converts into alcohol, giving a crisp and, for some palates, an assertive taste. The advantages of letting nature take its course are several. Firstly, it is less fattening when fully dry, much less so than an average pint of beer. The health benefits of a completely dry cider are such that the well-known Bulmer's Number 7, one of the driest on the market, is recommended as being perfectly safe for consumption by diabetics due to its low sugar content.

Secondly, you are getting a stronger drink with a dry cider. Cider will ferment out to as much as 7 or 8 per cent alcohol content by volume, about twice that of most draught beers. So, providing you are using public transport, have found a bed for the night, or have found someone else to do the driving, you can relax in the knowledge that pint for pint you are getting far better value for money than sticking to bitter.

Thirdly, dry cider offers you the pure, uncluttered taste of the bittersweet apple taken to its logical conclusion. Most cider tasting is undertaken with dry, properly to assess and appreciate the full character of the apples. People often say "cider's far too sweet for me", comparing it with beer. But confront them with a really dry cider and they have to admit defeat.

So try it dry. Like most good things it is an acquired taste. But it is a taste you may come to love.

Close to freezing

Received wisdom, spawned by close encounters of the American and Australian kind, is that all booze should be served "ice cold". If you live in Florida or Brisbane it may make sense to down a few tubes of freezing lager from time to time to keep your cool. I can personally vouch for the attraction of such treatment when stuck in the tropics, though had there been even keg cider on tap I'd have opted for that.

But in a cold climate over 50 degrees north of the equator, such an icy douche is more likely to give you a chill than a thrill. It is far more rational to maintain one's intake at average room temperature and for cider this is recommended. With a very cold drink, cider or whatever, the main sensation you experience is not taste but a shiver down the spine. Should you be seeking icy innards you might as well have a knob of ice in a glass of water, it comes far cheaper.

And so, looking ahead . . .

Perhaps the ideal outlook for the true cider drinker should be: "Becoming drier, but remaining rather cloudy, with average temperature." That way, the long-term prospect should be fine.

Making the best of it

Even with the aid of this guide, there will be times when you find yourself thirsty and ciderless. Your usual haunt may have run out, you may be in a cider desert, or you may be snowed in and have exhausted your supplies. Having found myself in all of these extremities I have been forced to make my own.

The process is laborious, messy, and quite disgusting, starting with a kitchen grater to break down the fruit, and progressing to squeezing handfuls of mushy pulp, helped by a pair of net curtains. I say a pair deliberately, as one is needed for the pressing, the other to hang in the window to protect innocent passers by from the sight, which is a cross between milking a cow and changing a nappy. Acquaintances calling during this crucial period seldom visit again.

The result is, however, surprisingly authentic, considering that the raw material consists of nothing other than cooking apples and a smattering of eaters. What emerges from the airing cupboard in the fullness of time may be cloudy, may be clear, but invariably has a satisfying tang.

Gentle reader, I give you *Gibbon Strangler*, the only traditional cider regularly made by hand in the London Borough of Bromley. If you are brave enough to accept a bottle it should be drunk soon after opening – and so should you.

Recently, however, a colleague has announced a breakthrough in amateur cider making, which takes scrumpy into the age of technology. 1. Freeze the apples for 48 hours. 2. Thaw in a warm atmosphere. 3. Place in a pillow case. 4. Spin out juice, using a spin dryer. The freezing destroys the yeast, so this must be added back, but that apart you are then ready to ferment. This method sounds quick, efficient and trouble free, apart that is from a slight problem of persuading the domestic authorities that the week's wash will have to wait its turn. Actually John Hawkins, my informant, solved this difficulty by picking up a virtually new spin dryer from a junk stall for a fiver: he swears that once he gets his production line going it will mean the end of the Big Three. What he will do about a name for his product I'm not sure, but he won't be able to use his address. He lives, you see, in *Castlemaine Avenue*. . . .

Cider and . . .

What goes well, and what doesn't, with your pint.

Cider and . . . lemonade

It's a funny thing, but whenever I go down to the deep west for a taste of the real stuff, I always hear the locals, usually the younger ones, asking for a pint with "lemonade top". Now I ask you! When questioned (and you need to be a bit careful about this, and do it fairly early in the proceedings) they maintain that it "takes the edge off it". Mercy me, folk like me travel hundreds of miles to find an edge *on* it. But there you are, it takes all sorts, and cider, more than other drinks, is happy to share your palate with other tastes.

Cider and . . . blackcurrant

This does curious things to the colour, and may result in your friends thinking you are drinking the blood of your last victim. But as with lemonade, it *is* done and, if you want to try it, who am I to spoil your fun. One could be perverse, and say that if ever you are forced to drink blackcurrant cordial you should always demand that it comes with ten parts of cider to every one of blackcurrant.

Cider and . . . ginger beer

I first came across this at the Swan at Lympstone in Devon, where they talk of little else (when she's not listening). I have more sympathy with this one, as the combination of apple and ginger does seem to be complimentary, and you can sometimes even find a farmhouse cider with a hint of gingery flavour to it. Providing the ginger beer is not so fizzy that it swamps the cider, and you need warming up, give it a try.

Cider and . . . mulling spices

Talk of being warmed up reminds me that a splendid winter beverage can easily be made with mulled cider (and ginger). It has the advantage over mulled wine that you can enjoy more of it, and the effect of heating the cider, and the mulling spices, does much to bring out the subtle flavours. Too often we tend to treat cider as a summer drink (some pubs only stock it from Easter to September) but it is a drink for *all* seasons. There is nothing better for a party, or any social occasion.

Cider and . . . snuff

No, not in the cider, but a pinch in the hand from time to time during the evening's imbibing. There are as many flavours, or should it be fragrances, to snuff as to cider, and those who have tried it praise it highly. What with the vitamin C in the cider, and the full frontal attack of the snuff on the nasal passages, they swear that colds are a thing of the past. It's certainly not to be sneezed at.

Cider and . . . beer

One to be more careful with. The combination of lager in particular mixed direct with cider, the dreaded "snake bite", has done much to harm the reputation of cider in some pubs. Unless you want a thick head from the drink, and a thick ear from the landlord, lay off it. The old boys down west have a rhyme:

Beer on cider
Is a good rider—
But cider on beer
Makes you feel queer.

As with most old sayings, there is a lot of truth in it: if you start a session with cider, and then go on to beer, you will come to no harm – but start with beer, and then switch to cider, and you will feel the worse for it. It is a rule which I have found by experience to work. But never drink them together.

Cider and . . . beer festivals

In view of my remarks on beer you might think this to be tempting providence. But you will find that most beer festivals nowadays carry at least one, and often quite a choice of ciders, sometimes perry too. For many of the public this is the first time they have tried other than commercial cider and providing they remember the little ditty above it is an experience they will remember with pleasure. At the Great British Beer Festival, CAMRA's national annual shop window, there is a complete cider bar, with as many as 20 ciders from all over the country and half a dozen perrys. Next time there is a beer festival near you, do go along, not for the beer, but firstly for the cider, and make a point of spending a day or two at the GBBF, which takes place in the late summer. You can find details from the Campaign for Real Ale headquarters, though if you join you will automatically be fully informed.

Cider and . . . cheese

Ideally you should come to a glass of cider with a completely clean palate, so that nothing gets in the way of the aroma and flavour. But cheese has long been recognised as being particularly enhancing to cider. Jeff Williams, late of Long Ashton Research Station, tells me that in professional judging of ciders he always has a knob of cheese between each sample, to freshen his palate. There is much to be said for getting back to the *real* "ploughmans lunch", a large hunk of Cheddar and a pint of farmhouse cider.

Cider and . . . water

Not that you would think of diluting it before you drink it, but, perish the thought, it has been known for cider makers to "stretch" the output a bit by this means. I don't know about you, but I have already paid once for my water to the local water board, and I'm blowed if I'm going to pay again, perhaps for as much as half the contents of the glass. Genuine farmhouse and traditional cider has *no* water added; it is all pure fermented juice. But you can see the temptation, for a cider maker is taxed on the amount of fermentable juice he presses, not on the quantity of cider which he eventually sells. So the more he waters it down the more profit he makes. A good test to check on the integrity of your favourite brand it to put a little of it in the fridge: if there is no water added it should not freeze. If it does – change to another cider.

Cider and . . . libation

Yes, libation. It is perfectly respectable. If your grandfather lived in cider country he probably did it regularly in public.

It is in fact one of the old customs associated with cider. During the wassailing of the trees, cider was poured over the roots as an offering to the Goddess of the apple trees, Pomona: it was called libation, from the Latin "libare" – to pour a little of. This was of course only done once a year, but it was felt wise to keep on good terms with Pomona on a more regular basis, so a cider drinker, at the end of his pint, would tip the last few drops onto the floor. Sometimes he would do it at the start of the drink instead. This went on well into this century, though by that time it is doubtful if anyone knew much about the Apple Goddess, and regarded it as just a habit.

The universal pub carpet might make libation somewhat unpopular today, though much worse happens to it so perhaps another drop or two would not notice. There are practical advantages. At the start of the drink, you may easily spill a little from an overfull glass – next time you do this assure everyone it was deliberate, and an old cider custom. At the end of your pint, you may wish to tip out a few dregs before recharging – again a

spot of libation is the obvious answer.

Cider and . . . additives

Cider made by traditional methods is most unlikely to contain any chemicals such as tartrazine, used in some beverages to enhance the colouring or boost the colour. For one thing the smaller makers could not afford it. What will often have been added, at the initial stage, is a wine or champagne yeast for the fermentation process, the original wild yeasts in the fruit having been killed off – this is to ensure a predictable end result. Sometimes the natural yeasts can produce a splendid cider, but sometimes not: if you are selling to the public your first concern is to provide a consistent product. Small amounts of sulphur dioxide are also added during manufacture, to correct the balance of acidity, or to stop unwelcome secondary fermentation, but this should *not* be detectable in the final taste.

In the old days, whether the cider was sweet or dry depended solely on how long the fermentation was allowed to proceed: naturally all the sugars in the juice ferment out to alcohol. More often now the cider is fully fermented, and then sweetener is added back as required. If this is in the form of sugar it can restart the fermentation, and so some makers prefer to use an inert substance, such as saccharine. But unfortunately this can on occasion leave an unpleasant "off" flavour. Sugar may be added by some makers not for sweetening, but deliberately to increase the alcohol content.

GOOD BEER GUIDE
1 9 8 8

THE WARM WELCOME

CAMRA

CAMPAIGN FOR ~~~~
in association ~~~~
SOLID FUEL ADVIS~~~~

The Good Beer Guide is Britain's best, best-selling and best-value pub guide. It is the one drinking companion no pub-goer should be without, listing over 5,000 pubs throughout Great Britain and the beers they serve. Published by CAMRA the 1988 Guide is much more than just a beer buffs bible, for it is also packed with information on the many other facilities pubs offer. It can lead you to pubs serving bar food, pubs with restaurants, pubs with overnight accommodation, pubs with family rooms, pubs with gardens, pubs near stations, pubs with campsites, pubs in the country ~~~~bs in the town. And, of course, pubs serving traditional

~~~~t £5.95, it represents remarkable value for money.
~~~~ direct from CAMRA, 34 Alma Road, St. Albans,
~~~~1 3BW.
~~~~ues payable to CAMRA Ltd.

INFORMATION PLEASE (TICK & COMPLETE AS APPROPRIATE – BLOCK LETTERS PLEASE)

Please use this sheet to inform us of any alterations or additions to the DIRECTORY and return it to us.

I should like to recommend inclusion of the following:

NAME _____

ADDRESS _____

_____

TEL. NO. _____

NAME OF TRAD. DRAUGHT CIDER SOLD_____

METHOD OF DISPENSE: flagon ☐ polycask ☐ polypin ☐

handpump ☐ wooden cask ☐ electric pump ☐ plastic container ☐

FACILITIES:

Bar snacks ☐ Times _____ Full meals ☐ Times _____

Separate restaurant ☐ Accommodation ☐ Garden/terrace ☐

Children's room ☐ Games room ☐

Other features_____

_____

Landlord or owner's name & signature _____

I should like to recommend inclusion of the following:

NAME _____

ADDRESS _____ _____

_____

TEL. NO._____

NAME OF TRAD. DRAUGHT CIDER SOLD_____

METHOD OF DISPENSE: flagon ☐ polycask ☐ polypin ☐

handpump ☐ wooden cask ☐ electric pump ☐ plastic container ☐

FACILITIES:

Bar snacks ☐ Times _____ Full meals ☐ Times _____

Separate restaurant ☐ Accommodation ☐ Garden/terrace ☐

Children's room ☐ Games room ☐

Other features _____

_____

Landlord or owner's name & signature _____

Please return this form to: Traditional Cider Directory,
161 Ravensbourne Ave, Bromley, Kent, BR2 0AZ.

Please amend the details of the following entries:

NAME _____

AMENDMENT _____

_____

_____

DATE NOTED _____

NAME _____

AMENDMENT _____

_____

_____

DATE NOTED _____

NAME _____

AMENDMENT _____

_____

_____

DATE NOTED _____

NAME _____

AMENDMENT _____

_____

_____

DATE NOTED _____

NAME & ADDRESS OF INFORMANT _____

_____

_____

_____ TEL. NO. _____

m to: Traditional Cider Directory,
Bromley, Kent, BR2 0AZ.